The Architecture of the Germplasm

The Architecture
of the Germplasm

VERNE GRANT
Rancho Santa Ana Botanic Garden, Claremont, California

JOHN WILEY & SONS, INC., NEW YORK · LONDON · SYDNEY

for Karen

We can, in the first place, state with certainty that the germ-plasm possesses a fixed architecture, which has been transmitted historically.

—AUGUST WEISMANN, 1892 *

* Weismann, 1892, p. 61.

Preface

The problem of how the hereditary material, the genotype, of higher organisms is organized in relation to its complex functions is a fundamental, difficult, and not completely solved problem of biology. The purpose of this book is to discuss the organization of the diploid genotype as found particularly in higher plants.

In the history of genetics there have been, in general, two main approaches to the question before us. The Weismannian approach, viewing the germplasm or genotype as a unit in itself, attempts to relate it as a whole to the development and functioning of the organism. The outstanding modern attempt to carry out the holistic approach consistently is embodied in Goldschmidt's *Theoretical Genetics* (1955). The Mendelian approach, on the other hand, focuses attention on the elementary components of the genotype, the genic units, and then proceeds to consider their interactions in gene systems. The gene systems which can be, or at least those which have been, successfully analyzed in detail by the Mendelian method are, owing to technical difficulties, the relatively simple systems. The analysis of one or a few simple gene systems within a highly complex genotype undoubtedly leaves us far short of understanding the organization of the latter entity considered as a whole.

A third approach to the problem, and the one which I have attempted to carry out in this book, is a combination of the aforementioned two. We consider genes and simple gene systems as building blocks which are inadequate in themselves, but indispensable, for the creation of the whole edifice. This point of view pervades Darlington's classic work,

Recent Advances in Cytology (1932), from which I have drawn many of my ideas.

Of course the combined atomistic and holistic approach as followed out here does not provide us with a ready solution of our problem either. We still have a gap in theory between the building blocks and the edifice. And our efforts to bridge that gap by postulating such integrative factors as polygenes, modifiers, genic balance, and multi-factorial linkage could well be supported by a richer body of evidence than is available at present.

If, as Weismann suggested, the germplasm possesses an architecture which has been transmitted historically, then it follows that that architecture has been tested and perfected through many generations of natural selection with reference to its functional usefulness to the organism. It follows, indeed, that the existing complex germplasms have most probably been built up from simpler components during the long course of evolution. We still know too little about the architectural plan involved—or rather the plans—since different organisms have different sets of functions which must call for germplasms with different structural features. To discover the plans of organization, not only at the genic and subgenic levels, where so much research is being concentrated nowadays, but also at the chromosomal and genotypic levels, remains a century after Mendel one of the challenging problems of genetics.

In the present book, as stated at the outset, I have tried to piece together from the available evidence a picture of the diploid genotype in the higher plants. To this end, I have summarized some of the evidence of plant genetics, both classical and recent, both familiar and probably not so familiar to the general reader, with many details included but many other details omitted, so long as it has met the single criterion of relevance to the question at hand. Furthermore, although we are concerned primarily with the genotype of diploid plants in this book, I have neither wanted to avoid—nor been able to avoid—referring to Drosophila, Neurospora, viruses, and such-like members of other kingdoms, in cases where these organisms provide evidence that is especially pertinent to our discussion. On the other hand, in spite of the great importance of polyploidy in the plant kingdom, I have resisted with some difficulty the temptation to enter upon a discussion of the organization and functioning of the polyploid genotype, since a treatment of the latter subject would have extended the length of the book considerably.

In order to give an overall view of the subject within the limits of a relatively small book it has been necessary to reduce the number of examples, details, and discussions of tangential questions to a minimum, with the result, of course, that many valuable stories have had to be omitted. Technical terminology has likewise been kept to a minimum.

The first part of Chapter 1 on The Hereditary Material is elementary but basic and logically essential to the thesis. Chapter 2 on Gene Action deals with a rapidly advancing subject which is well outside my own field of research, but which at the same time is basic for the discussion of gene interaction and the gene concept in later chapters. In the preparation of Chapter 2, I have relied heavily on non-technical reviews by biochemical geneticists.

The inclusion of some elementary (and fundamental) subjects in the following pages should not mislead potential readers into supposing that the book is an introduction to genetics. *The Architecture of the Germplasm,* being an attempt to deal with a particular topic in basic genetics, is addressed chiefly to professional biologists and advanced biology students interested directly or indirectly in genetics. I have not, however, pitched the writing at an advanced level exclusively; but partly in the interest of a more complete and logical development of the thesis, and partly to reach as broad a range of readers as possible, I have tried to let the explanations of various questions proceed from the simple and elementary to the complex and advanced.

The manuscript for this book was written in 1961 and 1962. The literature used and cited herein is largely but not exclusively that which I was able to read and digest before commencing to write the book in 1961.

The bibliographical footnotes serve several purposes. They indicate, first of all, the actual literature sources, whether primary or secondary, for each statement in the text. On some topics it has been possible to include historical notes in the footnotes. Finally, for the benefit of students wishing to read further on any one of the many subjects not discussed fully in this book, I have given cross references in the footnotes to good general treatments.

Dr. Th. Dobzhansky provided the author with the much needed encouragement to write this book, and gave advice on several specific questions. Mrs. Karen Grant carefully read and discussed with me the entire manuscript, section by section, as it developed, and on the basis of her criticisms it has been possible to eliminate some errors and ambiguities. Dr. R. W. Allard read the final draft of the manuscript, making a number of very helpful suggestions. Many authors and publishers have generously granted permission to reproduce previously published illustrations, as noted in the captions. The editorial staff of John Wiley and Sons, finally, have been most helpful and cooperative in every way.

VERNE GRANT

Claremont, California

Contents

The hereditary material

1   The tendency of offspring to resemble their parents is due to the transmission of a material substance which causes the development of similar characteristics in successive generations. The doctrine of a material basis of heredity was stated as early as 1745 by Maupertuis in France and again in the nineteenth century by Mendel (1866), Darwin (1868), Weismann (1883), de Vries (1889), and others.[1] The nature of this hereditary material has been revealed to us gradually and in successive stages by hybridization experiments during the nineteenth and early twentieth centuries, by cytogenetic studies in the period from 1900 to the 1930's, by more refined genetic investigations of small chromosome segments from 1945 on, and in recent years by biochemical analyses.

The studies of inheritance in hybridization experiments, carried out mainly with plants in the early period of genetics, led to the idea that the hereditary material consists of numerous separate determinants. These hereditary determinants Mendel referred to in 1866 as elements or factors, de Vries in 1889 as pangenes, and Johannsen in 1909 as genes.

MENDELISM

Let us consider the life cycle of a typical plant or animal with respect to its genetic constitution. The individual begins as a single cell derived from the fusion of a sperm contributed by its male parent with an egg contributed by the female parent. Each sex cell or gamete carries one set of genes, and is accordingly haploid. The fertilized

---

[1] Glass, 1947. Grant, 1956a. Heimans, 1962.

1

egg or zygote inherits one set of genes from its mother through the female gamete and another set of genes from its father through the male gamete; it accordingly possesses two gene sets and is diploid. The zygote develops into a mature body by a series of mitotic cell divisions which perpetuate the original genetic constitution of the zygote. The individual plant or animal thus retains throughout its lifetime the particular combination of maternal and paternal genes which it received at zygote formation. When the individual reaches sexual maturity, it produces gametes of its own as a result of the complex process of meiosis. During meiosis the homologous maternal and paternal genes become separated and assorted to different gametes, which are consequently haploid.

Each kind of gene may exist in two or more alternative forms known as alleles. Thus in man there are different alleles of the gene for eye color leading to the development of brown eyes or blue eyes. Following a common usage, the term gene is used in this book to refer to the sum total of the homologous alleles. We designate a gene in this book by a capital letter in boldface type (thus **A**, **I**, or **S**) and its various alleles by lower-case letters in roman type with appropriate subscripts or superscripts (a_1, a_2, or i^B, i^O), or by capital and small letters in roman type (S, s).

If a gene **A** is present in two allelic forms, a_1 and a_2, different individuals can exist with the genetic constitutions or genotypes a_1a_1, a_2a_2, and a_1a_2. An individual or genotype possessing two identical alleles of the same gene or genes is said to be homozygous; thus the a_1a_1 and the a_2a_2 individuals in the foregoing case are both homozygotes. An individual or genotype carrying dissimilar alleles (i.e., a_1a_2) is called a hybrid or heterozygote.

An a_1a_1 individual produces gametes of the constitution a_1. Therefore, if a_1a_1 individuals interbreed with other a_1a_1 individuals, their progeny will be uniformly a_1a_1 genotypes. Similarly a_2a_2 genotypes produce all a_2 gametes and all a_2a_2 progeny. Homozygotes are true-breeding.

The heterozygote a_1a_2 is derived from the union of two types of gametes, a_1 and a_2, and when it forms gametes itself it produces the same two types in equal numbers. The random union of a_1 and a_2 male gametes with a_1 and a_2 female gametes at fertilization then leads to the formation of the daughter genotypes a_1a_1, a_1a_2, and a_2a_2 in regular ratios. If the gene **A** controls some visible characteristic which can be present in two alternative conditions, like brown eyes versus blue eyes, the progeny of the heterozygote will differ among themselves, or segregate, for this character. A heterozygote or hybrid does not breed true to type, but on the contrary yields variable or segregating offspring.

In one of the classical genetic experiments carried out by Mendel with the garden pea, *Pisum sativum,* true-breeding pea plants possessing yellow seeds were crossed with other true-breeding plants possessing green seeds. The first generation or F_1 progeny of this cross were yellow-seeded. The F_1 hybrids produced a second or F_2 generation progeny consisting of some yellow-seeded individuals and some green-seeded plants in the average proportion of 3 yellow to 1 green. As Mendel noted, both parental types reappeared "without any essential alteration" and in a definite numerical ratio in the F_2 generation. The F_2 plants with green seeds produced only green-seeded plants in the next or F_3 generation. Some of the yellow-seeded F_2 individuals also came true to type in the F_3 generation. About two-thirds of the F_2 plants with yellow seeds segregated in the F_3 generation into green-seeded types and yellow-seeded types [2] (Fig. 1).

Mendel demonstrated that these results could be explained by the hypothesis that the original parental types differed with respect to a "differentiating element" or as we would say today, a single gene, **A**, represented by two alleles.[3] (See Fig. 1.) The yellow-seeded parent had the homozygous constitution a_1a_1, and the green-seeded parent the homozygous constitution a_2a_2. Their F_1 progeny was a heterozygote, a_1a_2, and was yellow-seeded owing to the dominance, or greater effectiveness, of the a_1 allele over the a_2 allele. The two alleles separated at sex cell formation in the heterozygote, which accordingly produced a_1 and a_2 gametes in equal numbers. These gametes then united in different combinations to produce three F_2 types in the ratios 1 a_1a_1:2 a_1a_2:1 a_2a_2. The two homozygous classes bred true to type in the F_3 generation, but the heterozygotes continued to segregate in later generations.

Mendel repeated this experiment by crossing pea plants differing in other characteristics, such as the form of the seeds, the color of the flowers, the color of the pods, and the height of the stem. Plants with violet flowers were crossed to plants with white flowers. Their F_1 hybrid possessed violet flowers. Its progeny in the F_2 generation then segregated into violet-flowered individuals and white-flowered individuals. Mendel grew 929 F_2 plants, of which 705 had violet flowers and 224 had white flowers; the observed proportion of the two types was 3.15 to 1 and hence close to the expected segregation ratio of

---

[2] Mendel, 1866.
[3] *Ibid.*

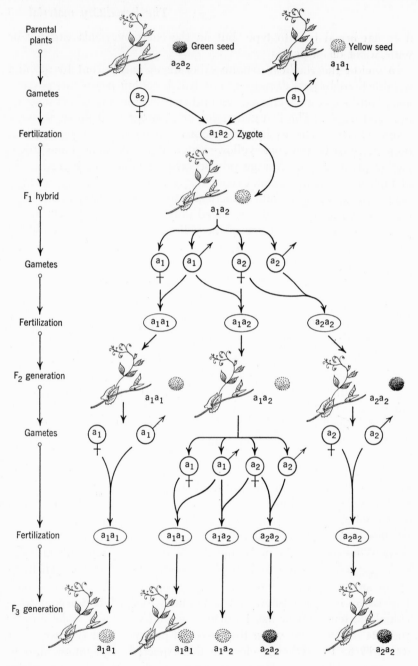

FIG. 1. Segregation for seed color and for the alleles of a gene **A** controlling this character in the offspring of a cross between two plants of the garden pea, *Pisum sativum.*

3:1. Again, parental plants with round seeds and parental plants with wrinkled seeds produced round-seeded F_1 hybrids, which in turn yielded segregating F_2 progenies containing round-seeded and wrinkled-seeded individuals in a 3:1 ratio. Altogether seven character differences were studied in pea plants during an eight-year period and were found to be inherited according to a common pattern.

Now if the seven different characters were inherited together, so that a pea plant with yellow seeds, round seeds, violet flowers, etc., and a plant with green seeds, wrinkled seeds, white flowers, etc., yielded F_2 progeny segregating into two classes (yellow-round-violet versus green-wrinkled-white), the results could be explained on the basis of a difference in a single gene, **A**, which controls all seven characters. But the different characters were not in fact inherited as a block. On the contrary, each character difference segregated independently of the other character differences.

Thus yellow round peas when crossed with green wrinkled peas produced F_1 hybrids with yellow round peas, and the F_1's in turn gave rise to an F_2 generation segregating into four types of individuals, namely, yellow round, yellow wrinkled, green round, and green wrinkled peas (Fig. 2). Therefore, the pea plants are segregating for two separate genes, **A** and **B**, which are assorted independently of one another to the gametes produced by the F_1 hybrids, and are united in all possible combinations in the F_2 zygotes (Fig. 2). Similarly, flower color is independent of seed form and seed color in inheritance. Violet flowers may become associated in any F_2 individual with either yellow or green seeds and with either round or wrinkled seeds, and white flowers equally may become associated with the various types of seeds. Therefore, a third gene (**C**), which governs flower color and is present in two allelic forms (c_1 and c_2), must be postulated in addition to the genes **A** and **B** for seed color and form in order to account for the observed segregations.

As Mendel noted: [4]

The relation of each pair of different characters in hybrid union is independent of the other differences in the two original parental stocks. . . . All constant [i.e., homozygous] combinations which in peas are possible by the combination of the said seven differentiating characters were actually obtained by repeated crossing. Their number is given by $2^7 = 128$. Thereby is simultaneously given the practical proof that the constant characters which appear in the several varie-

---

[4] *Ibid.* For a modern review of the factorial genetics of the garden pea see Yarnell, 1962.

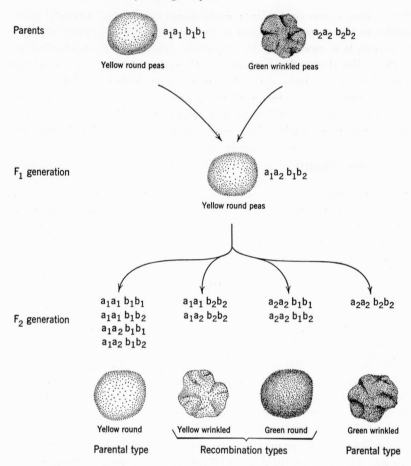

Parents

Yellow round peas $a_1a_1\,b_1b_1$

Green wrinkled peas $a_2a_2\,b_2b_2$

F_1 generation $a_1a_2\,b_1b_2$

Yellow round peas

F_2 generation

$a_1a_1\,b_1b_1$	$a_1a_1\,b_2b_2$	$a_2a_2\,b_1b_1$	$a_2a_2\,b_2b_2$
$a_1a_1\,b_1b_2$	$a_1a_2\,b_2b_2$	$a_2a_2\,b_1b_2$	
$a_1a_2\,b_1b_1$			
$a_1a_2\,b_1b_2$			

Yellow round   Yellow wrinkled   Green round   Green wrinkled

Parental type   Recombination types   Parental type

FIG. 2.   The formation of recombination types in the second generation progeny of a cross between a pea plant with yellow round seeds and a plant with green wrinkled seeds.   Because of dominance of a_1 over a_2 and of b_1 over b_2, the F_1 hybrid has the same seed characteristics as the first parent.   For the same reason certain different genotypes in the F_2 generation also look alike, and the 9 genotypes produced in the F_2 generation can be grouped into 4 phenotypic classes. Two of these phenotypic classes represent new character combinations not found in the parents.

ties of a group of plants may be obtained in all the associations which are possible according to the laws of combination, by means of repeated artificial fertilization.

The formation of new character combinations and new gene combinations unlike those of either parent is recombination.   Sexual reproduction, involving the independent assortment of different pairs of alleles to the gametes and the random union of these gametes at fertilization, is a mechanism for bringing about gene recombination.

From the study of segregation and recombination in peas Mendel was able to conclude that at least seven separable hereditary units exist in this plant. The heredity of pea plants is a mosaic of these (and many other) separate units or genes, which are transmitted from generation to generation in various combinations through the gametes.

THE CHROMOSOME THEORY OF HEREDITY

The genes had been inferred to exist as units of inheritance on the basis of breeding data in the nineteenth century. No one could say where the genes were located in the body. By the end of the nineteenth century, Roux, Weismann, and Hertwig in Germany and E. B. Wilson in the United States had come to the conclusion that the hereditary determinants were borne on the chromosomes within the nucleus of the cell. As Wilson stated in 1896: [5]

In its physiological aspect, therefore, inheritance is the recurrence, in successive generations, of like forms of metabolism; and this is effected through the transmission from generation to generation of a specific substance or idioplasm [hereditary material] which we have seen reason to identify with chromatin [chromosomes].

The characteristic form and number of the chromosomes had been described in accurate detail by the early German cytologists in the 1870's and 1880's. In this period Flemming, van Beneden, and others showed that mitosis involves a longitudinal splitting of the chromosomes in the nucleus of the original cell, and a migration of the daughter chromosomes to the two daughter nuclei. The chromosomes thus possess an individuality which is maintained through successive cell divisions. Furthermore, as suggested by van Beneden and Boveri, the number of chromosomes tends to remain constant in all the cells of the body and among the individuals of a species.[6]

The doctrine of the constancy of chromosome numbers could be reconciled with Oscar Hertwig's generalization, announced in 1875, that fertilization consists of the physical union of two nuclei contributed by the male and female parents, only by assuming that the regular equational division of the chromosomes is interrupted at some point prior to the formation of the gametes. A reduced number of

---

[5] Wilson, 1896, 326–327.
[6] Much of the account in this section is based on Grant, 1956a.

chromosomes in the gametes would be required in order to compensate for the doubled number in the product of their fusion, the zygote. The gametes of roundworms and of flowering plants were found by van Beneden and Strassburger, respectively, in the 1880's to contain half as many chromosomes as the body cells. A process reducing the chromosome number by one-half was predicted to occur once in the life cycle of every sexually reproducing organism.

The details of the complicated process of meiosis, by which the halving of the chromosome number is accomplished, were worked out by many cytologists at the close of the nineteenth century. Meiosis was found to consist of two successive nuclear divisions accompanied by only one division of the chromosomes. During the course of these nuclear divisions the members of each pair of chromosomes, one of which had been contributed to the zygote by the maternal and the other by the paternal parent, become assorted to separate gametes.

When the gametes are formed, two things happen: the complement of chromosomes is reduced from the diploid to the haploid number, and the maternal and paternal combinations of chromosomes are broken up. The homologous members of one chromosome pair are shuffled to separate daughter gametes independently of the distribution of the members of other chromosome pairs. Consequently, the daughter gametes differ from one another in their chromosomal constitution. (See Fig. 3.) And when the dissimilar gametes combine to form new diploid individuals, these too will usually differ from one another and from their parents in chromosomal constitution, since no two individuals in a limited number of trials are likely to inherit exactly the same combination of chromosomes.

At the turn of the century it became evident that several striking parallelisms existed between the behavior of the genes and the behavior of the chromosomes. Both the chromosomes and the genes possess the ability to duplicate themselves in cell division. Both the chromosomes and the genes are found in pairs in the body cells and singly in the gametes. The occurrence of a linear division of the chromosomes during mitotic cell divisions could explain equally the constancy of the chromosomal and the genetic constitution in the cells of the body. The homologous maternal and paternal chromosomes separate from one another at gamete formation, and so do the homologous alleles of a gene pair.

These parallelisms could be explained readily if the chromosomes, which were visible under the microscope, were the bearers of the hereditary determinants, the existence of which had been inferred indirectly from breeding data. The chromosome theory of heredity was foreshadowed by E. B. Wilson in *The Cell in Development and Inheritance* (1896–1900), formulated by Sutton in 1902–1903 and Boveri in 1904, advocated by Wilson in later editions of his book, and adopted and developed by T. H. Morgan and some of the other geneticists of the early twentieth century. The genes of Mendelism now had a known physical basis.

THE GENE AS A SECTOR OF A CHROMOSOME

The evidence presented so far might logically be interpreted to mean that the gene inferred from breeding data is identical with the chromosome observed cytologically. Other evidence obtained in the first decades of this century indicated, however, that numerous genes occur in a linear order on the same chromosome, and that each gene, consequently, represents a sector of a chromosome.

T. H. Morgan and his coworkers in the early studies of the genetics of the fruitfly, *Drosophila melanogaster*, found that eye color, which might be either red or white, was always associated or linked in inheritance with maleness or femaleness, indicating that different genes governing eye color and sex are borne on the same chromosome pair, which in this case happens to be morphologically distinguishable under the microscope. Many other instances were found of genic determinants controlling different characters but linked in inheritance. The phenomenon of linkage required a modification of Mendel's original law of the independent assortment of different pairs of alleles. It was, however, just the modification needed if two or more genes are borne on the same chromosome and are consequently linked together in transmission to the gametes. The discovery, finally, that the number of groups of linked genes, in Drosophila, peas, corn, and later in other organisms, is exactly the same as the haploid number of chromosomes completed the proof that the chromosomes are, individually, the bearers of numerous separate genes.

The reason why a chromosome has to be regarded as the bearer of several or many genes, and cannot be considered simply as a gene in itself, is that the members of a linkage group are not completely linked, but become separated from one another with a low but definite frequency. If **F** and **G** are adjacent sites or loci on a chromosome and are completely linked, so that the heterozygote $\dfrac{\text{F} \quad \text{G}}{\text{f} \quad \text{g}}$ always produces the two parental types of gametes (FG and fg), we would have no basis, operationally, for regarding **F** and **G** as different genes. However, if the linkage between **F** and **G** is incomplete, the heterozygote

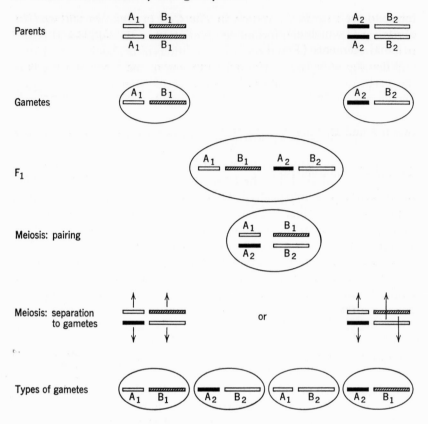

FIG. 3.   The consequences of meiosis in a heterozygote with two pairs of chromosomes and no crossing-over.

will produce not two but four classes of gametes.   Most of the gametes will be the two parental types (FG and fg), but in addition a small proportion of recombination gametes (Fg and fG) will be formed.

The recombination of **F** and **G** is due to crossing-over between these two points on the chromosomes during meiosis.   The process of meiosis is actually a good deal more complicated than the description in the preceding section of this chapter would suggest, in that the homologous maternal and paternal chromosomes, before separating, pair side by side, break at corresponding points along their length, and rejoin in new ways.   The homologous chromosomes cross over and exchange segments at these breakage points.   As a result of breakage and crossing-over in a chromosome pair, neither the maternal chromosomal material nor the paternal in any one chromosome is passed on intact to the gametes. Instead the gametes receive one chromosome of each pair which consists partly of maternal segments and partly of paternal segments (Fig. 4).

When the homologous chromosomes containing **F** and **G** are paired in the heterozygote $\frac{F \quad G}{f \quad g}$, breaks may occur occasionally between **F** and **G**, thus $\frac{F \qquad G}{f \qquad g}$, followed by crossing-over to give the new chromosome types $\frac{F \qquad G}{f \qquad g}$ (crossed). These then separate to form the recombination gametes (Fg and fG).

The actual mechanism of crossing-over is still poorly understood. Whether the homologous chromosomes actually break and cross over, as stated above, or achieve the same end result of recombination in some other way, is not known with certainty. It is convenient, however, here and elsewhere in this book, to use the terms breakage and crossing-over to describe the process leading to gene recombination in

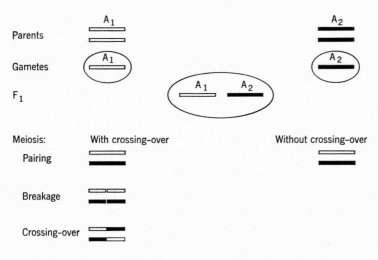

FIG. 4. The consequences of meiosis in a heterozygote with one chromosome pair which undergoes some crossing-over.

higher organisms, whether or not these terms later prove to be correct in a literal sense.

The recombination gametes may constitute up to 50% or down to nearly 0% of the total gametic output of the heterozygote, depending on the frequency of crossing-over between **F** and **G**. The frequency of crossing-over depends, among other factors, on the distance apart of **F** and **G** on the chromosome. If **F** and **G** exist at opposite ends of a chromosome, crossovers between them will occur regularly, and recombination gametes will arise up to a maximum frequency of 50%.[7] If, on the other hand, **F** and **G** lie very close together on a chromosome, breaks may occur only rarely in the region between them. In this case a low proportion, 1% or even less, of the total number of gametes produced by the heterozygote will carry the crossover chromosomes and hence the gene recombinations, Fg and fG.

By considering the amount of recombination between any two linked genes, therefore, their distance apart on the chromosome can be estimated. This distance is expressed in units of measurement known as crossover units on a so-called genetic map. One crossover unit is equivalent to 1% of crossing-over. If **F** and **G** cross over with a frequency of 5%, that is, if the heterozygote $\dfrac{F\quad G}{f\quad g}$ produces 95% parental type gametes and 5% recombination gametes, **F** and **G** can be said to be 5 crossover units apart on a chromosome. The study of the map distances can be extended to other genes on the same chromosome. **G** and **H**, for example, might be 15 crossover units apart. If then **F** and **H** turn out to be 20 crossover units apart, the serial order and relative positions of **F**, **G**, and **H** on the chromosome must be

. In this way extensive genetic maps showing the order and arrangement of the known genes were built up for the fruitfly (*Drosophila melanogaster*) and corn (*Zea mays*). (See Fig. 5.)

The different chromosomes constituting a haploid set frequently differ from one another in length, position of the centromere, and other morphological features by which they can be distinguished microscopically. By the use of cytogenetic techniques a group of linked

---

[7] To explain why 50% and not 100% is the upper limit of recombination between linked genes would require us to enter upon a more detailed account of the chromosomal mechanism than is necessary for our purposes here. The relevant cytogenetic details are given in genetics texts.

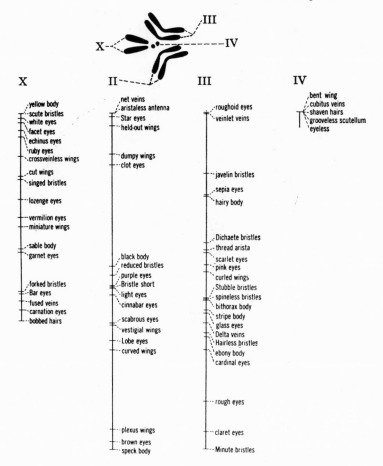

FIG. 5. Genetic map of the four chromosomes of *Drosophila melanogaster*. Only a few of the many known genes are shown. (Modified from *Principles of Genetics*, by Sinnott, Dunn, and Dobzhansky, copyright 1958, McGraw-Hill, New York, by permission.)

genes can be associated with one particular chromosome in the haploid complement. Further techniques enable the geneticist to locate the various genes in a linkage group at particular regions or points on the chromosome. (Figs. 6, 7.)

The laborious task of constructing chromosome maps, embodying the correlated data of breeding experiments and cytological investigations, was well advanced for Drosophila and corn by the 1930's and has been extended since that period for these and other organisms. The

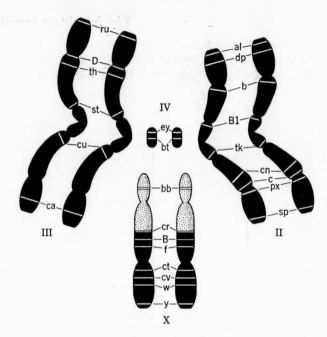

FIG. 6. Chromosome map of *Drosophila melanogaster* showing the location of various genes. Compare with Fig. 5. (Modified from *Principles of Genetics*, by Sinnott, Dunn and Dobzhansky, copyright 1958, McGraw-Hill, New York, by permission.)

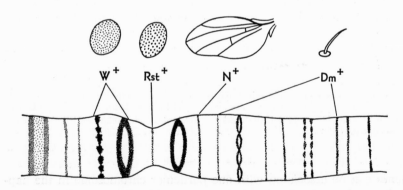

FIG. 7. Location of four genes in a short segment of the X chromosome of *Drosophila melanogaster*. The chromosome segment shown here is from the salivary glands of the larvae, where the chromosomes are exceptionally large and are marked at regular intervals by characteristic bands. The genes W, Rst, N, and Dm, for eye color, eye surface, wing outline, and body bristles respectively have the indicated spatial relationships to the chromosome bands. (From *Principles of Human Genetics*, by Stern, after Slizynska, copyright 1960, W. H. Freeman, San Francisco, by permission.)

chromosomes thus analyzed consist of a regular linear series of gene loci, which are separable from one another by crossing-over, and which individually control in a specific way the development of different phenotypic characteristics.

HEREDITARY DETERMINANTS IN THE CYTOPLASM

Fertilization in the majority of sexually reproducing organisms consists of the union of two morphologically dissimilar gametes, sperm and egg, which are alike in the amount of nuclear material but unlike in the quantity of cytoplasm they carry. The amount of nuclear material contributed by the mother and the father to the zygote at fertilization is just the same. The mother contributes, in addition, a great deal of cytoplasm to the zygote, whereas the father contributes very little or sometimes no cytoplasm to the new generation.

Reciprocal crosses between genetically and phenotypically different parents, viz., $A ♀ \times B ♂$ and $B ♀ \times A ♂$, can be expected to yield similar progeny, insofar as the genetic differences between A and B are carried in the nuclei. Mendel showed in his hybridization experiments with peas that the products of reciprocal crosses are indeed alike.[8] The similarity of reciprocal crosses has been confirmed again and again in numerous other organisms since Mendel's time. This result, combined with Hertwig's rule that fertilization involves the union of the nuclei of sperm and egg, points to the nucleus as the chief organ of heredity, a conclusion reached by Hertwig, Weismann, Strassburger, and others in the 1880's.

In a fair number of cases the hybrids derived from reciprocal crosses have been found to differ between themselves and to resemble the maternal parent in some phenotypic characteristic. In such cases the cytoplasm contributed to the zygote by the female parent can be suspected of determining the characteristic in question.

If the cytoplasmically controlled characteristic does not persist for more than one or two generations, as is frequently the case, it can be explained as a maternal effect, in which the nuclear genes of the mother, by imposing some condition on the cytoplasm of the egg, predetermine a phenotypic trait of the hybrid offspring. If the cytoplasmically controlled characteristic persists for a relatively few generations, but eventually disappears, as also happens, it is called a Dauermodifikation and explained in various ways.[9] If, finally, the

---

[8] Mendel, 1866.
[9] See Goldschmidt, 1955, 201 ff., for a discussion of this topic.

phenotypic trait determined by a particular kind of cytoplasm persists indefinitely through a succession of generations, we are forced to conclude that particles with the gene-like property of self-reproduction exist in the cytoplasm. An inheritance of characters through the cytoplasm has been verified for a number of plants, animals, protista, and fungi.

Striking reciprocal differences are found in the first generation hybrids derived from crossing *Epilobium hirsutum* and *E. luteum*. The hybrids of *luteum* ♀ × *hirsutum* ♂ have reclining branches, broad green leaves, large flower petals (10.7 mm. long by 9.2 mm. broad), and normally developed anthers, which produce 15 to 20% good pollen. By contrast the F_1 of *hirsutum* ♀ × *luteum* ♂ has erect pyramidal branches, narrow yellow-mottled leaves, small flower petals (4.6 mm. long by 3.4 mm. broad), and abortive and sterile anthers. In general, the products of crossing *hirsutum* ♀ × *luteum* ♂ show inhibitions of growth in different parts of the plant, as compared with the more normal progeny of the reciprocal cross, *luteum* ♀ × *hirsutum* ♂ .[10] (See Fig. 8.)

In Epilobium as in other plants the egg nucleus is surrounded by cytoplasm, but the sperm nucleus contributes little or no cytoplasm to the fertilized egg.[11]

In order to determine whether the special characteristics of the Epilobium hybrids are maternal effects or cytoplasmically inherited traits, Michaelis backcrossed the hybrids with the parental types for many generations. The backcrosses of the F_1 (hirs ♀ × lut ♂) ♀ × lut ♂ failed and the lines died out because of lethality and sterility, but the reciprocal backcross was continued through twenty-four generations. That is, the F_1 *luteum* ♀ × *hirsutum* ♂ was pollinated by *hirsutum* to produce the B_1 (lut × hirs) ♀ × hirs ♂ , and this first backcross generation was again pollinated by *hirsutum* to yield B_2 [(lut × hirs) × hirs] ♀ × hirs ♂ . The backcrossing was continued for over twenty years until the type B_{23} (lut ♀ × hirs ♂) ♀ × hirs ♂ was produced.[12]

Now, the proportion of the nuclear genetic material from the recurrent parent rises exponentially in the successive backcross generations, and the proportion of nuclear material of the other parent decreases correspondingly, while the amount of cytoplasm contributed by the female parent remains about constant. The relations are as shown in Table 1. It is evident that after a relatively few generations of

---

[10] Michaelis, 1954, 296.
[11] *Ibid.*, 295.
[12] *Ibid.*, 297.

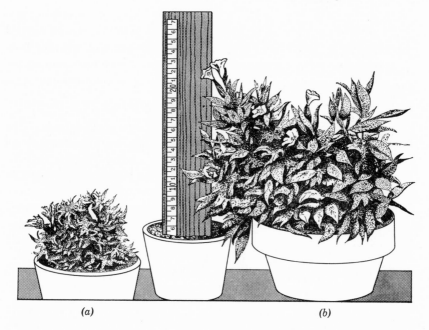

(a)   *(b)*

FIG. 8. Growth form of reciprocally different hybrids of *Epilobium hirsutum* and *E. luteum.* (*a*) *hirsutum* ♀ × *luteum* ♂. (*b*) *luteum* ♀ × *hirsutum* ♂. (Michaelis, 1929.)

TABLE 1   AVERAGE PROPORTIONS OF THE CYTOPLASMIC
AND NUCLEAR MATERIALS OF TWO PARENTAL TYPES, A
AND B, IN SUCCESSIVE BACKCROSS GENERATIONS [*]

Hybrid Generation		Cytoplasm	Nuclear Genes
F_1	A ♀ × B ♂	Virtually all A	$\frac{1}{2}B + \frac{1}{2}A$
B_1	(A × B) ♀ × B ♂	A	$\frac{3}{4}B + \frac{1}{4}A$
B_2	(A × B) × B	A	$\frac{7}{8}B + \frac{1}{8}A$
B_3	(A × B) × B	A	$\frac{15}{16}B + \frac{1}{16}A$
B_4	(A × B) × B	A	$\frac{31}{32}B + \frac{1}{32}A$
B_5	(A × B) × B	A	$\frac{63}{64}B + \frac{1}{64}A$
B_9	(A × B) × B	A	$\frac{1023}{1024}B + \frac{1}{1024}A$
B_{19}	(A × B) × B	A	$\frac{1{,}048{,}575}{1{,}048{,}576}B + \frac{1}{1{,}048{,}576}A$

[*] After Michaelis, 1953.

TABLE 2   THE CYTOPLASMIC AND CHROMOSOMAL CONSTITUTION
OF THE PROGENY DERIVED FROM VARIOUS RECIPROCALLY DIFFER-
ENT FIRST-GENERATION CROSSES, BACKCROSSES AND OUTCROSSES
BETWEEN TWO PARENTAL TYPES, A AND B

Parents	Progeny	Constitution of Progeny
(1) A♀ × B♂	F_1 A × B	A cytoplasm + A/B nucleus
(2) [(A × B) × B]♀ × B♂	backcross × B	A cytoplasm + B nucleus
(3) Backcross progeny 2♀ × A♂	outcross × A	A cytoplasm + A/B nucleus
(4) B♀ × backcross progeny 2♂	B × backcross	B cytoplasm + B nucleus
(5) Backcross progeny 4♀ × A♂	outcross × A	B cytoplasm + A/B nucleus
(6) B♀ × A♂	F_1 B × A	B cytoplasm + A/B nucleus

backcrossing (A × B) as a female to B as a male, the derived individuals consist for all practical purposes of the nuclear genotype of B in
the cytoplasm of A.[13]

Let us compare the genetic constitution of a backcross type with that
of the F_1 hybrids by reference to Table 2.   The F_1 hybrid A♀ × B♂
(from cross 1 in the table) has A cytoplasm and A/B chromosomes.
The reciprocal F_1 hybrid B♀ × A♂ (from cross 6) has B cytoplasm
and A/B chromosomes.   The two F_1 hybrid combinations are thus
alike in their chromosomal constitution but different in their cytoplasm.   The progeny of cross (2) in Table 2, the backcross type
B_n(A♀ × B♂)♀ × B♂, consists essentially of A cytoplasm and B
chromosomes.   It thus resembles the parental type A and the F_1
A × B in its cytoplasm, but is unlike these types in its chromosomal
constitution.   If, therefore, the phenotypic characteristics of the backcross progeny (2) are like those of the F_1 A × B, and different from
F_1 B × A, the characteristics in question must be determined by
hereditary factors in the cytoplasm of A.

The backcross derivatives of *Epilobium luteum* × *hirsutum*, namely
(lut × hirs) ♀ × hirs ♂, did in fact resemble the corresponding F_1
combination, lut ♀ × hirs ♂, in most of the characters in which the
latter differed from the reciprocally different F_1 hybrid, hirs ♀ ×

[13] Michaelis, 1953.

lut ♂ .[14] For example, the backcross (lut × hirs) ♀ × hirs ♂ possesses large corollas which are like those of the F_1 lut ♀ × hirs ♂ , and unlike the small corollas of the reciprocal hybrid, F_1 hirs ♀ × lut ♂ .[15] These and other characters which behave in a similar fashion are consequently determined by hereditary factors transmitted from generation to generation through the cytoplasm. The cytoplasmic constituents responsible for the characters in question maintain their identity and produce their specific action even though under the influence of a foreign nucleus for twenty-four generations.[16]

The validity of this conclusion can be tested by crossing the backcross derivatives reciprocally with the parental types. The critical outcrosses and the expected cytoplasmic and chromosomal constitution of their progeny are listed in Table 2. Crosses (1), (2), and (3) in this table form a consecutive series; crosses (1), (2), (4), and (5) form a reciprocal series; whereas cross (6) is the reciprocal of cross (1). Let us consider the two series of crosses—(1), (2), (3) versus (1), (2), (4), (5)—in detail.

The backcross progeny of (A × B) × B can be used as either a female or a male in crosses to the parental type B. If used as a female, the progeny will be as shown for cross (2) in Table 2. The backcross progeny (2) can now be outcrossed as females to parental type A in order to give the outcross type (3). The latter possesses A cytoplasm and A/B chromosomes. Accordingly, it is like the F_1 A × B (from cross 1) in both its cytoplasmic and chromosomal constitution.

The reciprocal outcross to A is derived by the following steps. The backcross progeny (2) is crossed as a male to B, yielding the backcross type (4). Backcross type (4) is then outcrossed as a female to A, to produce the outcross type (5). Outcross type (5), like the F_1 B × A (from cross 6), possesses B cytoplasm and A/B chromosomes. It thus differs in its cytoplasm but not in its nucleus from outcross type (3).

Michaelis produced the reciprocally different outcrosses from fourth generation backcross individuals in Epilobium. One of these had the derivation indicated by the formula O_1 [B_4 (lut × hirs) × hirs] ♀ × lut ♂ . It corresponds to outcross type (3) in Table 2. The other outcross, corresponding to type (5) in Table 2, was O_1 [hirs ♀ × B_3 ((lut × hirs) × hirs)] ♀ × lut ♂ .[17]

---

[14] Michaelis, 1929, 1953, 1954.
[15] Michaelis, 1929.
[16] Michaelis, 1954, 298.
[17] Michaelis, 1929.

TABLE 3   PHENOTYPIC CHARACTERISTICS OF RECIPROCALLY
DIFFERENT FIRST-GENERATION HYBRIDS AND LATER GENERATION
OUTCROSSES BETWEEN *Epilobium luteum* AND *E. hirsutum* *

Cross	Petal Size, mm.	Leaf Width, mm.	Anthers	Pollen Fertility
(1) F_1 lut × hirs	10.7 × 9.2	23.7	normal	15%
(3) O_1 [B_4 (lut × hirs) × hirs] × lut	9.6 × 7.8	23.4	normal	22%
(5) O_1 [hirs × B_3 ((lut × hirs) × hirs)] × lut	4.6 × 3.5	20.8	abortive	0%
(6) F_1 hirs × lut	4.6 × 3.4	20.8	abortive	0%

* Michaelis, 1929.

The phenotypic characteristics of the two outcross types and of the
two F_1 hybrids are summarized in Table 3 and illustrated in Fig. 9.
It is evident that the two outcross progeny differ phenotypically in the
same ways that the reciprocal F_1 hybrids differ. Outcross types (3)
and (5) differ from one another, not in their nuclei, but in their cytoplasm and in several phenotypic traits. And they resemble phenotypically the type of F_1 hybrid which has the same kind of cytoplasm.
Since the nucleus is the same in all hybrid combinations compared, the
observed correlation between the inheritance of certain phenotypic
characters and the inheritance of the cytoplasm proves that the two

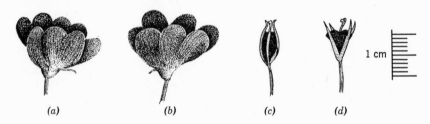

(a)   (b)   (c)   (d)

FIG. 9.   Flowers of reciprocally different F_1 hybrids and later generation outcrosses between *Epilobium hirsutum* and *E. luteum*.   (a) F_1 *luteum* ♀ × *hirsutum*.   (b) Outcross type 3 with *luteum* cytoplasm.   (c) Outcross type 5 with
hirsutum cytoplasm.   (d) F_1 *hirsutum* ♀ × *luteum*.   Further explanation in text
and in Tables 2 and 3.   (Redrawn from Michaelis, 1929.)

kinds of cytoplasm present in *Epilobium luteum* and *E. hirsutum* carry different hereditary factors.[18]

Evidence of cytoplasmic inheritance has been obtained from numerous crosses in Epilobium between the species *E. hirsutum, luteum, roseum,* and *parviflorum,* and between races of *E. hirsutum.* Not only morphological characters and pollen fertility, but also physiological characteristics, such as sensitivity to temperature and poisons and permeability and viscosity of the cellular protoplasm, are subject to control by persistent and hence self-reproducing constituents of the cytoplasm.[19]

Hereditary traits have been shown to be transmitted through the cytoplasm in Oenothera, corn, mosses, green algae, Neurospora, yeast, Paramecium, Drosophila, and other organisms.[20] The name plasmagene has been given to the cytoplasm-borne hereditary factors.

The nature of the hereditary factors in the cytoplasm has been the subject of numerous investigations and discussions, which we cannot review here for want of space. In many instances the plasmagenes can be shown to be particulate. The self-reproducing particles in the cytoplasm are easily seen under the microscope in the case of plastids in Oenothera and other plants, which in different mutant forms determine some cytoplasmically inherited phenotypic traits. The plasmagenes are much smaller in Paramecium, but are microscopically visible as particles after treatment with special stains.[21] In the alga Chlamydomonas the plasmagenes, though unseen as yet and perhaps submicroscopic in size, can still be inferred to have a particulate nature from the indirect evidence of segregation during cell division.[22]

Various authors have suggested that the submicroscopic plasmagenes may be viruses which live and reproduce in a specific cytoplasm and are transmitted from cell to cell in that medium. This may well be true in some cases. In Epilobium and Paramecium, however, the plasmagenes are regular components of the cells. Michaelis found that neither grafts nor sap infiltrations between strains of Epilobium differing in their cytoplasms led to an infection of plasmagenes,[23] whereas these entities are regularly transmitted to new individuals through the normal channels of sexual reproduction, as we have al-

---

[18] *Ibid.*
[19] Michaelis, 1953, 1954.
[20] For reviews see Caspari, 1948. Sonneborn, 1950*a*, 1950*b*. Darlington and Mather, 1949, Chapter 8. Michaelis, 1954. Wagner and Mitchell, 1955, 322–343.
[21] Preer, 1950.
[22] Sager, 1955.
[23] Michaelis, 1953.

ready seen. If such plasmagenes have some properties in common with viruses, they also have the properties of genes. Indeed, there does not seem to be any valid criterion for distinguishing in every case between plasmagenes and viruses which occur as normal components of the cell organization.[24]

THE CHEMICAL NATURE OF
THE GENETIC MATERIAL

The cytogenetic evidence pointing to a regular arrangement of different functional sites or genes in the chromosomes supported the view, held by some of the early geneticists, that the specific action of the hereditary material is traceable in the final analysis to its particular structural organization. As Wilson put it in 1896, "Hereditary traits are the outcome of a definite molecular organization of the idioplasm," idioplasm being synonymous with genetic material.[25] Similar views were expressed by Weismann, Goldschmidt, and others.[26]

Now if the molecular structure of the genetic material imparts a certain direction to the biochemical reactions within the cell, and controls the development of phenotypic characteristics, it becomes a matter of first importance to determine the chemical nature of this substance.

It was known since Miescher's researches on the chemical composition of salmon sperm in the late nineteenth century that the cell nucleus consists of both protein and nucleic acid.[27] The two constituents, referred to collectively as nucleoprotein, were later found by Feulgen and others to be associated in the chromosomes within the nucleus. Prior to 1944 it was generally believed that the genic activity resided in the protein component of the chromosomes.[28]

The proteins, infinitely complex and varied in their molecular structure, seemed to provide the requisite chemical basis for gene specificity. Proteins are built up, as is well known, from amino acids, of which some twenty types exist. A protein macromolecule consists of one or more chains of the various amino acids linked by peptide bonds. These polypeptide chains may contain scores or hundreds of

---

[24] Sonneborn, 1950*b*. Preer, 1950.
[25] Wilson, 1896, 301.
[26] Weismann, 1892. Goldschmidt, 1938, and his earlier works cited therein.
[27] Mirsky, 1953.
[28] A representative statement of this view was given, among others, by Goldschmidt, 1938.

amino-acid residues. The molecular weights range from 5733 in the hormone insulin, one of the smallest known proteins, to 300,000 or more in the largest proteins.[29] Each type of amino acid occurs at particular sites in the polypeptide chain. The number, types, and arrangement of the amino-acid residues produce the size and structural pattern of the protein macromolecule and determine its special characteristics.

The synthesis of a protein macromolecule with its complex and specific pattern requires a chemical organizer of great specificity. The only known substances with the necessary properties are the proteinases, or enzymes which are themselves also proteins. In view of the known occurrence of proteins in the chromosomes, and the known chemical organizing ability of the chromosomes, it was logical to conclude that the genetic material is a proteinase.

If the proteinases themselves are proteins and at the same time have the ability to synthesize other individual proteins then there must exist proteinases which have the ability to synthesize replicas of their own structural pattern and therefore are able to multiply in suitable surroundings.[30]

The postulated self-duplicating proteinases would be genes. Goldschmidt argued in 1938 that the chromosome is an enormously long and complex chain of proteinase, stabilized by nucleic acid, with different protein sites capable of directing the synthesis of different proteinaceous products.[31]

In 1944, however, Avery, Macleod, and McCarty found that hereditary characteristics could be transferred from one strain of bacteria to another by a substance identified chemically as nucleic acid.[32]

The pneumonia bacterium, Pneumococcus, exists in various true-breeding forms. Pneumococci of the form known as type III have cells coated with a polysaccharide, are virulent, and when grown on artificial media form large glistening colonies. Type II pneumococci lack the polysaccharide coat, and along with this are unable to infect an animal body; on an artificial growth medium they produce small rough-surfaced colonies (Fig. 10). The two types breed true for these morphological and physiological characters under ordinary growth conditions. If, however, type II pneumococci are grown in a medium containing the killed cells of type III or a sterile extract made

---

[29] Stein and Moore, 1961.
[30] Bergmann; quoted by Goldschmidt, 1938, 315.
[31] Goldschmidt, 1938, 315.
[32] Avery, Macleod, and McCarty, 1944.

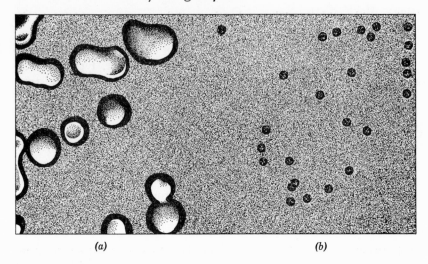

(a)   (b)

FIG. 10. Two types of colonies of the bacterium Pneumococcus when grown on an artificial medium. (*a*) Type III. (*b*) Type II. (Avery, Macleod, and McCarty, 1944.)

from type III cells, the type II bacteria acquired the virulence, polysaccharide cell coat, and large colonial structure of type III. The transformation of type II into type III, moreover, is permanent and hereditary.[33]

This hereditary transformation of pneumococcal types was first discovered by Griffith in 1928 from *in vivo* cultures in mice. Small amounts of living type II cells and large quantities of heat-killed type III cells were injected into mice. The non-virulent and "non-sugar-coated" type II cells gave rise after a period of growth and multiplication in the mouse tissue to virulent and "sugar-coated" cells of type III. Other workers repeated this experiment *in vitro*, using first whole killed cells of type III, and later a soluble extract of the dead type III cells, as the transforming substance. It was shown that type II could be transformed into type III in a test tube as well as in a living animal body by the lifeless cellular substance of III.[34]

The Pneumococcus cell contains proteins, nucleic acid, lipids, and polysaccharides. The early students of transformation in bacteria supposed, in accordance with the prevailing views of their period, that the transforming substance was the protein part of the cell.

---

[33] *Ibid.*
[34] *Ibid.*

Avery, Macleod, and McCarty isolated the biologically active fraction of the transforming substance in Pneumococcus and determined its chemical nature. They reported: [35]

The data obtained by chemical, enzymatic, and serological analyses together with the results of preliminary studies by electrophoresis, ultra-centrifugation, and ultra-violet spectroscopy indicate that, within the limits of the methods, the active fraction contains no demonstrable protein, unbound lipid, or serologically reactive polysaccharide and consists principally, if not solely, of a highly polymerized, viscous form of desoxyribonucleic acid.

Since the transforming substance of Pneumococcus is capable of replicating itself in reproduction and of determining the development of specific morphological and physiological characteristics, it has the properties of genetic material. And if the genetic material of Pneumococcus is a nucleic acid and not a protein, the time-honored assumption regarding the chemical nature of the genes must be re-examined.

Protein and deoxyribose nucleic acid (DNA) are generally found associated in chromosomes in a combination known as nucleoprotein. In the light of this fact, three hypotheses can be suggested to account for the chemical nature of the genetic material. (1) The genetic activity resides in the protein component. (2) The genetic activity resides in the combination. (3) The genetic activity resides in the nucleic acid. The chemical analysis of the transforming substance in Pneumococcus by Avery and his coworkers ruled out hypothesis 1, which had been tacitly assumed to be correct by earlier students, and reduced the possible explanations to hypotheses 2 and 3, which had received little consideration from previous students.

The evidence obtained by Avery and coworkers did not strictly discriminate between hypotheses 2 and 3. Their evidence seemed to them and to many other later workers to strongly favor hypothesis 3. They admitted, however, that:

It is, of course, possible that the biological activity of the substance described [the transforming material] is not an inherent property of the nucleic acid but is due to minute amounts of some other substance adsorbed to it or so intimately associated with it as to escape detection.[36]

In other words, hypothesis 2 could not be excluded as a possible explanation of the facts known up to that time.

Goldschmidt, who had previously advocated hypotheses 1 or 2, now

---

[35] *Ibid.*
[36] *Ibid.*

came out in favor of hypothesis 2, postulating that the genetic material is protein held together by a scaffold of DNA. The properties of replication and control of specific biochemical reactions reside in the protein component. The DNA fiber provides the scaffolding for the proteins which perform the primary genetic functions.[37]

Then in 1953 and 1956 Hershey reported on experiments with bacterial viruses or bacteriophages, which live as parasites on bacteria and multiply inside the bacterial cells.[38] Phosphorus forms a constituent of the DNA but not of the protein of the virus. Hershey tagged one strain of virus with radioactive phosphorus and permitted it to reproduce in bacterial cells. The daughter viruses were found to be radioactive. Another strain of virus was tagged with radioactive sulphur and allowed to reproduce in the same manner. Sulphur occurs in the protein but not in the nucleic acid of the virus. The daughter viruses in this case exhibited only traces of radioactivity, indicating that only 3% of the protein in the parental virus particles is carried over to the new generation. These results show that the hereditary link between successive generations of bacterial viruses consists primarily of DNA together with a trace of protein.

At about the same time (1956), Fraenkel-Conrat and his collaborators, working with tobacco mosaic virus from a different point of view, arrived at a similar conclusion.[39] The rod-like particles of tobacco mosaic virus, which live parasitically in plant tissues, consist of a protein shell and a long narrow core of nucleic acid (ribose nucleic acid or RNA in this case). Different kinds of tobacco mosaic virus exist which are distinguished by the particular type of protein in the shell. One strain known as HR differs from the common type of tobacco mosaic virus, designated as TMV, in the kinds and proportions of amino acids making up its protein sheath.

Fraenkel-Conrat and his coworkers separated the protein and nucleic acid components of tobacco mosaic virus by gentle chemical treatment. They found that when these two components were mixed together in a solution, they would combine again into a normal virus particle capable of infecting and growing in plant leaves. The hereditary characteristics of the reconstituted viruses, moreover, were determined by the nucleic acid component and not by the protein fraction. Thus reconstituted virus particles consisting of HR nucleic acid and TMV protein gave rise to progeny which are HR in both

---

[37] Goldschmidt, 1955, 40–42.
[38] See Beadle, 1957a; 1957b, 29–30.
[39] Fraenkel-Conrat, 1956. Fraenkel-Conrat, Singer, and Williams, 1957.

nucleic acid and protein. This shows that the protein is a product of gene action in this organism, and that the nucleic acid plays the role of genetic determinant.[40]

A slight difference could be detected between the original HR protein in the parental HR stock and the HR protein produced by the progeny of reconstituted particles containing an HR core and TMV protein sheath. Evidently the TMV protein did influence slightly the hereditary characteristics of the derived strain.[41] The genetic role of the protein is slight in comparison with that of the nucleic acid, however.

In higher organisms also there are strong indications that the genetically active part of nucleoprotein is the DNA rather than the protein. Beadle has recently called attention to evidence obtained by Stadler and Uber which pointed to this conclusion in 1942 but was interpreted otherwise at that time.[42]

It is known that ultraviolet radiation produces mutations in the genes, and that some wavelengths in the ultraviolet region of the spectrum are much more effective genetically than others. Stadler and Uber irradiated the pollen of corn (*Zea mays*) with ultraviolet rays of different wavelengths; the treated pollen was used to pollinate female corn flowers; and the frequency of certain mutant conditions appearing in the corn grains developing from the irradiated pollen was scored.[43] In this way it was determined that waves longer than about 3100 A. are nearly ineffective in producing gene mutations; that the shorter waves, 3000 A. or less long, are mutagenic or mutation-producing; and that some shorter wavelengths are much more strongly mutagenic in corn than others. In particular, the ultraviolet radiation with wavelengths in the range from 2500 to 2800 A. has the maximum effectiveness in altering the genes of corn.

Now DNA absorbs ultraviolet radiation mainly in one series of wavelengths and protein absorbs ultraviolet mainly in another range of the spectrum. Knowing the different characteristic absorption spectra of DNA and protein, therefore, and knowing the relative mutagenic effectiveness of the different wavelengths, it was possible to determine whether the genetically effective waves were those absorbed by the protein or those absorbed by the nucleic acid in the corn nucleus. The strong mutagenic wavelengths of ultraviolet radia-

[40] *Ibid.*
[41] *Ibid.*
[42] Beadle, 1957*b*, 27.
[43] Stadler and Uber, 1942.

tion were identified spectroscopically as those absorbed by nucleic acid; conversely, the genetically ineffective wavelengths were those that are not absorbed by nucleic acid.[44]

As Beadle notes in commenting on this case: [45]

When the mutations produced per unit energy were plotted against wave length, the resulting curve fitted within the limits of experimental error the known ultraviolet absorption spectrum of DNA but not that of protein. A simple and direct interpretation of this result indicated that DNA, not protein, is the genetic material. However, because of the prejudice of the time in favor of the protein structure of the gene, there was a strong tendency to invent alternative interpretations such as that the energy of the ultraviolet radiation might be absorbed by DNA but then transferred somehow to protein. In retrospect it is now clear that both geneticists and biochemists should have taken the direct interpretation much more seriously than they did.

The results obtained with bacterial virus and tobacco mosaic virus rule out any version of hypothesis 2 which holds that protein is a quantitatively important constituent of the genetic material. Hypothesis 3 that the genetic activity resides primarily in the nucleic acid is correspondingly strengthened by these same studies and by the experiments on corn. Whether the genetic material is composed *entirely* of nucleic acid, or predominantly of nucleic acid with slight supplementary amounts of protein, remains to be determined.

THE MOLECULAR STRUCTURE OF DNA

The probable structural organization of the DNA macromolecule was worked out by Watson and Crick in 1953 from chemical analyses and X-ray diffraction studies.[46] Briefly, DNA is a long chain of pentose sugars (deoxyribose), linked by phosphates, and bearing ring-like bases on side chains. A sugar molecule, a phosphate molecule, and a base collectively form a group known as a nucleotide. (Fig. 11*a*.) The sugar and phosphate groups are identical throughout the chain. There are four common types of bases: two purines, namely adenine and guanine; and two pyrimidines known as thymine and cytosine (Fig. 11*b*).[47] So far as is known, the bases can occur in any sequence along the pentose-phosphate chain.

---

[44] *Ibid.*

[45] Beadle, 1957*b*, 27.

[46] Watson and Crick, 1953. Crick, 1954.

[47] Two additional types of bases have been discovered as minor constituents of DNA.

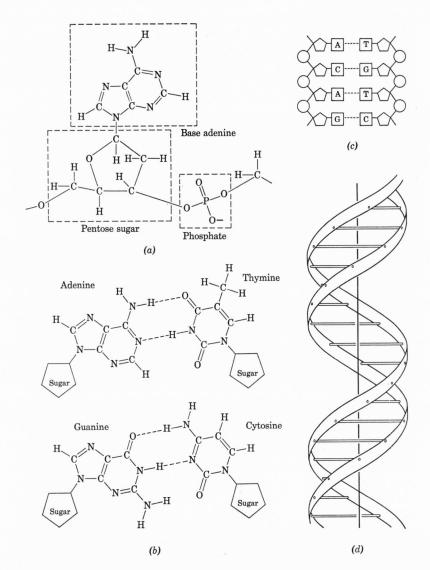

FIG. 11. Postulated structure of the DNA macromolecule. (a) The three building blocks which are repeated over and over in the DNA chain. The sugar and
phosphate groups are constant in structure and arrangement throughout the
chain; the base exists in four forms, one of which, adenine, is shown here. (b)
The four types of bases which make up the side chains of the DNA macromolecule. The bases are shown linked together in pairs by hydrogen bonds. (c) The
complementary order of bases on the two parallel sugar-phosphate chains. (d)
The double helix. The ribbons represent the sugar-phosphate chains, the hori-
zontal rods the base-pairs which hold the chains together, and the vertical line
indicates the axis of the macromolecule. (Rearranged from Crick, in *Scientific
American*, 1954, by permission.)

The DNA macromolecule is a double chain consisting of two parallel chains of sugar and phosphate held together by their bases. Two bases attached to each of the separate chains are linked by weak hydrogen bonds to form so-called base pairs (Fig. 11). Spatial relations in the two parallel chains require that a large base be paired with a small one, but two large bases will not fit together, and neither will two small bases. The purines are large and the pyrimidines small. One of the possible base pairs is adenine-thymine; the other is guanine-cytosine (Fig. 11*b*). Consequently, although the four bases may occur in a variety of sequences on one sugar-phosphate chain, their order on the other chain is not random but predetermined and complementary. For example, if the sequence of bases on one chain is A-A-C-T-G, the sequence at corresponding points on the parallel chain must be T-T-G-A-C (Fig. 11*c*).

The two parallel chains making up the backbone of the DNA macromolecule are coiled in a helix, as shown in Fig. 11*d*. The curvature of this backbone is postulated to be such that a complete turn of the helix occurs in a linear distance of 34 A. on the chain. Since bases are believed to lie 3.4 A. apart on the sugar-phosphate chain, 10 base pairs are included in every complete turn of the helix.[48]

The DNA thread of the much reduced bacterial viruses is variously estimated to contain between 80,000 and 200,000 nucleotide pairs in the case of phage T4,[49] 120,000 or more nucleotide pairs in phage T2,[50] and 5500 nucleotides in the smaller phage ϕX174.[51]

The chromosomes of higher organisms consist of many strands of DNA together with ribose nucleic acid (RNA), protein, lipids, calcium, and other substances.[52] The total length of the DNA in an average chromosome of a higher organism is estimated crudely to be of the order of 4 cm. or 400 million A., and to include more than 100 million nucleotide pairs.[53]

---

[48] Watson and Crick, 1953. Crick, 1954.
[49] Benzer, 1957. Beadle, 1957*a*. Crick, 1962.
[50] Beadle, 1962, 203.
[51] Beadle, 1960, 63.
[52] Ris, 1957. Steffensen, 1959. Kihlman, 1961, 49.
[53] Crick, 1954.

Gene action

2 The Watson-Crick model of DNA considered in the preceding chapter provides a plausible explanation in terms of molecular structure for the two essential properties of the genes: self-duplication and the control of specific biochemical reactions.

GENE REPLICATION

The physical structure of a DNA macromolecule can be perpetuated by a copying process, as Crick and others have suggested. The two chains of the double helix comprising the DNA macromolecule could separate, by unwinding or in some other way which is not yet understood, whereupon each separate chain may build up from a supply of precursor units floating in the cell a new complementary chain. The precise pairing of the bases, A with T and C with G, insures that the new bases will be attached to the old chain in exactly the same sequence as were the old bases. And since a similar but complementary synthesis of new strands is going on in both of the single chains separated from the old double helix, two pairs of chains will be built up exactly like the original one.

Assume for example that a short segment of the original double chain has the sequence $\begin{array}{cccc} \text{T} & \text{G} & \text{T} & \text{C} \\ | & | & | & | \\ \text{A} & \text{C} & \text{A} & \text{G} \end{array}$, as in Figure 11c, and let the two strands separate. Each separate single chain will act as a mold on which the complementary chain can be synthesized. Thus $\begin{array}{cccc} | & | & | & | \\ \text{A} & \text{C} & \text{A} & \text{G} \end{array}$ will rebuild

31

itself as $\begin{matrix} T & G & T & C \\ | & | & | & | \\ A & C & A & G \end{matrix}$, and $\begin{matrix} T & G & T & C \\ | & | & | & | \end{matrix}$ will form a new double structure

$\begin{matrix} T & G & T & C \\ | & | & | & | \\ A & C & A & G \end{matrix}$. Given a supply of precursors, DNA is capable of repli-

cating itself.[1]

The predicted replication of DNA has recently been shown to occur experimentally in a solution containing the four bases together with a primer of natural DNA and some other substances.[2] The original DNA primer synthesizes from the raw materials in the solution more DNA like itself. That the newly synthesized DNA is like the original DNA is indicated by the similarity in chemical composition between product and primer. The DNA products of the *in vitro* reaction have the same proportions of A + T to C + G as the DNA primer, regardless of the relative concentrations of the bases in the solution. The quantity of DNA can increase up to tenfold in the test tube.

GENE SPECIFICITY

Although the backbone of the DNA macromolecule is a monotonous concatenation of identical sugars and phosphates, the bases attached to the sugars are of four main kinds (A, C, G, T), and the base pairs are likewise of four kinds (A-T, T-A, C-G, G-C). These base pairs may be arranged in a variety of sequences along the sugar-phosphate chain.

As suggested by Crick, Beadle, and others, the four types of base pairs can be likened to the different letters in a four-letter alphabet. The different possible combinations of the four letters will then spell out an enormous diversity of words and phrases differing from one another in the number and order of the letters. There are, for example, 4^{1000} possible ways of arranging the 4 base pairs in a segment of DNA 3400 A. long containing 1000 base pair units.[3] A segment of DNA of this length may approximate the size of some genes or functional gene groups. (See Chapter 6.) The number 4^{1000} is incomprehensibly large, and even though only a fraction of the possible combinations are functionally useful, this fraction of potential molecular diversity in a short segment of DNA about the size of one gene is still very great.

---

[1] Crick, 1954.
[2] Kornberg and coworkers; see Beadle, 1960, 1962; and Allfrey and Mirsky, 1961.
[3] Beadle, 1957*b*, 34.

Any one sequence of base pairs within the limits of a single gene may direct in a specific way the course of a biochemical reaction and the formation of some chemical product. The molecular specificity of the gene is transferred somehow to the primary product of gene action, which possesses a corresponding specificity.

A good example of the relationship between a gene and a protein product resulting from its action is provided by the hemoglobin in human blood and the gene **Hb** which controls, partly at least, the synthesis of hemoglobin. The large and complex macromolecule of hemoglobin consists of some 600 amino acids linked into four polypeptide chains, to which four iron groups are attached. This pigment, as is well known, occurs in the red blood cells, where it serves to transport oxygen from the lungs to the body tissues and carbon dioxide back to the lungs.[4]

Ten or more different types of hemoglobin are known in man, three of which are relevant to our present discussion. The normal type, called hemoglobin A, forms disc-shaped red blood cells. A second type, hemoglobin S, forms sickle-shaped cells which do not function efficiently in oxygen transport, in consequence of which individuals carrying only S hemoglobin in their blood suffer from a usually fatal anemia. A second abnormal type of hemoglobin, also associated with anemia, is hemoglobin C.[5]

The differences between these three types of hemoglobin are due to differences in the single gene, **Hb**. The allele hb^A determines the formation of hemoglobin A; the allele hb^S causes hemoglobin S to form; and the allele hb^C produces hemoglobin C. Individuals homozygous for hb^A carry all type A hemoglobin in their blood. Homozygotes for hb^S or hb^C have only hemoglobin S or hemoglobin C. The blood of the heterozygotes hb^A hb^S and hb^A hb^C contains mixtures of the normal and abnormal types of hemoglobin.[6]

Ingram found that the difference between hemoglobins A, S, and C is confined to one small section in two of the polypeptide chains. In hemoglobin A, glutamic acid occurs at a particular place in each of two chains; in hemoglobin S the corresponding sites in the chains are occupied by valine; and in hemoglobin C, lysine is substituted for glutamic acid in the same places. The other corresponding links in the polypeptide chains of the three forms of hemoglobin are apparently the same. The differences between the three kinds of hemoglobin

---

[4] *Ibid.*, 17–19; 1960, 55.
[5] *Ibid.*
[6] Neel, 1949. Beadle, 1957*b*.

can thus be resolved into differences in the amino acid groups inserted at one particular point in the chains.[7]

The various alleles of the gene **Hb** must, therefore, be similar to one another in their general features, for they direct the synthesis of generally similar hemoglobin macromolecules. The only differences that need to be postulated between the alleles hb^A, hb^S, and hb^C in order to account for the known differences in their protein products are such as could determine the kind of amino acid forming one link in a long chain. Perhaps all the alleles of the gene **Hb** have the same sequence of base pairs except at some localized point, where the base pairs differ from one allele to another in ways connected with the insertion of different amino acids at specific points on a polypeptide chain.

GENES AS DETERMINANTS OF BIOCHEMICAL REACTIONS

Critical evidence for the hypothesis that individual genes control particular steps in a sequence of biochemical reactions was obtained from combined genetical and nutritional studies of the red bread mold, *Neurospora crassa*. Normal strains of this fungus possess the ability to synthesize most of the complex substances they require for growth. The mold can be grown in test tubes on an agar medium containing sugar, one of the B vitamins (biotin), and various inorganic salts (nitrate, sulfate, phosphate, etc.). From these simple materials the mold builds up twenty-odd types of amino acids, which it then combines in diverse ways to form a great variety of proteins. Similarly, it synthesizes several kinds of vitamins, polysaccharides, fats, and various other substances.[8]

Mutant strains of Neurospora, which arise spontaneously in low frequencies, or in higher frequencies when the spores are exposed artificially to X-rays or ultraviolet light, are unable to synthesize the various complex materials which this fungus requires for its life processes. The mutant strains fail to survive on the minimal medium of sugar, vitamin B and salts which supports the growth of the normal strains of the same organism. The mutant molds can often be made to grow on a so-called complete medium provided with the higher sugars, amino acids, and vitamins. This shows that the gene mutations block a biosynthesis at some point or points along a metabolic path-

[7] Ingram, 1956. Beadle, 1960, 55.
[8] Beadle and Tatum, 1941.

way, and that the gene-controlled metabolic deficiency can be by-passed artificially by feeding the more complex metabolites to the mutant organisms.[9]

By appropriate techniques it is possible to identify the step in a metabolic pathway which is blocked in any given mutant type of the mold. Suppose that Neurospora requires a product D for growth. Suppose further that the normal strain of Neurospora can synthesize D from the raw materials present in a minimal medium, but that an assortment of various mutant strains of Neurospora grow only if D is furnished in a complete medium. Suppose finally that the synthesis of D is known from biochemical studies to take place in a series of successive stages, $A \rightarrow B \rightarrow C \rightarrow D$, where A is some precursor present in the minimal medium. The problem now is to find out which step in this pathway is blocked in each of the various mutant types unable to synthesize D.

This can be determined by culturing the mutant strains on a series of progressively more complete media. If B, which is absent in the minimal medium, is added to that medium in a form in which it can be absorbed by the mold, and if a mutant strain can survive and hence by inference synthesize D on the B-enriched medium, it can be concluded that the nutritional mutant in question is deficient for the ability to carry out the metabolic step $A \rightarrow B$, but can carry out the subsequent steps $B \rightarrow C$ and $C \rightarrow D$. This mutant strain can be designated arbitrarily as type I (see Fig. 12).

Other mutant strains of the mold may be unable to grow even when provided with $A + B$ in their medium, but survive on a medium to which C is added. These mutant types are deficient for the ability to carry out the metabolic step after B, for otherwise they would have been screened out with the type I mutants. They can, however, perform the step after C. The inhibition in this case, therefore, exists at the stage after B and before C, or in other words at $B \rightarrow C$. These mutants are evidently different from the type I mutants, and can be distinguished from the latter as type II (see again Fig. 12).

Still other mutants may fail to grow on either an A, a B, or a C medium, but will grow on the fully complete medium containing D. These type III mutants can be concluded to be lacking in the ability to carry out the final metabolic step $C \rightarrow D$.

In practical laboratory work it is often convenient to work backwards from the complete medium to the minimal medium, rather than forwards from the minimal medium. Thus D can be furnished in

---

[9] *Ibid.*

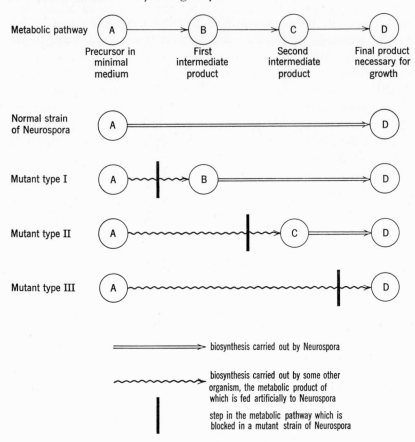

FIG. 12. Nutritional mutants of Neurospora deficient in the ability to carry out different steps in a metabolic synthesis.

the first tests to separate out the whole group of D-deficient mutants. In the second series of screening tests these mutants are grown on a medium containing C but not D. Some mutant molds will grow on the C medium while others will not; the former are type III and the latter are a collection of other types. The unknown mutant types are next assayed by culturing on a medium containing B but not C or D; those which grow on the B medium are type II and those which do not are type I.

By crossing a normal individual of Neurospora with an individual of mutant type I, and growing the progeny of this cross, it is possible to show that the difference between the parental strains in ability to carry out the reaction A → B is due to differences in the alleles of a single gene. By the same standard genetical technique we can show that the metabolic differences between type II and normal molds and between type III and normal molds are likewise inherited as single gene differences. Finally, by intercrossing types I, II, and III in every possible combination, and testing for and excluding the possibility of allelism between the various mutants, it can be established that each type carries a mutation at a different gene locus.

Tatum, Beadle, Horowitz, Srb, and other students of the biochemical genetics of Neurospora have found that many of the single genes in this fungus do control particular reactions in a metabolic pathway. Some 484 nutritional mutants of Neurospora have been obtained, isolated in pure cultures descended from single spores, and put through a series of screening tests designed to reveal the exact nature of their metabolic deficiency. Of these 484 mutant types, 405, or 84%, have been found to require a single specific chemical substance for growth.[10]

As an example we may consider the group of mutant types deficient for the ability to synthesize arginine. This essential amino acid can be synthesized by normal strains of Neurospora, which grow perfectly well on a medium deficient in arginine. Arginine is built up from its precursors in the sequence of steps shown in Fig. 13. The conversion of glutamic acid to ornithine probably takes place in several steps. Ornithine is probably converted to citrulline in two successive steps, and citrulline is converted to arginine in a single reaction.[11]

There are seven mutant types of Neurospora that cannot synthesize arginine due to the failure to synthesize one or another of its precursors. One mutant strain, and hence the mutant allele of one gene, is unable to carry out the single step citrulline → arginine. Two mutant types correspond to the change from ornithine to citrulline, which from chemical considerations probably takes place in two successive steps. Hence two different genes are concerned with this two-stage reaction. Four other mutant types, which are non-allelic *inter se,* can utilize ornithine to synthesize arginine. Therefore, at least four other genes are known in Neurospora, and others probably exist, corresponding to the various steps in the reaction chain leading from glutamic acid to ornithine.[12]

As noted earlier, many other genes are known in Neurospora which

[10] Horowitz, 1950.
[11] Srb and Horowitz, 1944.
[12] *Ibid.*

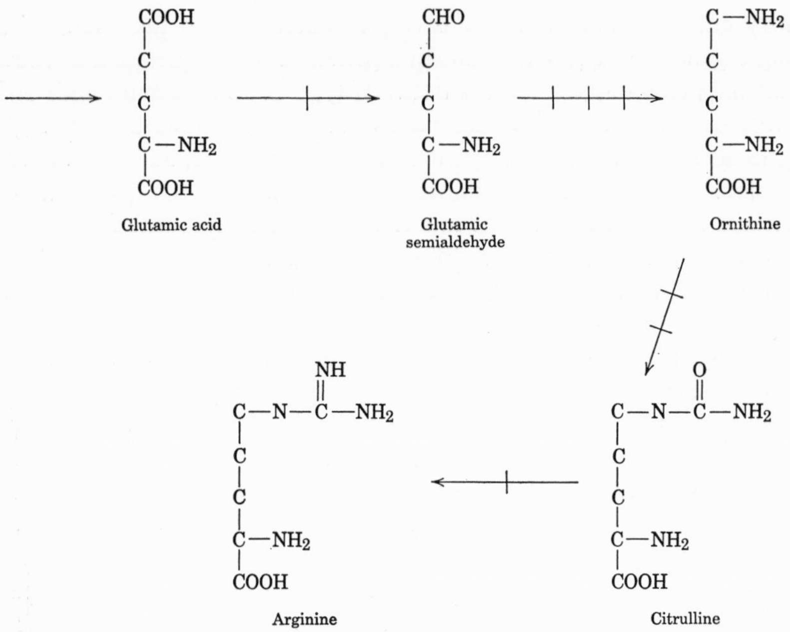

FIG. 13.   Main steps in the synthesis of arginine.   The cross bars in the arrows indicate the positions of known genetic blocks.   (Reprinted with modifications from *Genetics and Metabolism*, by Wagner and Mitchell, copyright 1955, John Wiley, New York, by permission.)

control specific biochemical reactions.[13]   Nutritional mutants deficient in the ability to carry out a particular metabolic step have been found in other fungi, such as Aspergillus, Penicillium, and yeast, and in the colon bacterium (*Escherichia coli*).[14]   Genes known to be responsible for various metabolic disorders in man and other mammals, and for the formation of color pigments in the flowers of plants and in the coats of animals, can likewise be related to particular biochemical reactions or sequences of reactions.[15]   The control of biochemical reactions is probably one of the primary effects of gene action in all organisms, animals and plants as well as microorganisms.

The evidence of biochemical genetics does not entitle us to conclude, however, that all genes are alike in terms of specificity of action.

---

[13] Wagner and Mitchell, 1955, Chapter 8, for review of examples.

[14] *Ibid.*, 109.

[15] Reviews in Srb and Owen, 1952, Chapter 17; and Wagner and Mitchell, 1955, Chapters 7, 8.

We cannot say that each gene in every organism has but a single primary function, apart from self-duplication, namely to direct a single biochemical reaction. A direct correlation between single genes and single metabolic steps has been established for many genes in Neurospora and other organisms. It is recognized by the Neurospora workers, however, that the experimental technique used in the studies of nutritional mutants is such as to select and accumulate the types of mutations which block particular steps in a metabolic sequence. The numerous mutant types that do not have simple metabolic effects and hence do not respond to single precursor substances are automatically eliminated from the research program by their own inviability under the specialized nutritional conditions prevailing in the culture media. The class of intractable mutants may include numerous cases of genes which have two or more primary functions and consequently control more than one chemical reaction.

Among any representative sample of genes of known primary effects, many would be expected to direct single biochemical reactions, while others might control two or more reactions. Still other genes might be difficult to classify according to their mode of action, because it is not always possible to decide what constitutes a single gene or what constitutes a single primary function. But whether genes have single or multiple primary functions, they exert their influence by directing the course of biochemical reactions.

GENES AND ENZYMES

It has long been known that biochemical reactions are controlled by enzymes, which have a specificity equal to that of their products. The genes are also seen to control biochemical reactions in specific ways. As Beadle and Tatum pointed out in 1941, many studies "tend to support the assumption that gene and enzyme specificities are of the same order." [16] Since genes and enzymes have similar effects in the cell, it was logical to suggest that genes either act directly as enzymes or indirectly through enzymes. This inference was drawn by Garrod in *Inborn Errors of Metabolism* (1909–1923), by Goldschmidt in 1916 and later in *Die quantitativen Grundlagen von Vererbung und Artbildung* (1920),[17] by Wright in 1927, Haldane in 1937, Beadle and Tatum in 1941, and various other workers.

---

[16] Beadle and Tatum, 1941.
[17] See Goldschmidt, 1938, for references.

The hypothesis that the genes *are* enzymes had an appealing simplicity which accounts for its wide acceptance at one time. But the enzymes which have been obtained in purified form and determined for chemical composition have turned out to be proteins, whereas the genes that have been identified chemically have turned out to be predominantly or entirely nucleic acid. The remaining possibility is that the genes produce specific enzymes which in turn direct and regulate specific reactions.

Direct evidence that genes act through enzymes has been obtained in a number of cases. A classical case studied by Garrod is that of a hereditary disease in man known as alcaptonuria. The urine of alcaptonuric persons turns black on exposure to air. The blackness of the urine is due to the abnormal accumulation in the urine of an organic acid, which in normal persons is broken down into simpler components by an enzyme present in the blood. The difference in the urine of normal persons and alcaptonuric persons can be reduced to the presence or absence of a certain enzyme. Since alcaptonuria is inherited as a single recessive character, the presence or absence of a critical enzyme in the blood can be traced ultimately to the normal or mutant alleles respectively of a single gene.[18]

Correlations have been shown to exist between single genes and enzymes in a number of other instances. Genes are known which affect the enzymes controlling sugar fermentation in yeasts, cyanide production in white clover (*Trifolium repens*), and the hydrolysis or breakdown of the alkaloid atropine by rabbits.[19]

In Neurospora it is known that different genes control different metabolic steps, and it is probable that the steps in the reaction chain are also controlled by different enzymes. A good correlation thus exists between the known action of each gene and the presumed action of each putative enzyme. The difference between the normal and mutant alleles of one gene may be such as to determine the action or failure of a specific enzyme. And the different genes for which mutant alleles are known could be inferred to control different enzymes in a stepwise series of reactions. These considerations have led Horowitz to suggest that the primary function of those genes which act on specific steps in a reaction sequence is to control the production or action of a specific enzyme.

---

[18] Reviews in Srb and Owen, 1952, 352–354; and Wagner and Mitchell, 1955, 165–166.

[19] See Wagner and Mitchell, 1955, 161–188, for review.

Horowitz states: [20]

. . . with one or two doubtful exceptions, the analyzed biochemical mutants of Neurospora behave as if the only effect of the mutation is to abolish a single reaction in the synthesis of an essential metabolite. This has led to the hypothesis that a large class of genes exists in which each gene controls the synthesis of, or the activity of, but a single enzyme, a supposition which has come to be known as the "one gene–one enzyme hypothesis."

As we have seen in the preceding section, it is possible or even probable that some genes in Neurospora may control two or more separate chemical reactions. The corollary, which is implicit in Horowitz's statement quoted above, is that while some genes may exert their effects through single enzymes, other genes may determine the action of two or more enzymes.

THE IMMEDIATE PRODUCT OF GENE ACTION

If the genes are not themselves enzymes, but organizers of enzymes, the question which logically follows is how do genes control enzymes? Do genes produce enzymes directly, or do they produce the precursors of enzymes? What, in other words, is the immediate product of gene action?

Many of the gene-controlled, enzyme-directed biochemical reactions occur outside the nucleus in the cytoplasm of the cell, whereas enzyme activity is generally slight within the nucleus.[21] A direct connection between genes and enzymes is usually precluded by the spatial distribution of the two entities in the cell. An intermediary to establish the required connection between genes and enzymes should, therefore, be found in the cell.

A second type of nucleic acid, ribose nucleic acid or RNA, occurs in both the nucleus and the cytoplasm. RNA like DNA consists of long sugar-phosphate chains with base side-chains, but the sugars in RNA are ribose and contain one more oxygen atom each than the deoxyribose sugars of the DNA macromolecule. RNA not only occurs in both the nucleus and cytoplasm, but moves from nucleus to cytoplasm, and becomes concentrated in regions of active protein synthesis.[22] This suggests that RNA carries a genetic message, so to

---

[20] Horowitz, 1950, 60.
[21] Haldane, 1954a, 118.
[22] Mirsky, 1953.

speak, from the genes to the sites of enzyme activity and protein synthesis.

Good evidence that RNA is directly concerned with protein synthesis is furnished by the studies of Fraenkel-Conrat and his coworkers on tobacco mosaic virus mentioned in Chapter 1. It will be recalled that a particle of this virus consists of a central core of RNA surrounded by a sheath of protein. Different strains of the virus are distinguished by the particular species of protein macromolecule in the sheath. The protein and RNA constituents of each of two virus strains can be separated experimentally and the two constituents can be reassembled in new combinations. The daughter virus particles descended from such "hybrid" combinations are then found to possess the type of protein characteristic for each strain of RNA and not the type of protein possessed by the reconstituted parent. Therefore, the protein of tobacco mosaic virus does not reproduce itself but is built up anew in each generation by the RNA of this organism. Furthermore, the specific type of protein macromolecule is determined directly by the specific type of RNA present.

It will be recalled that enzymes and other proteins are composed of amino acids linked together in polypeptide chains. There are some twenty different types of amino acids. The types and sequence of these amino acid units in the polypeptide chain determine the characteristics of each species of protein. The synthesis of a given kind of protein macromolecule thus depends on the lining up of the various types of amino acids in a particular sequence. There is evidence to support the hypothesis that the formation of specific kinds of enzymes and other proteins, though controlled ultimately by genes, is guided directly by RNA intermediaries in the following way.[23]

A particular sequence of nucleotides in a relatively short section of DNA, acting as a template, forms an equally short chain of RNA with a complementary order of nucleotides. The DNA chain forms the RNA chain by a copying process similar to that which under other conditions leads to the formation of new complementary DNA strands. The short RNA chain thus produced, called transfer RNA, has a specific affinity for a particular type of amino acid. Presumably there exists a different type of transfer RNA for each of the twenty-odd kinds of amino acid. The various kinds of transfer RNA hook on to their respective types of amino acids and carry them to the sites of protein synthesis in the cytoplasm.

---

[23] The account given here is based largely on an excellent non-technical review by Allfrey and Mirsky, 1961, to which the reader is referred for more details and for mention of the research workers involved. See also Hoagland, 1959.

Present in these protein-synthesizing centers is a second form of RNA, known as template RNA, which consists of a long chain, coiled in a helix, and subdivided into sections—each of which has a base order complementary to that of one of the various types of transfer RNA. When the short chains of transfer RNA come into contact with the long chain of template RNA, each type of transfer RNA fits into its mirror-image section on the template chain. As the molecules of transfer RNA get into place on the helical template RNA macromolecule, the amino acids which they carry are also aligned in the proper sequence to form the polypeptide chain characteristic of a particular species of protein.

It will be noted that only four types of nucleotides are available in the DNA chain and in the RNA chain derived from it to specify the identity of twenty types of amino acids in the polypeptide chain of a protein. How can the "genetic information" contained in the four-letter code of DNA and RNA be translated into the twenty-letter alphabet that spells out protein structure? It has been suggested that, whereas single nucleotides would be inadequate for this task, different combinations of three adjacent nucleotides, termed triplets, could easily provide the requisite diversity. Thus the triplet TGC on the DNA chain might correspond to one kind of amino acid, ATG to another, CAA to still another amino acid, and so on.[24]

ENZYME ACTION

The enzymes, once formed in a cell, then enable that cell to carry out the numerous biochemical reactions and synthesize the many other substances necessary for life. The specificity of each enzyme, which causes it to guide a specific chemical reaction in a very precise way, is believed to be due to the surface configuration of the enzyme molecule, which is due in turn to its particular chemical structure. Each enzyme is supposed to fit its substrate like a key fits a lock.

An enzyme is produced by green mold which ferments and breaks down the dextro form of tartaric acid but not the levo form of the same compound. These two stereoisomers are exactly the same chemically but differ in the direction of rotation of the molecular axis.[25] Apparently the enzyme of green mold has a molecular structure enabling it to fit dextrotartaric acid, but not the mirror-image molecules of levotartaric acid.

The oxidation of acetic acid is catalyzed by a certain enzyme which

---

[24] Allfrey and Mirsky, 1961. Beadle, 1962. Crick, 1962.
[25] Pasteur in 1860; see Pfeiffer, 1948.

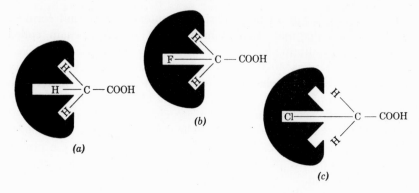

FIG. 14. Diagrammatic representation of the lock and key relationship between an enzyme and its substrate. (*a*) The enzyme (shown black) and part of an acetic acid molecule. (*b*) The same enzyme with monofluoroacetate. (*c*) With monochloroacetate. Explanation in text. (From Pfeiffer, in *Scientific American*, 1948, by permission.)

is believed to correspond closely in structure to the size and shape of one end of the acetic acid molecule. (See Fig. 14*a*.) This enzyme brings about the breakdown of acetic acid but not of the closely related compounds, monofluoroacetate and monochloroacetate, which contain a fluorine or a chlorine atom in the position occupied by one of the hydrogen atoms in acetic acid. (Fig. 14*b* and *c*.) These molecules differ in the length of the link between the terminal group of three atoms and the rest of the molecule, this link being 1.09 A. long in acetic acid, 1.41 A. long in monofluoroacetate, and 1.76 A. in monochloroacetate. The enzyme probably has a structure into which the acetic acid molecule but not the other types of molecules can fit properly.

There is a further difference between monofluoroacetate and monochloroacetate. Although the enzyme cannot catalyze the oxidation of either of these two compounds, the former renders the enzyme impotent to oxidize acetic acid, while the latter has no such inhibiting effect on the enzyme. This result can be explained by supposing that monofluoroacetate, which differs only slightly from acetic acid in the length of the terminal link, is able to fit into the structural configuration of the enzyme molecule and block its action on acetic acid; whereas monochloroacetate, being more dissimilar from acetic acid in its dimensions, does not fit into the enzyme molecule well enough to inhibit its activity (Fig. 14). The enzyme in relation to acetic acid is like a key that turns a lock; in relation to monofluoroacetate it is like a key that fits a lock but does not work it; and in relation to mono-chloroacetate it is like a key that cannot fit into the lock.[26]

The way in which the structure of the enzyme molecule may enable it to catalyze one particular chemical reaction and not others has been explained in clear and simple terms by Pfeiffer in an article written for non-chemical readers.[27]

The lock-key theory implies that there is some sort of fleeting union between enzyme and substrate, an implication which has been backed by many experiments. As a matter of fact, the spectroscope has permitted biologists to "see" the union taking place. This was attempted for the first time [in 1936] by Kurt G. Stern, then at Yale University. Using the enzyme catalase and a hydrogen peroxide derivative as substrate, he observed first the spectral light pattern characteristic of catalase and then a new pattern, presumably that of the enzyme-substrate union. A short while afterward, however, the original catalase spectrum appeared again, indicating that the enzyme had performed its duty and was ready for more work.

What is the purpose of the brief combination of an enzyme with its substrate? The answer to the question hinges on [the fact that] not all collisions between molecules produce chemical reactions. In a 100-cubic-centimeter solution of ethyl bromide and diethyl sulfide, for instance, there are 1.6×10^{34} . . . collisions a second, but fewer than one out of every billion billion collisions results in a chemical reaction. The reason for this low proportion of successful hits is that molecules are relatively stable structures, and most of them bounce off each other a bit jarred but essentially unscathed.

Now enzymes do not increase the speed of molecules in solution, nor do they increase the frequency of collisions. Instead they increase the number of fruitful collisions by weakening the structure of substrate molecules so that they react more readily. In combining briefly with its substrate (in the case of catalase the combination lasts less than one 85,000th of a second), an enzyme somehow distorts the architecture of the substrate molecule, converting it from a relatively stable to a highly reactive state. There is evidence that in some cases this effect is achieved by removing electrons and transforming the substrate molecules into a charged ion.

GENES AND DEVELOPMENT

The molecular structure of a genic segment of DNA is the beginning, but only the beginning, of a complex chain of events which culminates in the development of a morphological or physiological character. The ultimate phenotypic expression of a gene—the physiological prop-

---

[26] Barron; see Pfeiffer, 1948.
[27] Pfeiffer, 1948.

erty or morphological character of the organism—is removed from the primary biochemical action of the gene by many, usually poorly understood developmental steps.

In an analogous fashion the fine physical structure in the grooves of a phonograph record is the beginning, but just the beginning, of a process which may result in the production of a characteristic sound by a phonograph. Each specific pattern of waves in the grooves of the record predetermines a specific sound. The variety of wave patterns and of sound effects is apparently as unlimited as the variety of genes and of phenotypic effects. The ultimate sound expression of a record is, however, many steps removed in the chain of causes and effects from the structural configuration engraved in its grooves.

Single causes commonly produce multiple primary effects, each of which then determines multiple secondary effects. As the cause-effect sequence progresses through time the number of effects increases at a compound rate. A multiplicity of end effects thus follows from simple initial causal factors.[28] The multiplication of effects is as true of the causal relations between gene action and the development of phenotypic characteristics as of other types of causal sequences in living and non-living systems.

The large number of developmental steps intervening between gene and character, and the opportunity for a compounding of effects on a wide scale during a long stepwise process, make it very difficult to trace out the developmental sequence in detail. The biochemical geneticist can sometimes work forward from a gene to its secondary or tertiary gene products, and the developmental geneticist can sometimes work backwards from a mature character expression to its onto-genetical antecedents, but it is rarely possible to account for each step in the whole long process of development from gene to character.[29]

We have seen, for example, that different alleles of the gene **Hb** in man determine the formation of different kinds of hemoglobin molecules. The action of the gene **Hb** does not stop with hemoglobin synthesis, however, but continues further in the formation of different types of red blood cells. The various kinds of red blood cells have effects of their own on the phenotypic characteristics of the individual. Persons carrying hemoglobin C in their blood have one set of clinical symptoms of anemia; persons with hemoglobin S exhibit anemic symp-

[28] Spencer, 1884, Chapter 20.

[29] With regard to the subject of this section, the reader's attention is called to a recent authoritative treatment by Waddingon, *New Patterns in Genetics and Development* (1962), which comes to hand as the present manuscript goes to press.

toms of a different sort; and persons carrying hemoglobin A do not have anemia of the foregoing types. We are still not ended with the phenotypic effects of the **Hb** gene, however, for the heterozygote hb^A hb^S with mixtures of both hemoglobin A and hemoglobin S is more resistant to malaria than the non-anemic homozygous genotype carrying only hb^A alleles and producing only type A hemoglobin.[30]

The term pleiotropy is used to denote the occurrence of diverse phenotypic effects as a result of the action of a single gene. Since gene action ordinarily does lead to a multiplicity of phenotypic effects, there is reason to believe that pleiotropy is a general phenomenon.

Several cases of pleiotropy have been worked out by Grüneberg, Dunn and others in mice and rats. A good example is summarized in Fig. 15. A certain mutant allele in the rat, which brings about the death of the newborn young, affects various different organs—heart, lungs, nose, teeth, etc. These diverse pleiotropic effects can all be traced back to a defective formation of cartilage in the embryo, as shown in Fig. 15.

In the tobacco plant, *Nicotiana tabacum,* a gene **S** affects the form of the leaves, calyx, corolla, the anthers of the stamens, and the seed pods or capsules. The allele S produces leaves with long petioles and acuminate tips, calyces with long slender teeth, corolla lobes with slight points, long anthers, and capsules with a long narrow form. (See Fig. 16.) Plants homozygous for the recessive allele s have the contrasting leaf, flower, and fruit characters shown in Fig. 16, namely unpetioled and oval leaves, short-toothed calyces and unpointed corollas, and roundish anthers and capsules. These pleiotropic effects could be due to a single mode of action of the gene **S** during development. The allele S may cause all of the lateral organs of the plants, the various flower parts as well as the foliage leaves, to grow long and narrow, while the allele s brings about a short broad growth of the same organs.[31]

The relation between gene action and character expression is complicated by at least two other factors in addition to the large number of developmental steps and the pleiotropic multiplication of effects. One of these additional complicating factors is interaction between different genes. The various genes constituting an organism's genotype do not act singly but in concert. Most characters, in other words, are determined not by the action of any single gene but by several

[30] Allison, 1956.
[31] Stebbins, 1959.

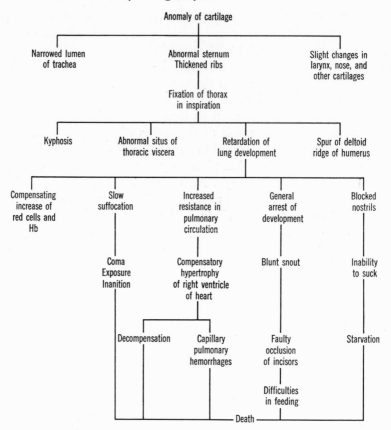

FIG. 15. The pleiotropic effects of a certain lethal allele in the rat. (From *Animal Genetics and Medicine,* by Gruneberg, 1947, by permission of Cassell, London.)

or many genes. The development of some character is likely to be controlled by the coordinated action of several genes concerned directly with different stages or facets of the development; and in addition many other genes in the complement, which have other primary functions of their own and are not directly concerned with the character in question, may nevertheless contribute to its development as so-called modifying genes or modifiers.

With regard to the intricate relationship between genes and characters, Stern has the following to say: [32]

---

[32] Stern, 1949*b*, 15.

For most characters of multicellular organisms the relation between genes and character is not that of "one-to-one" but that of a long multi-dimensional network of interrelations between numerous genes and their interweaving reaction sequences. Consequently, changes in many genes may affect the "same" character. Thus, in corn (*Zea mays*) at least 50 genic loci in chromosomes have been discovered all of which are concerned with the production of chlorophyll. A change in any of these loci may result in absence or abnormality of pigment. In *Drosophila* more than 40 loci are known to affect eye color, and at least 43 jointly to be responsible for normal, flat wings. Reduction in wing size, an evolutionary important trait, has been found to be caused by each one of 34 different loci. In mice, shortness of tail is known to be due to any one of 10 different loci.

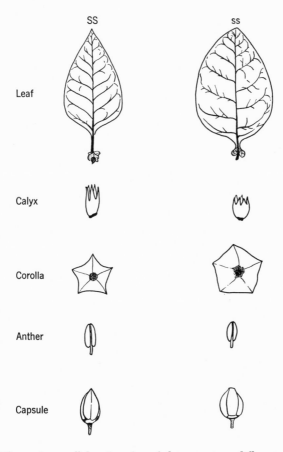

FIG. 16. Effects of two alleles, S and s, of the gene **S** on different organs in the tobacco plant. (From Stebbins, in *Vistas in Botany*, copyright 1959, Pergamon Press, New York, by permission.)

It is evident that if a character is determined directly by the joint action of several genes primarily concerned with the trait in question, and is affected indirectly by many other modifying genes, and if furthermore these genes each produce pleiotropic effects, it will be very difficult to trace the interwoven pathway from gene to character. The complexity of this pathway has been described by Horowitz and Leupold:[33]

The ultimate effect of a mutation is the result of an enormous magnification of the initial gene change, brought about through a system of reactions which, originating at the gene, rapidly branches out in various directions and coalesces with similar networks deriving from other loci to form a reticulum of as yet indeterminate extent and complexity.

Finally, the effects of gene action are modified by the environmental conditions. One and the same allele will produce different phenotypic effects in different environments. Clonal divisions of the perennial herb *Potentilla glandulosa,* with the same genetic constitution but grown in different environments, develop short branches and small leaves in the open sun, and long branches bearing large leaves in the shade.[34] The environmental factors in this case are external to the organism. Of equal importance perhaps as a modifying condition, though less easy to observe, is the internal environment, the physical and chemical factors surrounding the sites of gene activity within the cell.

Enzymes are usually active only within a certain range of temperatures, or at certain levels of acidity or alkalinity in the solution, etc. If an enzyme which controls the synthesis of a pigment is capable of acting only at certain temperatures, the product of the enzyme activity will be formed at the critical temperatures and will not be formed otherwise. The gene that produces the enzyme which produces the pigment will then also have one phenotypic expression under one set of temperature conditions, and a different phenotypic expression at other temperatures.

These considerations may be summarized by a generalized scheme showing the manifold influences of modifier genes and environmental factors on a developmental pathway leading from gene to character.[35] (See Fig. 17.) It is evident from the diagram of Fig. 17 that the phenotypic character is determined not only by the one or more genes

---

[33] Horowitz and Leupold, 1951.
[34] Clausen, Keck, and Hiesey, 1940.
[35] Timofeeff-Ressovsky, 1934. Stern, 1960, 325.

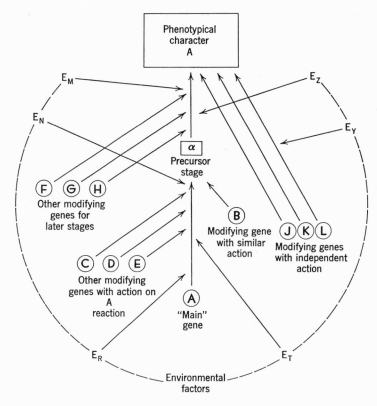

FIG. 17. Generalized scheme showing the influence of various kinds of modifying genes and environmental factors on the developmental pathway leading from gene to character. (From *Principles of Human Genetics,* by Stern, after Timofeeff-Ressovsky, copyright 1960, W. H. Freeman, San Francisco, by permission.)

principally involved, but also by innumerable modifying influences—genetic and environmental—that come into play at different points in the developmental sequence.

EPILOGUE

The genes are comparable to the sections of a phonograph record, in that both entities have a specific physical structure which determines a specific but modifiable expression that can be copied exactly in reproduction. It is tempting to extend the analogy by comparing the individual gene with a musical chord on the record. The gene consists of smaller units—nucleotides, triplets, and subgenes—just as the chord consists of separate notes. In the same way that chords are built up into phrases, some genes are organized, as we shall see later in Chapter 6, into functional units of a higher order occupying a continuous segment on a chromosome—linked serial genes and supergenes. The chromosome as a whole is comparable to a part or movement, and the genotype is symbolized by the whole composition.

The "genetic constitution" of a phonograph record—the particular wave pattern in its grooves—is fixed at the time it is made and remains constant during its lifetime. The record gives forth essentially the same sounds when played on different phonographs and in different rooms. But everyone knows that the quality of the sounds produced by a record does vary according to the particular phonograph on which the record is played, and the acoustical properties of the room in which the phonograph is located. The modifying influence of the phonograph on the performance of a phonograph record is like the action of the internal environment on the expression of a gene or gene system, and the influence of the room may be likened to the external environment.

Allele interaction

3 Nearly all animals, many plants, and many protistans are diploid. The individual organism in such cases carries, in most cells of its body, two sets of chromosomes and hence two alleles of each gene. There are, to be sure, exceptions to this rule, for some tissues of a predominantly diploid body may contain more or less than two chromosome sets, and the diploid cells of the same body may carry certain chromosomes and the genes borne on them in a single or multiple rather than a double dose; nevertheless, the diploid condition prevails for most genes in most tissues of the body of a great many organisms.

The two homologous alleles of each gene in the diploid cell may be alike (as in homozygotes) or unlike (in heterozygotes). In either case an opportunity exists for complex interactions between the two alleles of a gene. The ultimate phenotypic expression of the gene is affected by this interaction of the two alleles, as well as by the influences of other genes and the environment. In this chapter we shall attempt to interpret, in terms of the principles of gene action summarized in Chapter 2, the control exercised by pairs of alleles on the development of phenotypic characteristics.

DOMINANCE

When the phenotypic characteristics of an individual heterozygous for one pair of alleles are compared with the phenotypes of the corresponding homozygotes, the results are found to vary according to the particular gene involved. The heterozygote may exhibit characteristics which are just like those of one homozygous type (complete

54   The architecture of the germplasm

dominance); or the heterozygote may be very similar phenotypically to one homozygote (incomplete dominance); or intermediate between the two homozygous parents (intermediacy, codominance); or, finally, dissimilar from either homozygote (overdominance or heterosis). The various phenotypic expressions of heterozygotes will be discussed below in this order.

Mendel discovered in his hybridization experiments with peas that the heterozygous F_1 individuals generally exhibited the same characteristics as one of the two contrasting parental types. Thus in crosses between round-seeded plants and plants with wrinkled seeds, the heterozygotes have round seeds. The heterozygous type b_1b_2 has the same observable characteristics as the homozygous type b_1b_1 but is unlike the other homozygous type b_2b_2 (Fig. 2). Evidently one of the two alleles present in the heterozygote, namely b_1, is somehow more effective in determining the shape of the seeds than is the other allele, b_2. The former is said to be dominant and the latter recessive. Dominance of one allele over another has been found to be a widespread, though not universal, feature of heterozygotes, not only in peas, but also in fruitflies, corn plants, man, and many other organisms.

Dominance occurs when one allele, present singly in a heterozygote, brings about the same phenotypic effect as arises when the same allele is present doubly in a homozygote. The development of a character then follows essentially the same course and arrives at essentially the same final product under the controlling influence of either the genotype a_1a_2 or the genotype a_1a_1. This result could be due to three possible relationships between the two alleles in the heterozygote.[1] First, the dominant allele a_1 may act, while the recessive allele a_2 is inactive, so that the phenotypic product of a_1a_2 is the same as that of a_1a_1. Secondly, both alleles a_1 and a_2 may act in similar ways, but a_1 has stronger effects than a_2. Thirdly, the two alleles may act in opposite directions, as where a_1 causes one biochemical reaction and a_2 another alternative reaction, but the effects of the gene action of a_1 prevail over those of a_2.

If we symbolize the type of action of an allele by the direction of an arrow, and the strength of the allele action by the length of the arrow, the three modes of relative action between two alleles, a_1 and a_2, which lead to phenotypic effects similar to those of a_1a_1, may be written as follows.

---

[1] Muller in 1932; see Stern 1949a; 1960, 48–49. Also Wagner and Mitchell, 1955, Chapter 9.

(1) Inactivity of one allele: $a_1 \longrightarrow$
(a_2)

(2) Cumulative action of both alleles: $a_1 \longrightarrow$
$a_2 \rightarrow$

(3) Competition between the two alleles: $a_1 \longrightarrow$.[2]
$\leftarrow a_2$

The relations between two of the several known alleles of the gene **I** controlling the type of blood in man provide an example of the first case cited above. The homozygous individuals $i^0 i^0$ have type O blood; the homozygotes $i^A i^A$ have type A blood; and the heterozygotes $i^A i^0$ also have blood of type A, as though the i^0 allele is nearly or quite inactive in the heterozygous individuals.[3]

Case 2, where different alleles work in the same direction but with unequal effectiveness, may be a very common situation. This can be illustrated by the effects of different combinations of two alleles of the gene **Y** controlling the vitamin A content of corn endosperm. The endosperm of corn grains contains three sets of chromosomes. The two alleles, the dominant Y and recessive y, can therefore be combined in four genotypes: yyy, yyY, yYY, and YYY. The vitamin A content of the endosperm closely parallels the dosage of the Y allele. The number of vitamin A units per gram in each of the four genotypes is:

0.05 units in yyy

2.25   yyY

5.00   yYY

7.50   YYY

The dominant allele Y is thus chiefly responsible for the formation of vitamin A in this tissue, and the effects of two or three Y alleles are additive and equal, but the y allele probably also produces some vitamin A, as indicated by the presence of traces of this product in the homozygous recessive genotype yyy.[4]

Competition between different alleles (case 3 above) can be illustrated by the gene **Ci** controlling the development of a certain wing vein known as the cubital vein in *Drosophila melanogaster*. The mutant allele (ci) of this gene has the effect of interrupting the continuity of the cubital vein, from which it has gained the name "cubitus inter-

---

[2] Stern, 1960, 48–49.
[3] *Loc. cit.*
[4] Mangelsdorf and Fraps in 1931; see Goldschmidt, 1955, 383.

(a)   (b)   (c)   (d)

FIG. 18. Wings of female flies of *Drosophila melanogaster* with normal and various mutant conditions of the cubital vein. (*a*) Normal. (*b*) Vein thin in one
region. (*c*) Short gap in vein. (*d*) Broad gap in vein. (Stern, 1943.)

ruptus." The normal allele (ci^+ or simply $+$) causes a continuous
cubital vein to develop. The normal wing venation is shown in Fig.
18*a* and the mutant phenotype in Fig. 18*c* and *d*.[5]

The two alleles may be present in various combinations and dosages.
The principal homozygous and heterozygous classes are, of course,
ci/ci, $+/+$, and $+/$ci. In addition, exceptional flies with an extra
chromosome may have the genotypes ci/ci/ci and $+/$ci/ci. Finally,
hemizygous types, which are deficient for one of the two homologous
chromosome segments carrying the **Ci** gene, may have the constitution
ci/o or $+/$o.

Flies with the constitution $+/+$ or $+/$o have normal wing veins of
the type shown in Fig. 18*a*. Flies carrying only the ci allele have
mutant wings. The amount of reduction in the cubital vein varies,
however, from a slight thinning in one region (Fig. 18*b*) to a broad
gap (Fig. 18*d*), in proportion to the number of doses of the ci allele.
Stern found that the genotype ci/o brings about strongly mutant wings
as in Fig. 18*d*; ci/ci produces wing veins with short to broad gaps
(18*c* or *d*); and the phenotypic expression of the genotype ci/ci/ci is
a wing vein with a thin region or a short gap (18*b* or *c*). Contrary to
expectation, therefore, increasing the dosage of the mutant allele does
not lead to a more strongly mutant expression, but rather to an approach to a normal phenotype.

Now the cubital vein is formed developmentally by the activity of
the **Ci** gene in converting a substrate material into a vein structure.
The $+$ allele in one or two doses builds a normal vein. The ci allele

[5] Stern, 1943.

in one dose fails to form a good vein, in two doses forms a vein with a wide gap, and in three doses builds a slightly interrupted vein. One dose of the + allele leads to the formation of more vein structure than three doses of ci allele, and therefore the normal allele is more effective than the mutant allele in producing the cubital wing vein.

We note, however, that either allele when present in a sufficient dosage can build a normal or nearly normal vein. The like alleles combined in the various homozygous flies work in the same direction and have additive phenotypic effects.[6]

But in heterozygous flies of the constitution +/ci/ci the wing veins are broken by a broad gap, as in Fig. 18*d*. The combination of unlike alleles brings about a strong inhibition of vein formation. This fact suggests that there are alternative ways of building a vein, the ci allele working in one way and the + allele in another. The different alleles may carry out reactions that are opposed to one another, so that when combined in a cell their actions are antagonistic.[7]

INTERMEDIACY, INCOMPLETE
DOMINANCE, AND CODOMINANCE

As noted earlier, the dominance of one allele over another is by no means a universal feature of the relations between different alleles in heterozygous genotypes. It is well known, for example, that the heterozygous plants derived from the crossing of true-breeding red-flowered four-o'clocks (*Mirabilis jalapa*) with true-breeding white-flowered four-o'clocks have pink flowers. Both alleles exert their effects on the phenotype of the heterozygote, which is intermediate in character, and dominance is consequently absent.

In some cases where dominance is present, it has been possible after a more thorough examination to show that the heterozygote is slightly different from the dominant homozygous class. The dominance is, therefore, incomplete. Mendel observed that the round form of pea seeds is dominant over the wrinkled form. Later workers, re-examining this case during the early period of Mendelian genetics in the present century, found that heterozygous smooth peas differed from homozygous smooth peas in the microscopic appearance of the starch grains.[8] The recessive allele for wrinkled seeds thus has a

---

[6] *Ibid.*

[7] *Ibid.*

[8] For references see Sirks, 1956, 125–126; and Yarnell, 1962, 474.

definite but slight phenotypic effect in the heterozygote. The dominance of the round form of peas, in other words, is not complete.

Stern and his collaborators investigated the effects on viability of seventy-seven recessive lethal alleles in *Drosophila melanogaster*. The viability of the normal homozygous flies was taken to be a standard value of 100%; the homozygous recessive types were, of course, lethal and did not live. The viability of the heterozygotes differed from that of the corresponding homozygous dominant type in every case. In most of the heterozygous combinations the viability was between 92% and 97% of that of normal homozygous flies. From these average levels the viability of flies heterozygous for a "recessive" lethal allele ranged down to 60% in some cases and up to 130% of normal viability in other instances. The recessive alleles of many different genes in Drosophila thus generally produce a detectable effect, though usually a slight one, in the heterozygotes.[9]

The two different alleles may function somewhat independently of one another in the heterozygous combination. The phenotype of the heterozygote is neither dominant nor intermediate, but exhibits a mixture of the products formed by the two respective alleles. This situation, known as codominance, is exemplified by one of the combinations of the blood group alleles in man. The allele i^A produces blood solely of type A in the homozygote $i^A i^A$; similarly the allele i^B when homozygous produces solely type B blood; while the heterozygote $i^A i^B$ produces blood containing a mixture of the A and B substances.[10] Again, as mentioned in the preceding chapter, persons heterozygous for different alleles of the gene **Hb**, concerned with hemoglobin synthesis, have mixtures of different types of hemoglobin in their red blood cells. Thus the heterozygote $hb^A hb^S$ produces both hemoglobin A and hemoglobin S.

It may be wondered whether codominance, as seen when the biochemical products of allele action are examined, may not be responsible for some cases of morphological intermediacy of heterozygotes. We shall see below that codominance may also be a preliminary step towards overdominance or heterosis.

SINGLE GENE HETEROSIS

Certain paired combinations of dissimilar alleles of a given gene **A** may lead to a greater productiveness than is brought about by the

---

[9] Stern, Carson, Kinst, Novitski, and Uphoff, 1952.
[10] Stern, 1960, 51.

corresponding homozygous combinations. The heterozygote then exceeds the mean of the corresponding homozygotes for some measurable phenotypic character, like size, weight, vigor, seed output, or egg production. The condition where Aa > AA or aa is referred to as overdominance or single gene heterosis.

Some heterozygous combinations in the Drosophila study carried out by Stern and his coworkers and described above proved to have a viability much greater than the most viable parent. One of the two alleles present in such flies was lethal when homozygous; the other allele when present in two doses produced normal viability; but the combination of a lethal and a normal allele resulted in supervital flies with a viability 30% greater than the norm. Similarly, in man we have seen that the heterozygote hb^A hb^S has a greater resistance to malaria and is more viable in a malarial environment than the homozygotes. In this case both alleles are active in a way that brings about codominance at the molecular level and heterosis at the organismic level.

Cases have been reported in Drosophila, man, mice, corn, barley, and snapdragons (*Antirrhinum majus*) where individuals heterozygous for some particular gene are superior in growth, viability, or fecundity to the corresponding homozygotes.[11] In these cases the observed differences in phenotypic traits are correlated mainly but not entirely with the various heterozygous or homozygous combinations of alleles at a single gene locus. On the basis of this correlation a number of students have accepted the hypothesis that heterozygosity for a single gene *may* have an enhancing effect on the development and functioning of the phenotype.[12]

The hypothesis of single gene heterosis is rejected by other workers on the grounds that the effects of interactions between the alleged heterotic allele pair and other genes of the complement cannot be excluded from the picture.[13] This argument loses much of its force in certain cases in barley, where a heterotic F$_1$ hybrid is heterozygous for a single gene but homozygous for the other genes of the complement, which consequently form a constant genetic background in relation to the heterozygous allele pair.[14] The cogency of the argument

[11] Whaley, 1952. Da Cunha, 1953. Stubbe, 1953. Hagberg, 1953. Schuler, 1954. Dunn and Suckling, 1955. Allison, 1956. Mukai and Burdick, 1959. Schnick, Mukai, and Burdick, 1960.
[12] This interpretation is favored by the authors cited in footnote 11, except Schuler, and by various other authors, myself included, some of whom are cited in footnotes 15 and 17.
[13] Schuler, 1954. Mather, 1955. Jinks, 1955.
[14] Hagberg, 1953.

against single gene heterosis is again weakened, and for a similar rea-son, in its application to an example described in Neurospora.

Although the nuclei of Neurospora are haploid, nuclei derived from different parental strains can become associated in a single fungus body. A hybrid fungus containing separate haploid nuclei of different parentage is known as a heterocaryon. In a genetical and physio-logical sense a heterocaryon is comparable to a heterozygote in dip-loid organisms. In an experiment carried out by Emerson, a particu-lar heterocaryon containing nuclei which differed in the alleles of a single gene, and not in other genes of the complement, grew better than either pure or homocaryotic parental strain.[15]

The biochemical basis of the single gene heterosis was worked out in this case. One homocaryotic strain, and hence one allele, when present alone apparently synthesizes too little of a vitamin (para-amino-ben-zoic acid) necessary for growth. The other homocaryotic strain and hence the alternative allele produces a deleterious excess of the same growth substance. But the heterocaryon in which the two alleles are present together achieves a balance which promotes optimum growth.[16]

Haldane has suggested that, in general, homozygotes may be able to produce only single kinds of enzymes for each gene, and may be restricted on this account to specialized reactions taking place within a narrow range of environmental conditions. Heterozygotes, on the other hand, by producing a mixture of different enzymes, may be able to function in more diverse ways and over a wider range of environ-mental conditions.[17] The superior fitness of some heterozygotes is then favored by a biochemical complexity brought about by the joint action of related but somewhat different alleles.

Heterosis or hybrid vigor is of widespread occurrence in plants and animals. Most actual cases of hybrid vigor, as observed for example in hybrid corn, are due to the actions and interactions of numerous genes. The genetic mechanisms involved are very complex and, despite much study by plant and animal breeders, are still not fully understood. We are concerned here, not with the whole complex problem of heterosis as such,[18] but rather with evidence suggesting that inter-actions between alleles of one gene may, in special cases, produce

---

[15] Emerson, 1952.   Beadle, 1953.

[16] *Ibid.*

[17] Haldane, 1954*a*, 121.

[18] For further reading on this subject see Gowen, 1952, and Allard, 1960.   We will discuss another aspect of heterosis in Chapter 9.

heterotic effects. The simplified model of single gene heterosis may provide a useful key for explaining a part of the more complex phenomena found in actual situations.

PHYSIOLOGICAL HOMEOSTASIS

Organisms generally exhibit some degree of stability or constancy in the face of changing environmental conditions. This buffering of the individual against fluctuating external conditions is known as physiological homeostasis. There is a good deal of evidence indicating that physiological homeostasis, in many though not in all higher organisms, is associated with heterozygosity. This evidence is based on comparisons between related heterozygotes and homozygotes of Drosophila, chickens, mice, and several kinds of plants with respect to the phenotypic constancy exhibited by certain characters under varying environmental conditions.[19]

Mather measured the variation in style length between flowers of the same plant in long inbred lines of the primrose, *Primula sinensis*, and in their F_1 hybrids. The phenotypic variation due to differences in the development of separate homologous organs on the same plant turned out to be much less in the heterozygotes than in the related homozygotes produced by inbreeding. The variance of the intra-individual style lengths was 0.12 in the F_1's as compared with 0.36 in the inbreds in 1946, and 0.21 for the F_1's versus 0.41 for the inbreds in 1948. Evidently the heterozygous genotypes are more stable than the homozygotes in the development of styles.[20]

Similarly in *Drosophila melanogaster*, the difference between the number of hairs (sternopleural chaetae) on the two sides of an individual fly is more variable in inbred lines of the Oregon and Samarkand strains than it is in their F_1 hybrids.[21] The variation in time of vaginal opening in the house mouse is fairly closely correlated with the degree of homozygosity, which is high in long inbred strains, low in their F_1 hybrids, low also in the B_1 and B_2 generations, and high again in the homozygous B_{11} and B_{22} generations.[22] A lower variance and hence a greater phenotypic stability in heterozygotes than in the corresponding homozygotes has been found also for the rate of growth

---

[19] For an excellent and stimulating review see Lerner, 1954, 41–62. Moos (1955) adds some later references.
[20] Mather, 1950.
[21] Mather, 1953.
[22] Yoon, 1955.

in tomatoes, the average number of chiasmata at meiosis in rye, and plant height and ear weight in corn.[23]

The homeostasis of heterozygotes affects not only various morphological characters which may or may not enhance the fitness of the individuals manifesting them, but also physiological characters related to fitness.   In *Drosophila pseudoobscura, persimilis, prosaltans* and *melanogaster,* the rates of survival of flies heterozygous or homozygous for particular chromosomes were determined in replicated crowded cultures.   Environmental conditions varied somewhat from culture to culture.   The homozygotes showed significantly different survival rates in the different cultures, whereas the heterozygotes were generally uniform among the replicates.   The viability of the homozygous flies, in other words, was modified by environmental conditions to a much greater extent than was the viability of the corresponding heterozygotes.[24]

Apparently some physiological processes related to viability in Drosophila are better buffered against environmental fluctuations in heterozygotes than in homozygous flies.   In *Drosophila pseudoobscura* these physiological traits have been identified with the processes affecting egg-laying rate, larval viability, adult longevity, and growth rate, all of which showed a greater uniformity in response to environmental diversity in heterozygotes of the type ST/CH than in the homozygotes ST/ST and CH/CH.[25]   (ST and CH symbolize blocks of genes or supergenes borne in inverted segments of homologous chromosomes, as will be discussed later in Chapter 9.)

Individuals which possess internal self-regulating mechanisms buffering them against changing environmental conditions can perform successfully in a variety of environments.   Less homeostatic individuals are likely to perform well only in a narrow range of conditions.   The homeostatic types will thus exhibit a higher average fitness in various environments and hence a higher degree of heterosis than their less homeostatic relatives.   The correlation between heterosis and homeostasis, taken together with the fact that heterozygosity is connected with both phenomena, suggests that heterosis may be due in part at least to the superior homeostatic properties of some heterozygous combinations of alleles.[26]

---

[23] Mertens, Burdick and Gomes, 1956.   Rees and Thompson, 1956.   Adams and Shank, 1959.

[24] Dobzhansky and Wallace, 1953.   Dobzhansky and Levene, 1955.

[25] Moos, 1955.

[26] Dobzhansky and Wallace, 1953.   Lerner, 1954.

The property of a heterozygote which could provide the basis for both its homeostasis and its heterosis could be its relatively great biochemical complexity as compared with homozygotes.[27] The two identical alleles of any gene in a homozygote may produce a single type of enzyme. The dissimilar alleles of the same gene in a heterozygote may determine the formation of two slightly different enzymes. Now a biochemically homogeneous enzyme may have a sharp optimum for pH or temperature, whereas a pair of related enzymes is likely to be active over a broader zone of conditions. A mixture of enzymes resulting from heterozygosity would, therefore, be advantageous in an organism exposed to a wide range of environmental conditions.[28]

PARAMUTATION

It has been assumed in the preceding discussion that the two homologous but dissimilar alleles in a heterozygote, while acting in different ways physiologically, do not themselves change, but replicate their respective forms in later generations. This assumption of the integrity of the contrasting alleles in heterozygotes and of the purity of the gametes produced by such heterozygotes is supported by much experimental evidence dating back to Mendel's work on peas. The principle of the constancy of alleles in heterozygotes is not universally valid, however, for Brink has described, under the term paramutation, an interesting exception in *Zea mays*.[29]

The **R** gene in corn determines the color of the endosperm in the kernels. The normal allele R gives rise to self-colored endosperm, while the allele R^{st} gives stippled endosperm, and the recessive allele r produces colorless endosperm. The heterozygote R/R^{st} and the homozygote R/R were testcrossed as males to r/r females. The R/r progeny of the two testcrosses should be phenotypically alike on Mendelian theory. In fact they were phenotypically different. The R allele in male gametes produced by the R/R^{st} heterozygotes gives rise to a different phenotypic effect in the R/r offspring from that resulting from the R allele in male gametes of R/R. The pigment-producing activity of the R allele from R/R^{st} plants is much lower than that of R alleles from R/R plants.[30]

Evidently, therefore, the R allele in the R/R^{st} plants is altered in

---

[27] Lerner, 1954, 112. Haldane, 1954a.
[28] Haldane, 1954a, 1954b.
[29] Brink, 1956, 1958.
[30] Brink, 1956.

some way. The alteration is hereditary, moreover, inasmuch as the altered form of the R allele is transmitted through the male line to a subsequent generation.

The change in R is reversible, as can be shown by putting the altered R alleles from R/Rst heterozygotes in the homozygous condition R/R, and observing their performance in the progeny of the testcross r/r ♀ × R/R ♂. The R alleles in these R/R homozygotes can be seen, in the testcross progeny, to have regained approximately the standard level of pigment-producing action characteristic of never-altered R alleles.[31]

CLASSIFICATION OF THE MODES
OF ALLELE INTERACTION

When the phenotypes of heterozygotes are compared with those of the corresponding homozygous classes, the heterozygous phenotypes may be variously described as dominant, recessive, intermediate, heterotic, and so on. The phenotypic characteristics of heterozygotes reflect the various modes of interaction between different but homologous alleles. The modes of allele interaction are clearly more fundamental than the phenotypic characteristics resulting from them. A knowledge and classification, not of the phenotypes of heterozygotes, but of the relative actions and interactions of homologous alleles is desirable.

The number of links in the chain of events between primary gene action and ultimate phenotypic expression is very great and as yet poorly understood. Geneticists can work backwards a few links in the development of a character, or forwards a few links from gene action, but must be content to draw inferences regarding the rest of the chain, at least at the present time. Desirable as a classification of the modes of allele interaction may be, therefore, the information necessary to devise a sound one which can be related to phenotypic expressions does not appear to be available yet, and until such information is available we must get along with preliminary attempts.

The examples presented earlier in this chapter suggest that the following modes of allele interaction are realized in actual cases.

1. One allele active, the other inactive.
2. Both alleles active and producing the same primary product, but

---

[31] *Ibid.*

one allele bringing about a greater quantitative effect than the other.

3. The two alleles unequally active (as in 2), but directing the formation of different primary products along different biochemical pathways:

   (a) The primary effects of the separate reactions additive.

   (b) The separate reactions mutually inhibiting or antagonistic, and their primary effects consequently subtractive.

4. The two alleles controlling different biochemical reactions (as in 3), but equally strong in terms of the amount of primary product formed:

   (a) The effects of the separate reactions additive.

   (b) Subtractive.

The terms used to describe the various phenotypic characteristics of heterozygotes, and the concepts underlying these terms, were largely worked out in the early period of Mendelian genetics from a body of breeding data unenlightened by much understanding of gene action. It is not surprising, therefore, that some phenotypic expressions in heterozygotes (like intermediacy or dominance) can be the result of several different modes of allele interaction, or that, contrarily, one mode of allele interaction may exhibit one phenotypic expression at one stage in development (i.e., codominance) and another expression at a later stage in development (i.e., intermediacy or heterosis).

We can tentatively relate the phenotypes of heterozygotes to the types of allele interaction as follows, preserving the same numeration as in the classification of allele interactions outlined above.

1. Only one allele active—*complete dominance, incomplete dominance, intermediacy.*

2. Both alleles active in the same direction but quantitatively unequal —*complete dominance, incomplete dominance, intermediacy.*

3. Alleles active but in different directions and with unequal strengths:

   (a) Primary effects additive:

      (i) Ultimate effects not synergistic—*codominance* at an early stage of development; some form of *dominance* or *intermediacy* at a late stage.

      (ii) Ultimate effects synergistic—*codominance* at an early stage; *heterosis* or *homeostasis* at a late stage.

   (b) Primary effects subtractive (the reactions controlled by the separate alleles being antagonistic)—*incomplete dominance, intermediacy.*

4. Alleles active in different directions with equal strengths:

(*a*) Primary effects additive:

  (i) Ultimate effects not synergistic—*codominance* at an early stage; at a late stage some form of *dominance* or *intermediacy*.

  (ii) Ultimate effects synergistic—*codominance* at an early stage; *heterosis, homeostasis* at a late stage.

Serial gene systems

4 A phenotypic characteristic is an advanced stage, often an end point, in a developmental sequence, the individual steps of which may be governed by different genes. The synthesis of the amino acid arginine in Neurospora, for instance, takes place in at least seven steps, each one of which is controlled by a different gene. Beadle and others have suggested that the relation between separate genes and the successive steps in a reaction chain may follow the generalized scheme depicted in Fig. 19.[1]

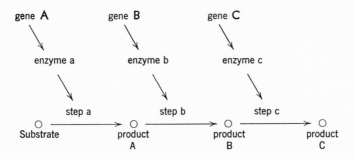

FIG. 19. Generalized relation between different genes and different steps in a biochemical reaction chain. (After Beadle, 1955.)

It is evident that the formation of the final product (product C in Fig. 19) is dependent upon the cooperation of several genes (genes **A**, **B**, and **C** in the figure) working on different steps in the develop-

---

[1] Beadle, 1955.

mental sequence. For convenience we will refer to the various genes controlling different steps in a developmental sequence as a serial gene system.

If any single critical gene in a serial gene system is represented by a mutant allele which does not properly activate an essential step, product C will not develop and the individual will appear as a mutant type deficient in C. There are, moreover, different C-deficient mutants which on a first classification by phenotypic characteristics would be regarded as the same, but which on further genetic analysis could be proved to be non-allelic. The interaction between the separate genes comprising a serial gene system may take various forms, which we will now consider.

COMPLEMENTARY FACTORS

In the setup outlined in Fig. 19 a character C is the end product of a stepwise development requiring the successive action of three genes, **A**, **B**, and **C**. Assume that an organism is diploid and homozygous for the dominant alleles, A, B, and C, of these genes, which together bring about a normal phenotype. The genotype is normally AA BB CC, and the phenotype normally exhibits the product C. Assume further that two mutant types exist, one of which carries mutant alleles for the **A** gene and the other mutant alleles for the **B** gene. The former has the constitution aa BB CC, the latter the constitution AA bb CC. Both are alike phenotypically in that the character C is lacking. Intercrossing of two such C-deficient individuals will, however, lead to the production of normal individuals, for the first mutant type produces gametes aBC, the second mutant produces gametes AbC, and their zygote Aa Bb CC contains the right alleles to carry the normal development through to completion. If the genes **A** and **B** are on separate chromosomes, they will segregate independently to form the four types of gametes, AB, ab, Ab, aB. The random union of these gametes will then yield normal individuals and C-deficient mutants in the ratio of 9:7 in the next generation.

Since the two genes complement one another in the production of a given phenotype, the gene interaction just described is appropriately called complementary factor inheritance. The classical case, worked out by Bateson, Saunders, and Punnett in 1906, involved flower color in sweet peas (*Lathyrus odoratus*). Two true-breeding white-flowered forms produced a blue-flowered F_1 which segregated in the F_2 generation into individuals with colored flowers and those with white flowers in a 9:7 ratio.[2] Since then numerous other examples have been described in both plants and animals, and complementary gene interaction can be regarded as a general phenomenon.

The absence of product C might be normal for a certain organism. The normal C-deficient phenotype could be produced by a genotype containing, in addition to genes for C, also a gene inhibiting the formation of C. The inhibitor gene could operate by simply blocking one of the precursor stages in the developmental sequence leading to C. Thus in the genotype AA bb CC, in the same hypothetical model considered earlier (Fig. 19), the allele b inhibits the formation of product C and can be regarded as an inhibitor of the gene **C**.

One and the same gene **B** may thus be a complementary factor in one allelic form (B) and an inhibitor in another (b). Complementarity and suppression represent, in many setups at least, positive and negative aspects of the same basic form of gene interaction. In a species the normal allele of a gene may have a complementary action and can properly be called a complementary gene. Or the normal allele might have the inhibitory action, in which case the gene will be identified for all practical purposes as an inhibitor gene.

The wild pansy, *Viola tricolor,* normally possesses a dark spot or nectar guide in the flowers, but spotless forms also occur. Crosses between the spotted and spotless forms of *V. tricolor* give segregations indicating that the formation of spots requires the presence of both a positive gene for spot (**S**), and a complementary gene (**K**) necessary for the expression of **S**. A closely related species of pansy, *Viola arvensis,* usually lacks spots, though plants with spots are occasionally found. A study of the progeny of spotted × spotless types of *V. arvensis* shows that this species possesses genes for spots, and also one or two suppressor genes (**I** and **H**) inhibiting spot formation. The spotless condition which is normal in *V. arvensis* is thus due to the presence of about four genes with antagonistic effects: two genes working in the direction of spot formation, and two genes which suppress spot formation, perhaps by blocking some precursor stage of development.[3] The related species, *V. tricolor* and *V. arvensis,* therefore, differ phenotypically in the usual presence of spots in the former

---

[2] Brief summary by Clausen and Hiesey, 1958, 160.

[3] Clausen, 1926; 1951, 59. Clausen and Hiesey, 1958, 188.

and absence in the latter. These phenotypic differences do not result from a simple presence or absence of spot-forming genes in the two species. Each species is seen to possess positive genes for spots combined with complementary genes (in *V. tricolor*) or inhibitor genes (in *V. arvensis*). The characteristic differences between the two species are due to different balances between the positive and negative factors.[4]

Systems of genes with opposing effects have been described by numerous workers in many organisms. As Clausen has emphasized, such oppositional systems have been found very widely in plants wherever a thorough genetic analysis of the inheritance of flower color or other traits has been made.[5] Clausen and Hiesey studied the inheritance of 16 multifactorial characters in *Potentilla glandulosa* in sufficient detail to determine whether inhibitor genes were present or absent in the various gene systems. Half of the well analyzed gene systems were found to contain inhibitor genes or, at least, to consist of genes with opposing effects.[6]

EPISTASIS

A form of gene interaction discovered in the early period of Mendelian genetics was that wherein one gene masks the effects of another, so that the phenotype is determined effectively by the former and not by the latter when both genes are present together. The phenotypic effects are comparable to those produced by the combination of a dominant and a recessive allele of one gene, but the genotypic setup responsible for these phenotypic effects differs in that the dominant characteristic results from the interaction between separate genes rather than from the allelic interactions of a single gene. This relation of dominance and recessiveness between separate genes is known as epistasis.

The term epistasis is being used currently by population geneticists and quantitative geneticists to refer to gene interactions of various kinds. In this more general sense of the word, all of the topics considered in this chapter, and some of those to be discussed in the next chapter, could be described as epistatic interactions. The same terminology was introduced by Bateson in 1907 and used by the early Mendelian geneticists in a more restricted sense for a special type

---

[4] *Ibid.*
[5] Clausen, 1951, Chapter 5. Clausen and Hiesey, 1958, Chapter 4.
[6] Clausen and Hiesey, 1958, 109.

of gene interaction, as defined above. It is in this special sense that we will use the term epistasis here.

In searching for an explanation of epistasis in terms of gene action and interaction, we may consider a modification of the developmental sequence shown in Fig. 19. The pathway of development is not necessarily linear, as represented in the figure, but may be branching. Suppose that at step b in Fig. 19 the pathway is capable of being sidetracked towards the formation of a product which we may call beta. The gene **B** controlling step b in the reaction then plays a critical role, for different alleles of **B** might either (1) prepare the way for the gene **C**, (2) simply block the action of **C**, or (3) switch the metabolic pathway in a new direction toward the formation of beta. In case 1 the gene **B** is complementary to **C**; in case 2 **B** is an inhibitor of **C**; and in case 3 **B** is epistatic to **C**.

In the case of epistasis, therefore, an allele β of the gene **B** in the genotype AA $\beta\beta$ CC not only inhibits the action of the gene **C** but also has a separate and divergent action of its own. The phenotype resulting from the action of this genotype consequently lacks the product C and, in addition, possesses the alternative product beta. In other words, the genotype BB CC produces character C, whereas the genotype $\beta\beta$ CC produces character beta instead of character C.

Nilsson-Ehle crossed oats with black spikelets to oats with yellow spikelets. The F_2 and F_3 generations segregated in ratios consistent with the idea that the parental types differ in two independent genes, **S** and **Y**, which determine the formation of black and yellow pigment respectively. If **S** is represented by its recessive allele s in the genotypes ss YY, ss Yy, and ss yy, the spikelets are yellow. But if **S** is represented by its dominant allele S in any combination with the **Y** alleles, the spikelets are black. The genotypes SS YY and SS Yy possess an allele for the production of yellow pigment, but this potentiality is not realized owing to the masking effect of the epistatic allele S, which causes the spikelets to be black.[7]

It can be supposed that the yellow and black pigments develop by divergent pathways from some common precursor, and that the gene **S** controls a stage at or before the point of divergence. The alleles s and S are then capable of switching the development towards yellow or black respectively.

An oversimplified version of the genetic determination of spikelet color in oats is presented here deliberately to illustrate the general features of epistasis. Clausen and Hiesey have shown that Nilsson-

[7] Nilsson-Ehle in 1909; see Sirks, 1956, 149–152.

Ehle's data for all crosses in oats combined are best explained in terms of a series of at least four epistatic genes, in which **S** is the top epistatic and **Y** the bottom hypostatic member. The top epistatic gene **S** for black predominates over a second gene **Gr** for gray, which in turn predominates over a third gene **W** for white, until the bottom hypostatic gene **Y** for yellow is reached.[8] The more complex epistatic gene system could be taken to mean that the developmental pathway leading to spikelet color is equally complex. The alternative routes in pigment formation are not merely twofold, black versus yellow, as suggested in the preceding paragraph, but are manifold and probably follow a series of branchings.

In *Viola tricolor* several genes combine to produce a black coloration in the flowers. The normal color of the mature flowers is violet. The conversion from black to violet is accomplished by an epistatic series of five genes, the dominant alleles of which predominate over one another in the following order: $M_1 \rightarrow M_2 \rightarrow M_3 \rightarrow M_4 \rightarrow M_5$. Plants homozygous recessive for all five **M** genes ($m_1m_1 \; m_2m_2 \; \cdots$) have jet black flowers. Plants homozygous recessive for the top four **M** genes but carrying one or two dominant alleles of the hypostatic member ($m_1m_1 \; m_2m_2 \; \cdots M_5$) have velvety black flowers. Successively lighter shades of violet are produced by the alleles M_4, M_3, and M_2 respectively; thus the genotype ($m_1m_1 \; m_2m_2 \; m_3m_3 \; M_4 \; \cdots$) gives rise to deep velvet colors, whereas the genotype ($m_1m_1 \; M_2 \; \cdots$) produces light velvet colors. The top epistatic allele M_1 when present in a genotype with either recessive or dominant alleles of the other **M** genes (viz., $M_1 \; \cdots$) brings about the normal violet color.[9]

This series of epistatic genes implies the existence of a series of successive steps in the conversion of black pigment into violet pigment, with the different genes controlling the different steps. The biosynthetic pathway probably consists of a succession of branchings leading in one direction to black and in the other to velvet or violet. The different alleles of the genes $M_1 \; \cdots \; M_5$ could switch the biochemical reaction into one or the other alternate route at each successive branching.

Epistasis, like complementary and inhibitor factors, is common and widespread, numerous examples having been found in both plants and animals.

---

[8] Clausen and Hiesey, 1958, 163.
[9] Clausen, 1926. Clausen and Hiesey, 1958, 188–190.

Multiple gene systems

5 The development of many of the general characters of organisms probably requires the presence of several or many genic sites elaborating the same or similar growth substances or growth regulators and thus cooperating to bring about a large quantitative effect. Such characters as the size and proportion of organs or of the whole body, the rate of growth and time of maturation, and the density of pigmentation or of hairiness, are especially likely to be inherited as though they are controlled by several or many genes with cumulative effects.

QUANTITATIVE CHARACTERS
CONTROLLED BY MULTIPLE FACTORS

We know that one dose of the Y allele in corn produces 2.25 units per gram of vitamin A in the endosperm, as mentioned in Chapter 3, and that two doses of this allele produce 5.00 vitamin units per gram. If it were advantageous for a corn plant to have kernels with large quantities of vitamin A, this result could be attained most simply by multiplying the number of Y alleles up to the desirable concentration. For example, the quantitative effect of 15 or 20 vitamin units per gram could be produced by the cumulative actions of 6 or 8 Y alleles respectively, if the supply of precursor substances were not limiting.

It is significant that cells and tissues which perform nutritive or secretory functions, and which consequently must produce some growth substance in great amounts—like the salivary glands in Drosophila, silk glands in moths, intestinal and liver cells in mammals, tapetum in the stamens of flowering plants, endosperm in the seeds of plants, etc.—frequently possess several or many chromosome sets

73

(polyploidy) or chromosome strands (polyteny).[1]   Tapetal cells in plants frequently possess twice or four times as many chromosome sets as the normal tissues of the same body.   It is calculated that the giant salivary gland chromosomes of Drosophila are composed of about 1000 parallel strands.[2]   The significance of the large number of chromosome sets or chromosome strands in the cells composing such tissues may consist in the multiplication of gene sites.   By multiplying the number of active gene sites through polyploidy or polyteny, the tissue may be able to carry on an extraordinary metabolic activity.

Most tissues in the body of a diploid organism are, of course, diploid. There is no reason to suppose that the normal diploid tissues of an organism are exempt from the problem of producing various growth substances in quantity, which is so apparent in the case of glandular and nutritive tissues.   On the contrary, the latter reveal in a striking way a type of cellular activity leading to quantitative effects which may be general throughout the body.

The diploid cells cannot, by definition, increase the number of working gene sites by adding extra chromosomes, but they can achieve the same net result by having multiple genes permanently built into the normal chromosome constitution.   The formation of 12 vitamin units per gram in a plant, by a gene (Z) which produces 2 units per gram per z allele, could conceivably be accomplished by either the polyploid multiplication of chromosomes carrying the Z gene up to the hexaploid level, or by the scattering of the Z genes in three sites on each haploid chromosome set of a diploid cell.   In either case the cell in a plant homozygous for z would contain 6 z alleles and would produce the required quantity of the vitamin.

A series of two or more separate genes having similar effects on some character, usually a quantitative character, is referred to as multiple factors.   In the period from 1909 to 1916 it was demonstrated that some of the character differences in plants are in fact controlled by multiple factors.   The existence of multiple factors was later confirmed for many characters in many organisms.

Nilsson-Ehle showed in 1909–1911 from the segregation ratios obtained in the progeny of hybrids between wheat plants with red kernels and plants with white kernels that the color of the kernel in wheat is controlled by three independent genes with similar effects, R_1, R_2, and R_3.   Clausen and Hiesey, reanalyzing Nilsson-Ehle's data,

---

[1] See Goldschmidt, 1955, 295 ff., for examples and references.
[2] Herskowitz; see Goldschmidt, 1955, 296.

have recently pointed out that a series of four rather than three **R** genes is probably involved in the inheritance of kernel color in wheat.[3]

In 1910 and 1913 East and his coworkers studied the inheritance of ear size and various other characters in corn.[4] A variety of popcorn has short ears which are usually 6 or 7 cm. long, while the long ears of a variety of sweet corn are usually 14–19 cm. long. Their F_1 hybrids mostly have ears 10–13 cm. long and are thus intermediate. The ears of the F_2 progeny range continuously from short (7 cm.) to long (21 cm.), with most of the F_2 ears being medium long (10–14 cm.). The range and distribution of the F_1 and F_2 indicate that the differences in ear length between the parental varieties of corn are due to allelic differences in multiple genes.

The theory of multiple factor inheritance was applied to variation in a quantitative character in man in the same years (1910 and 1913) by Davenport, who showed that the difference between Negroes and Caucasians in skin color is due largely to two genes with equivalent and cumulative effects.[5]

In 1914 Shull reported duplicate factor inheritance in the shepherd's-purse (*Capsella bursa-pastoris*) of the mustard family (Cruciferae). One parental type with triangular capsules and another parent with oval capsules yielded F_1 hybrids with triangular capsules. The F_2 generation segregated in a ratio approximating 15 triangular to 1 oval. Some of the triangular-fruited F_2 individuals bred true to type in the F_3 and F_4 generations; others gave segregating F_3 and F_4 progenies. Some of the segregating F_3 and F_4 families gave 3:1 ratios and others 15:1 ratios for the shape of the capsule. These results are explained by the hypothesis that the differences in capsule shape are due to two independent genes with similar effects (i.e., by duplicate factors), which are represented in the triangular-fruited parents by dominant alleles and in the oval-fruited parents by recessive alleles.[6]

Two years later East (1916) showed that the difference in flower size in *Nicotiana longiflora* between a long-tubed and a short-tubed variety is controlled by a series of multiple genes with generally similar and cumulative effects. This classical experiment of East furnished the conclusive verification of the multiple factor hypothesis.[7]

---

[3] Clausen and Hiesey, 1958, 162.
[4] Emerson and East, 1913.
[5] Stern, 1960, 351 ff.
[6] Brief summary by Clausen and Hiesey, 1958, 174.
[7] East, 1916; see Allard, 1960, 77–82, for a good recent summary of East's experiment.

TYPES OF MULTIPLE GENE SYSTEMS

We may inquire what modes of action are taken by the various members of a system of multiple genes. We shall approach this problem deductively by asking how a given quantitative effect can be produced by the joint action of multiple genes. We can answer our questions with a series of hypothetical models. Then by searching for actual examples we can see whether the hypothetical cases have any relation to reality or not.

Let us elaborate on the hypothetical case mentioned earlier of multiple genes (Z_1, Z_2, Z_3) concerned with the formation of a vitamin in a plant. The alleles z_1, z_2, and z_3 of these genes produce 2 vitamin units per gram each. If the effects of the separate allele actions are additive and equal, the cell of a homozygous diploid, containing 6 alleles manufacturing 2 units each, will produce the vitamin in the concentration of 12 units per gram. Such a system of multiple genes with equal and additive effects is known technically as a polymeric system.

Suppose now that the concentration of vitamin most advantageous for the welfare of the plant is 17 units per gram. This level of vitamin concentration represents an adaptive situation for the plant and an adaptive goal which the plant lineage may evolve toward. The multiple gene system of the ancestral plant, producing only 12 units, must be changed if its descendants are to reach their adaptive goal. What kinds of genetic changes might bring about the new and better adapted phenotype?

1. Mutations might occur in each **Z** gene from the old allelic form producing 2 vitamin units per gram to new mutant alleles capable of manufacturing 3 units per gram. The diploid cell homozygous for the mutant alleles will then produce vitamins in the concentration of 18 units per gram.

2. Or the plant could change from a multiple factor system composed of three **Z** genes to one composed of four genes. One additional **Z** gene could be inserted in the chromosomes at some point by the duplication of one of the three chromosomal segments containing one of the three original **Z** genes. Without any mutational changes in the genes themselves, there are now 8 z alleles in a diploid cell collectively manufacturing 16 units per gram.

Now the concentration of this material which is most advantageous and adaptive for the plant is, by assumption, 17 units per gram, not 18 (as arrived at by solution 1) or 16 (as in solution 2). Living organisms, however, frequently have to compromise with their circumstances and get by with imperfect adaptations. At least 16 or 18 units comes closer to the adaptive goal of the plant than the ancestral 12 units. Furthermore, the optimum condition for some quantitative characters appears to have relatively broad limits, whereas the optimal range is much more narrow in the case of other characters. If the vitamin concentration in the plant happens to have a broad optimal range, solutions 1 or 2 will represent satisfactory and genetically feasible ways of bringing about a well-adapted phenotype. But if for some physiological reason the vitamin concentration must be adjusted within fine limits, some other course will have to be followed.

3. Mutations could occur in each Z gene from the standard z allele, producing 2.00 units, to a new mutant allele, producing precisely 2.83 units per gram each. The triple mutant homozygote would then manufacture almost exactly 17 units per gram.

Mutant alleles having the required precision of action might or might not be functionally possible, or might or might not arise during the history of the plant population. The occurrence of three independent mutational events bringing about a new level of activity which is at once precise and equivalent in three different genes is at any rate improbable. As a means of building up to the level of 17 units, solution 3 is conceivable but improbable, because other and genetically simpler means exist by which the plant can achieve the same result.

4. One or two of the three Z genes might mutate to new alleles with enhanced vitamin-synthesizing activity. Since the mutational changes occurring in the different Z genes are independent events, it is likely that the strengths of action of the separate mutant alleles will turn out to be different. A combination of three genes with different strengths could, however, engender a well-adapted phenotype containing 17 vitamin units per gram. For example, if the mutant alleles of the Z_1 gene produce 4.5 units each (instead of 2), the Z_2 and Z_3 genes remaining unmutated, the new homozygous genotype will synthesize $9 + 4 + 4 = 17$ units per gram. Or if the Z_1 gene mutates to an allele with a strength of action equal to 4 units, and if the Z_2 gene mutates to a new allele with a strength of 2.5 units, and if the Z_3 gene does not change, the new homozygous gene combination will again produce 17 units, though by an alternative route $(8 + 5 + 4)$. The result in this case is a system composed of multiple genes with additive but unequal effects.

The plant's chances of acquiring by mutation three unequal additive genes, the effects of which add up to 17 units, are greater by far than its chances of obtaining three mutations with precise and equal effects totalling 17 units. Solution 4 is more feasible genetically than solution 3. Nevertheless, a strong chance does exist that mutant alleles having the cumulative effect of exactly 17 units will not arise.

Suppose that the only mutations available to the plant are new allelic forms of the Z_1 gene with a vitamin-synthesizing strength of 4 units, and mutant alleles of the Z_2 gene with a strength of 3.5 units, the Z_3 gene remaining unchanged. The cumulative effect of the mutant alleles of Z_1 and Z_2 and the standard alleles of Z_3 in the homozygous condition is, therefore, not the 17 units required for adaptation, but 19.

5. Under these conditions a fine adjustment of the phenotype could be brought about by incorporating into the multiple factor system a counterbalance in the form of a gene working in the opposite direction to Z_1, Z_2, and Z_3. If the strength of the pairs of alleles of the three Z genes is respectively +8, +7, and +4, and if the strength of one allele pair of an antagonistic gene (I) newly introduced into the system is −2, the combination of Z and I genes will produce the phenotypic characteristic of 17 units per gram.

Gene combinations of this sort are variously referred to in the literature as oppositional systems,[8] or systems of plus and minus modifiers, depending upon the particular balance of forces involved, and the gene with antagonistic effects is called an inhibitor or suppressor (and is commonly designated I or S). For our purposes the essential point to note is that a prescribed quantitative character can be produced, not only by multiple genes with additive effects, but also by multiple genes with antagonistic and subtractive effects.

We have reckoned so far on the assumption that the Z genes mutate in the direction of enhanced vitamin productivity. What if the Z genes remain stable? Or what if the mutations that do arise in them are functionally useless to the plant in any possible gene combination? Another route leading from the ancestral phenotype with 12 quantitative units to the new and better adapted phenotype with 17 units may be followed under these conditions.

6. The total vitamin production of the three original Z genes, which are now assumed to remain stable, could be supplemented by additional genes having individually minute effects but present in large numbers. Twenty-five such genes, each producing 0.1 unit per allele or 0.2 unit per allele pair, with additive effects, would produce in the

---

[8] Clausen and Hiesey, 1958, 263.

aggregate the 5 units needed to make up the difference between the ancestral condition of 12 units and the adaptive goal of 17 units.

An assemblage of multiple factors of this type, consisting of one or more genes with large effects and numerous genes with minute effects, the latter acting mainly but not necessarily entirely in the same direction, is referred to generally as a system of major genes and modifiers or in certain contexts as a polygenic system, and the factors with small effects are variously called modifier genes or polygenes. The important lesson for us here is that a system of genes with very unequal effects represents one of the possible routes to a fine adjustment of the phenotype.[9] For polygenes can be incorporated into the genic system in numbers up to the point where a phenotypic character is produced with the precise quantitative level required for adaptation.

The degree of inequality between the major genes and the modifiers can, of course, range widely. The relative strengths of action of the various multiple genes were assumed to be in the approximate proportion of 2:1 in case 4 above, and in the proportion of 20:1 in case 6. This proportionate activity of the major and minor genes could have any intermediate value.

In summary, the relative actions of the genes comprising a system of multiple factors and concerned with the production of a quantitative character may take various possible forms. The effects of the different multiple genes in such a system may be:

1. Additive and equal (*polymery*).
2. Additive and moderately unequal (*anisomery*).
3. Subtractive and unequal (*oppositional systems*).
4. Mainly additive, and extremely unequal (*systems of major genes and modifiers; polygenic systems*).

MULTIPLE GENES WITH CUMULATIVE
EFFECTS: HYPOTHETICAL MODELS

An analysis of the multifactorial control of a phenotypic character can be carried out by hybridization experiments with related and interfertile organisms differing quantitatively in this character. The F_1 hybrid will usually be intermediate between the parental types with respect to the character in question. The F_2 progeny will segregate into a continuous or nearly continuous array of forms ranging from

---

[9] Mather, 1949.

the quantitative expression found in one parent to that found in the other. The frequency distribution of the various F_2 types forms a bell-shaped curve with a peak in the intermediate range. This curve may be symmetrical or skewed.[10]

Some of the properties of a given multiple gene system, such as the approximate number of independent genes involved, their relative strengths of action, and the presence or absence of dominance, can be inferred from the distribution of phenotypes in the F_1 and F_2 generations, and the inferences can be verified by reference to the data obtained in F_3 and later generations. The elementary approach to the problem before us, therefore, is to consider a series of purely hypothetical models in which the foregoing factors are made to vary one at a time.

Such models have both a strength and a weakness. Being over-simplified, they cannot be applied directly and without qualifications to actual cases, which are invariably complex. On the other hand, in spite of their unrealistic simplicity, or perhaps because of it, they are useful in revealing the different patterns of phenotypic variation expected from the segregation of different types of multiple gene systems.

The number of independent (viz., unlinked) multiple genes for which a hybrid is segregating can be inferred from the frequency with which the parental types are recovered in the F_2 generation. One parental type is recovered in the following proportions in an F_2 generation segregating for g multiple factors: [11]

$$g = 2, \quad \frac{1}{16}$$

$$g = 3, \quad \frac{1}{64}$$

$$g = 4, \quad \frac{1}{256}$$

$$g = 5, \quad \frac{1}{1024}$$

$$g = n, \quad (\tfrac{1}{4})^n.$$

---

[10] The account of multiple factor inheritance given in this and other sections of the present chapter is oriented in relation to the central theme of this book. Consequently some aspects of the subject have been emphasized, while other aspects, which are important in their own right but not essential to our present line of argument, are omitted. Fortunately, since this chapter was written, Allard's *Principles of Plant Breeding* (1960) has appeared. The excellent discussion of continuous variation and quantitative inheritance in Chapters 7 to 10 of Allard's book is recommended to readers wishing a more complete treatment of the subject than can be given here.

[11] Anderson, 1949, 29.

The numerator in the above fractions may represent either parent if the multiple genes are truly polymeric with equal and additive effects and without dominance. In more complex multiple factor systems complicated by the existence of dominance or antagonism between the component genes, the numerator must represent the bottom recessive type.

If, of course, the multiple genes are borne on the same chromosome and hence are linked in inheritance, the ratios will be like those due to the segregation of fewer genes, as was noted by the early students of multifactorial inheritance.

The segregation of a quantitative character observed in the progeny of a hybrid does not necessarily expose for analysis all of the multiple genes involved in the development of that character. The segregation reveals only those genes that are represented by different alleles in the two parents. The hybrid progeny derived from a cross between two plants or animals differing in stature or growth rate do not segregate for stature or growth rate as such; they segregate with respect to the quantitative differences between the parents in those traits and with respect to the allelic differences responsible for the character differences. The number of segregating genes is probably much fewer in most cases than the total number of multiple genes concerned with the particular character, for the parents can be assumed to be genetically alike and their F_1 hybrids homozygous with respect to some of the genes comprising the multiple factor system. Hybridization experiments thus give us only a glimpse, not a complete picture, of the gene systems controlling various characters, but incomplete though it is, it is the only insight we have.

Let us next take some constant number of multiple genes with cumulative actions, say three, and consider the effects of different relative strengths of action of the three genes and of different degrees of dominance on the pattern of phenotypic variation in F_1 and F_2.

We will assume that two forms of a plant differ in some quantitative trait determined by three independent genes (**A**, **B**, and **C**) with additive effects. The character in which the parental types differ could be the amount of some vitamin, the height or weight of the body, the number of days or weeks required for development to maturity, etc. Whatever the character, let the value of 18 be assigned to one parent (P_1) and the value of 6 to the other (P_2). The allelic differences in the three multiple genes responsible for the phenotypic difference can be expressed by writing the genotype of P_1 as AA BB CC, and that of P_2 as aa bb cc.

It will be assumed further for the purpose of the following discussion that the various alleles produce their full phenotypic effects in some standard environment in which the parental types and hybrid progeny are raised. More specifically, the heritability of the phenotypic character undergoing segregation, that is, the proportion of the observed variation in this character that is due to genetic as opposed to environmental causes, is assumed to be as high as 100%. Now this assumption of complete heritability is unrealistic, since the heritabilities of quantitative characters are invariably reduced and are often quite low. We cannot discuss the complicating effects of reduced degrees of heritability here.[12] The theoretical distributions presented in the following discussion can be taken as referring to characters possessing complete heritability, or more realistically, to the genotypic component of the observed variation in characters with normal reduced heritability values.

Let us now examine the variation patterns expected in F_1 and F_2 generations segregating for three independent genes with additive *and equal* effects, under various conditions of dominance.

1. If the effects of the genes **A**, **B**, and **C** are equal as well as additive, and if, furthermore, no dominance is present between the homologous alleles (A and a, etc.), the cross of P_1 with a character measured as 18 units by P_2 with 6 units yields an F_1 hybrid with 12 units, which is exactly intermediate between the parents. The genotypes of the parents and F_1 and the phenotypic values determined by these genotypes are:

$$P_1 \quad AA\ BB\ CC \quad 6 + 6 + 6 = 18$$

$$P_2 \quad aa\ bb\ cc \quad 2 + 2 + 2 = 6$$

$$F_1 \quad Aa\ Bb\ Cc \quad 4 + 4 + 4 = 12.$$

The frequency distribution of F_2 types will then form a symmetrical bell-shaped curve with extremes at 18 and 6 and a peak at 12, as shown in Fig. 20*a*.

2. If, next, dominance is present in the **A** gene but not in the **B** and **C** genes, so that Aa has the same value as AA, but Bb is intermediate between BB and bb and Cc is similarly intermediate, and if the effects of all three genes are still equal and additive, the genotypes and corresponding phenotypic values of the parents and hybrid will be as follows:

---

[12] For good discussions of heritability see Lerner, 1958, 57 ff.; Allard, 1960, 83 ff.; and Falconer, 1960, 165 ff.

$$P_1 \quad AA\ BB\ CC \quad 6 + 6 + 6 = 18$$

$$P_2 \quad aa\ bb\ cc \quad 2 + 2 + 2 = 6$$

$$F_1 \quad Aa\ Bb\ Cc \quad 6 + 4 + 4 = 14.$$

The F_1 hybrid, though intermediate, is not exactly so, but is skewed in the direction of the parental type carrying the one dominant allele

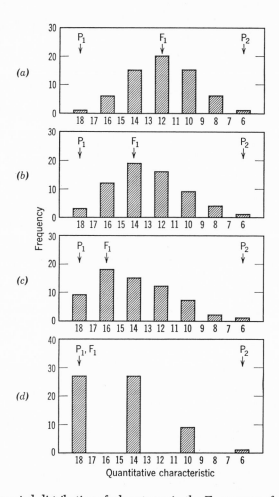

FIG. 20. Expected distribution of phenotypes in the F_2 progeny of a hybrid seg-regating for three unlinked multiple genes with equal and additive effects. The characteristics of the F_1 and the two parental types are indicated by arrows. (*a*) No dominance. (*b*) Dominance in one gene. (*c*) Dominance in two genes. (*d*) Dominance in all three genes.

pair. (See Fig. 20*b*.) The F_2 generation now forms a frequency curve which is also skewed towards the P_1 type. (Fig. 20*b*.)

3. If two genes, **A** and **B**, exhibit dominance of A over a and B over b, while the third gene **C** has no dominance, the other conditions of equality of effects between the separate genes remaining the same, the characteristics of the F_1's and F_2's will be still more strongly skewed towards the dominant parent. (Fig. 20*c*.)

4. If, finally, dominance is present in all three genes with their equal additive effects, the expected results in F_1 and F_2 will be as indicated in Fig. 20*d*.

We will next deal with the case of three genes with additive *and unequal* effects. Assume that the **A** gene has quantitative effects which are twice as strong as those of **B** or **C**. The presence or absence of dominance in the strong gene will then lead to the following expectations.

1. If no dominance is manifested in the interaction between A and a or between the other pairs of alleles, the parental types and F_1 will have the following quantitative values:

$$P_1 \quad AA\ BB\ CC \quad 9 + 4.5 + 4.5 = 18$$

$$P_2 \quad aa\ bb\ cc \quad 3 + 1.5 + 1.5 = 6$$

$$F_1 \quad Aa\ Bb\ Cc \quad 6 + 3 + 3 = 12.$$

The frequency curve for the F_2 generation will be symmetrical with a peak at 12, like the curve for case 1 with equal additive genes. (Compare Figs. 20*a* and 21*a*.) A larger number of phenotypic classes is present in the F_2 generation in the present case, however, and the variation is more continuous. Furthermore, the peak is lower, the curve in Fig. 21*a* being lower and broader than that in Fig. 20*a*.

2. If the genes **A**, **B**, and **C** have the same relative strengths of action as above, but dominance is assumed to be present in **A** though not in **B** or **C**, then:

$$P_1 \quad AA\ BB\ CC \quad 9 + 4.5 + 4.5 = 18$$

$$P_2 \quad aa\ bb\ cc \quad 3 + 1.5 + 1.5 = 6$$

$$F_1 \quad Aa\ Bb\ Cc \quad 9 + 3 + 3 = 15.$$

The F_1 and F_2 are now skewed towards the dominant parent. (Fig. 21*b*.)

3. With dominance present in both **A** and **B**, the score value for the F_1 hybrids and for the modal number of F_2 individuals is 16.5 and is thus still more off center. (Fig. 21*c*.)

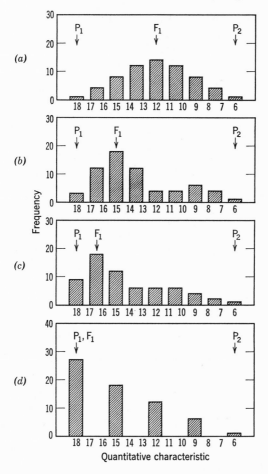

FIG. 21. Expected distribution of phenotypes in the F_2 progeny of a hybrid segregating for three unlinked multiple genes with additive but unequal effects. Further explanation in text. (*a*) No dominance. (*b*) Dominance in the strong gene. (*c*) Dominance in the strong gene and in one weak gene. (*d*) Dominance in all three genes.

4. If dominance is present in all three genes, finally, the F_2 distribution is strongly skewed, as seen in Fig. 21*d*.

Thus to generalize, as the number of independently segregating multiple genes with additive effects becomes larger, the F_2 generation exhibits a lower frequency of the parental types, a larger number of phenotypic classes, and consequently a more continuous series of variations.

For any given number of additive multiple factors, the height and breadth (or kurtosis) of the curve describing the frequency distribution of the F_2 phenotypes is affected by the relative strengths of action of the different multiple genes. Multiple factor systems composed of genes with additive but unequal effects segregate into a larger number of phenotypic classes than do systems of equivalent genes. Consequently the F_2 variation derived from the segregation of unequal genes is more continuous, more spread out, and exhibits a lower frequency of types with the mean value, than does the F_2 variation resulting from the segregation of the same number of genes with equal effects. In other words, although the frequency distribution curve describing the F_2 variation is bell-shaped for any system of segregating multiple genes with additive effects, this curve has a normal peak when the effects of the different genes are equal, and a lower broader top (i.e., is more platykurtotic) when the effects of the several genes are unequal.

Skewness of the F_2 variation is related to the presence of dominance and recessiveness in the different pairs of alleles. If dominance is not present in any of the multiple genes, the bell-shaped curve representing the F_2 variation is symmetrical, the peak and the mean being centered between the two parental values. This is the case whether the multiple genes have equal or unequal effects (contrary to some statements found in the literature). If dominance is present in one of the segregating allele pairs comprising the multiple gene system, the distribution of phenotypic variations in the F_2 generation will be skewed in the direction of the parental type contributing the dominant allele. In general, the greater the number of genes possessing dominant alleles, the greater is the skewness of the F_2 frequency distribution.

The effect of decreasing heritability, finally, is to make the frequency curve of observed phenotypic variation in F_2 more continuous, for any given number of segregating genes under any condition of dominance.[13]

MULTIPLE GENES WITH CUMULATIVE
EFFECTS: EXPERIMENTAL RESULTS

It will be instructive now to look at some typical results obtained in F_1 and F_2 progenies segregating for quantitative characters. We would like to be able to relate the experimental observations to particular gene models. Perhaps in no case can this task be carried out

---

[13] Allard, 1960, 84–85.

TABLE 4   INHERITANCE OF WINTER DORMANCY IN
Potentilla glandulosa *

Degree of Winter Activity	Coastal Race	Alpine Race	F_1	Observed Segregation in F_2	Expected Segregation with 3 Polymeric Genes
Fully active	+			43	15
Fairly Active				139 ⎫	⎧
Intermediate			+	601 ⎬ 918	945 ⎨
Fairly dormant				178 ⎭	⎩
Entirely dormant		+		14	15

* Clausen and Hiesey, 1958, 102.

beyond an approximation to the true situation. Owing to the complexity of actual gene systems and to the difficulties posed by low heritability of quantitative characters, even elaborate hybridization experiments going well beyond the F_2 generation usually fail to reveal the nature of the underlying gene systems in all their detail.[14] On the other hand, experimental progenies do exhibit different types of variation patterns which correspond to the different hypothetical models considered in the preceding section, suggesting that some common factors are involved. It is reasonable to suppose that the various modes of gene interaction and allele interaction discussed in hypothetical terms in the preceding section are realized in actual cases.

Two of the races of *Potentilla glandulosa* differ in their seasonal periodicity. A coastal race from Santa Barbara, California, remains active during the winter, while an alpine race from the Sierra Nevada becomes dormant in winter, even when grown in a lowland transplant garden. Clausen and Hiesey crossed the two races and scored the degree of winter activity of the F_1 hybrids and F_2 progeny. The F_1 hybrids had a moderate growth in mid-winter and were exactly intermediate between the parents. In the F_2 generation 975 individuals ranged from fully winter active to entirely winter dormant, with a peak in the intermediate range, as shown in Table 4.[15]

[14] See Comstock, 1955, for a discussion of some of the problems involved.
[15] Clausen and Hiesey, 1958, 101–102, 109.

The frequency of one of the parental types recovered in the F_2 generation, 14/975, comes close to the 1/64 ratio expected for three independently segregating genes, and for this reason the differences in winter activity between the two races are attributed by Clausen and Hiesey to a multiple factor system composed of approximately three genes. None of the F_2 individuals were more extreme in their phenotypic expression than the parental races; for reasons which will be explained in the next section, this fact is consistent with the idea that the (approximately) three genes have additive effects. It is not possible to decide from the data whether the genes have equal or unequal strengths, but quite possibly, as Clausen and Hiesey suggest, their effects are about equal. Since the modal condition in the F_1 and F_2 generations is unskewed, dominance can be concluded to be absent in each of the several pairs of alleles.

In his study of the inheritance of corolla size in crosses between large-flowered and small-flowered forms of *Nicotiana longiflora,* East recorded a similar intermediacy in the F_1 and a similar continuous and symmetrical distribution of phenotypes in F_2 with a peak in the intermediate range. Since corolla size in *N. longiflora* has a relatively high heritability (about 75%), extrapolations from measurements of phenotypes to the underlying genotypic conditions can be made with considerable reliability. The observed pattern of phenotypic variation in the F_1 and F_2 generations, therefore, indicates that the character in question is controlled by several independent genes with cumulative effects and little or no dominance. East was able to obtain confirmatory evidence for the multiple factor hypothesis in this case by growing a series of F_3, F_4, and F_5 families derived from different F_2 types.[16]

The inheritance of capsule shape in *Capsella bursa-pastoris* described by Shull and mentioned in an earlier section of this chapter provides an example of multiple factors in which allelic relations of dominance and recessiveness exist. It will be recalled that one parental type of shepherd's-purse had triangular seed-pods and the other oval-shaped pods. Their F_1 hybrid had triangular pods like those of the first parent. The observed distribution of phenotypes in the F_2 generation was 2429 triangular capsules and 111 oval capsules.[17] The recovery of the recessive type in about one sixteenth (actually in one twenty-third) of the F_2 progeny indicates that about two genes are responsible for the phenotypic difference between the parents. The

---

[16] East, 1916. Allard, 1960, 77–82.
[17] Summary by Clausen and Hiesey, 1958, 173–175.

TABLE 5 FREQUENCY DISTRIBUTION OF INDIVIDUALS WITH VARIOUS GIVEN LENGTHS OF STIGMA LOBES IN *Gilia capitata capitata, G. capitata chamissonis,* AND THEIR HYBRID PROGENY *

	Length of Stigma, mm.													
	0.3	0.4	0.5	0.6	0.7	0.8	0.9	1.0	1.1	1.2	1.3	1.4	1.5	N
P ca	+	+												
P ch												+	+	
F_1				+	+									
F_2			1	11	43	57	33	24	3	2	1		1	176
B_1 (ca × ch) × ca	1	3	9	1	1	1	1							17
B_1 (ca × ch) × ch					3	1	3			1	1			9

* Grant, 1950, 288.

strong skewness of the F_1 and F_2 generations towards the triangular-fruited parent indicates further that that parent carries dominant alleles for each of the two genes.   Shull, like East, was able to confirm his factorial hypothesis by growing F_3 and F_4 generations.

Two of the races of *Gilia capitata,* an annual plant belonging to the Polemoniaceae, differ in the size of the stigma lobes in the flower. In *Gilia capitata capitata* from the California Coast Ranges the stigma lobes are 0.3 or 0.4 mm. long, while in *G. capitata chamissonis* from maritime sand dunes the stigmas are 1.4 or 1.5 mm. long.   Their F_1 hybrid is off-center in the direction of *G. capitata capitata,* with stigmas 0.6 or 0.7 mm. long.   The F_2 generation contains a continuous series of stigma lengths, as seen in Table 5.   One parental type is recovered among 176 F_2 progeny, suggesting that the difference in stigma length between the two races of Gilia is due to differences in about 3 or 4 genes. The frequency distribution of F_2 types is skewed towards short stigmas, as shown by Table 5.   This skewness is manifested again in the backcross progeny derived from crossing the F_1 hybrids with either parental race.[18]   The degree of skewness is not very great, being about the same as that shown in Fig. 21*b,* which suggests that dominant alleles are carried by *G. c. capitata* for only a fraction, say about one out of three, of the additive genes involved.

It is difficult to find cases in which an interpretation can be made

---

[18] Grant, 1950, 288–289.

as to whether the underlying system of additive multiple factors consists of genes with equal or unequal strengths of action. One might distinguish between the two situations on the basis of the degree of curvature or kurtosis of the F_2 frequency curve, which as noted earlier is more platykurtotic or flat-topped for unequal genes than for equal ones. But the difference in kurtosis of the curves representing equal and unequal gene effects is slight in comparison with all the other variable factors affecting the observable results in a hybridization experiment. The experimental data do not permit a decision between the alternative possibilities where other sources of error have overriding effects.

To be sure, some cases of quantitative inheritance have been attributed in the literature to unequal strength of multiple genes on the basis of skewness of the frequency distribution. But the skewness is a criterion of some other condition, namely dominance as we have already seen, and therefore some reported examples of unequal additive multiple factors cannot be accepted as such.

Nevertheless, the type of multiple gene system with unequal additive effects is probably quite common. Indeed, we might expect systems of unequal additive genes to be more common than systems of equal additive genes, considering the greater probability of producing any given quantitative result by the summation of various combinations of genes with unlike strengths of action than by the summation of equally potent genes.

MULTIPLE GENES WITH OPPOSITIONAL EFFECTS

The genes comprising a multiple factor system do not necessarily all work in the same direction, but some genes may have effects antagonistic to the others, in which case we can speak of an oppositional system.

We may consider a hypothetical case for purposes of illustration. Let two individual plants or animals differ in some quantitative character having the respective values 18 and 6, as in the models considered previously. Let these phenotypic differences be due to allelic differences in three independent genes, **A**, **B**, and **C**, the phenotypic effects of which are fully expressed, again as in the previous models. But now the genes are antagonistic and unequal, the quantitative phenotypic expression being due to the summation of some positive effects and some negative effects. Thus the two parental forms might be supposed to achieve their respective phenotypes by the following modes of action of the three genes:

P_1 AA BB CC $+26 -4 -4 = 18$

P_2 aa bb cc $+10 -2 -2 = 6.$

Among the F_2 progeny derived from the cross $P_1 \times P_2$ are types which are more extreme phenotypically than either parent. The occurrence of transgressive segregation, as this phenomenon is known, is due to the formation of new gene combinations in which the balance of forces present in the parental genotypes is broken up by recombination. For instance, the genotype AA bb cc which can arise in the F_2 generation will have the effect $+26 -2 -2 = 22$, and will consequently have a quantitatively greater expression of the character in question than that of the greatest parental type. Conversely, the genotype aa BB CC, with a value of $+10 -4 -4 = 2$, will produce a phenotype with a quantitatively smaller score value than that of the smallest parent.

Let us now consider the effects of dominance in an oppositional gene system of this sort.

1. If no dominance is present in any gene, the phenotypic rating of the hybrid as compared with the parents will be:

P_1 AA BB CC $+26 -4 -4 = 18$

P_2 aa bb cc $+10 -2 -2 = 6$

F_1 Aa Bb Cc $+18 -3 -3 = 12.$

The F_1 is thus exactly intermediate. The F_2 generation will have the distribution of phenotypes shown in Fig. 22a.

2. If dominance is present in the gene **A**, the quantitative measure of the F_1 hybrid will be:

F_1 Aa Bb Cc $+26 -3 -3 = 20.$

This is an interesting situation in which not only some F_2 types but *also the F_1's exceed either parent* phenotypically. (See Fig. 22b.)

3. With dominance in the two genes, **A** and **B**, the F_1 hybrid is again transgressive, though not as strongly so. (See Fig. 22c.)

4. With dominance in all three genes, the phenotypic expression of the F_1 hybrid coincides with that of the parent carrying the dominant alleles. The distribution of phenotypes in F_2 is now more strongly skewed towards the dominant parent than in any previous case. Nevertheless, the occurrence of transgressive segregants in the F_2 generation remains as a revealing clue of the type of gene interaction involved. (Fig. 22f.)

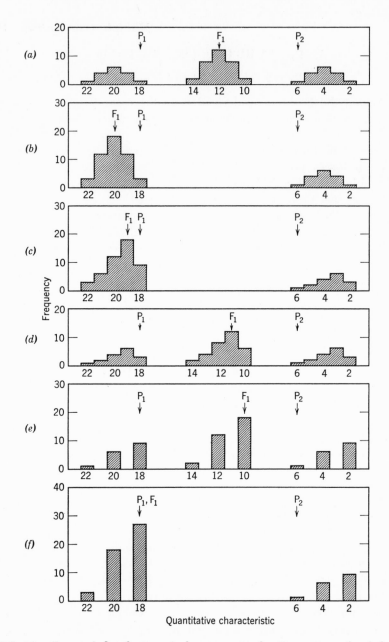

FIG. 22. Expected distribution of phenotypes in the F_2 progeny of a hybrid segregating for three unlinked multiple genes with unequal and oppositional effects. The characteristics of the F_1 and the two parental types are indicated by arrows. Further explanation in text. (a) No dominance. (b) Dominance in the one strong gene. (c) Dominance in the strong gene and in one weak gene. (d) Dominance in one weak gene. (e) Dominance in two weak genes. (f) Dominance in all three genes.

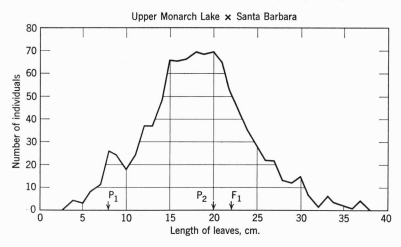

FIG. 23. Frequency distribution of the length of the rosette leaf among 996 F_2 progeny of an interracial cross in *Potentilla glandulosa*. (From Clausen and Hiesey, 1958; photograph by courtesy of Drs. Clausen and Hiesey.)

Transgressive F_1 hybrids are not rare in plant hybridizations. The F_1 hybrids derived from numerous interracial and interspecific crosses in Gilia were transgressive for 9 of the 203 characters scored.[19] This transgressiveness in a character which segregates in later generations into more or less distinct phenotypic classes is symptomatic of complementary gene interaction, which we discussed in the preceding chapter. The syndrome of features consisting of transgressiveness in F_1, a similar transgressiveness in F_2, and continuous variation in F_2, for a character with high heritability, is also found occasionally, and also needs to be explained in terms of a definite factorial model. We see on hypothetical grounds that this syndrome can be produced by the segregation of a multiple factor system in which the genes have oppositional actions, unequal potencies, and dominance in the strong genes but not in all factors.

In *Potentilla glandulosa* the leaves range in size from small in the alpine race to large in the coastal race. The F_2 progeny of the interracial cross shows continuous variation in leaf size, with a low frequency of one parental type, indicating that multiple genes are involved. Transgressive segregation is found in the F_2 generation, some individuals having leaves smaller than the alpine parent, and many individuals possessing larger leaves than the coastal parent. (See Fig.

---

[19] Grant, 1956c, 58.

23). This fact suggests the possibility that the multiple genes may form an oppositional system.[20]

We also see in Fig. 23 that the F_1 hybrid transcends in leaf size the coastal parent. The observed pattern of variation in F_1 and F_2 shown in Fig. 23 is similar in its general features to the hypothetical pattern shown in Fig. 22b. It is possible that this similarity is coincidental; it is also possible that it points to factors common to both cases. The skewness of both the F_2 and the F_1 beyond the limits of normal variation of the coastal parent could be explained by the hypothesis that the two races of *P. glandulosa* differ in multiple genes with antagonistic effects, some of which are represented by dominant alleles in the coastal plants. A study of advanced generations would be needed to verify this hypothesis.

MODIFIER GENES

The existence of modifier genes was first demonstrated in *Drosophila melanogaster* by Bridges and by Sturtevant in the period from 1916 to 1919. A classical case studied by Sturtevant involves the number of hairs in a group on the back of the fly. Normal flies have four bristles in each group on the back of the thorax, whereas a mutant form called "dichaete" possesses fewer bristles per group. The difference between the normal and the reduced number of bristles is due primarily to allelic differences in a single gene, **D**, the normal flies being homozygous recessive (d/d), and the dichaete flies heterozygous for a dominant allele (D/d). The genotype D/D is lethal.

Among a series of dichaete flies with the uniform constitution D/d and reared in a uniform environment, the average number of bristles varies significantly in different lines. Thus some D/d flies may have two bristles, and other lines with the same constitution for the **D** gene may have one, zero, three, or even four bristles. It has been shown that the D/d genotypes with different bristle numbers differ with respect to other genes of the complement, which have relatively slight effects on the bristle character and do not modify the expression of this character at all in normal d/d flies. These modifier genes do, however, affect the expression of the D allele in the D/d flies.[21]

Many different modifier genes are known to affect the dichaete character. Some of the allelic forms of one or more of these modifiers enhance the expression of the D allele; other modifier alleles act to

[20] Clausen and Hiesey, 1958, 90.
[21] Sturtevant in 1918; see Stern, 1960, 310–311.

suppress the effects of the allele D. The enhancers or plus modifiers account for the phenotypes of D/d with extremely reduced numbers of bristles, while the suppressors or minus modifiers lead to phenotypes that are normal or nearly so in D/d flies.[22]

In short, the number of bristles in a group on the back of the Drosophilas is controlled mainly by the gene **D**, but secondarily by one, several, or many other genes with relatively slight individual effects. The former can be referred to as a major gene and the latter as a system of modifiers.

The concept of modifying genes was later taken up by Harland in a series of studies from 1929 to 1936 to explain some of the variations observed in F_2 and backcross generations derived from hybrids in cotton. The two closely related and interfertile species of New World cotton, *Gossypium hirsutum* and *G. barbadense*, possess a number of homologous genes in common. In certain cases identical alleles of the same genes are found in each species. Thus the gene **S** controlling petal spot is represented by both the dominant allele S for spot and the recessive allele s for spotless in the two species. Similarly, the dominant and recessive alleles, R^B and r^B, causing the plant body to become red or green respectively, are present in both species of cotton.[23]

These and many other character differences segregate as single gene differences in crosses within either species. For example, if a form of *G. barbadense* with purple spots at the base of the petals is crossed with a spotless form of the same species, the F_1 hybrid is spotted, and the F_2 segregates into two clearly distinguishable phenotypic classes, spotted and spotless, in a 3:1 ratio. Similar results are obtained when spotted and spotless forms of *G. hirsutum* are hybridized.[24]

But the same character differences, which segregate in a simple Mendelian ratio in the F_2 generations derived from intraspecific crosses, exhibit continuous variation suggestive of multifactorial control in the progeny of interspecific crosses. Thus if a spotted plant of *G. barbadense* is crossed with a spotless plant of *G. hirsutum*, the F_1 is intermediate in the intensity of the petal spots, and the F_2 generation contains 22 degrees of spotting varying by minute stages from complete absence of spots to the presence of spots more intense than those of *G. barbadense*. The same graded series of petal spots is found in the F_3 generation.[25]

---

[22] *Ibid.*
[23] Harland, 1936.
[24] *Ibid.*
[25] *Ibid.*

Other character differences, such as the red or green color of the plant body, the crinkled or even margins of the leaf, etc., exhibit the same contrasting behavior in intraspecific and interspecific crosses.

Since the alleles of the major genes concerned with petal spots, plant color, leaf margin, and other characters are the same in *G. barbadense* and *G. hirsutum,* the continuous variation in the F_2 generation of interspecific crosses is probably a result of allelic differences between the species in other parts of the two genotypes. Harland suggested that the simple and clearcut segregation of a character difference in an intraspecific cross is due to the fact that the rest of the genotype provides a relatively constant genetic background against which the dominant and recessive phases of a major gene can express themselves clearly. By contrast, the genotypes of the two species differ in many other modifying genes besides the one major gene under consideration, and the segregation of these modifiers in the interspecific crosses produces many different genetic backgrounds upon which the major gene must manifest itself. The continuous variation in the F_2 and F_3 generations of the interspecific crosses is a consequence of the segregation of the different alleles of numerous modifier genes affecting the expression of the dominant and recessive alleles of the major genes. The species of cotton thus differ in their assemblages of modifier genes.[26]

This hypothesis can be tested by transferring an allele of a major gene controlling some character from one species to the other by means of repeated backcrossing. If the continuous variation in this character in the interspecific crosses is due, as postulated, to the influence of segregating modifier genes, the inheritance of the character in question should cease to be multifactorial and should become simple Mendelian as soon as the genetic background is made uniform. And the genetic background can be made uniform by backcrossing the hybrids repeatedly for several generations to one parental species, which for practical reasons is the parent carrying the dominant allele of the particular major gene under investigation.[27]

The hybrid of spotted *barbadense* × spotless *hirsutum* was backcrossed generation after generation to the spotted *barbadense* parent. In this way the recessive allele for spotless (s), originally derived from *G. hirsutum,* was transferred to the genetic background of *G. barbadense.* After several generations of backcrossing, the variation in the degree of spottedness ceased to be continuous and became, in-

---

[26] *Ibid.*
[27] *Ibid.*

stead, discontinuous. Heterozygous individuals in later backcross generations, on selfing, yielded progeny segregating into distinct phenotypic classes, normal spots versus weak spots, in a simple 3:1 ratio.[28] These and similar results obtained for other character differences between the two species of cotton confirm Harland's hypothesis that the two species differ with respect to many modifier genes.

When the hybrid is backcrossed to *G. barbadense,* the alternative phenotypes are normal petal spots or weak spots. From the fact that the spotless alleles produce weak spotting in the genetic background of *G. barbadense,* it can be concluded that the assemblage of modifiers of this species has the general effect of enhancing the expression of the gene for spots. When, on the other hand, the reciprocal backcross is made between the hybrid and *G. hirsutum,* the spotting becomes gradually weaker each generation and eventually disappears. This result indicates that the modifier complex of *G. hirsutum* tends to suppress the formation of petal spots. In other words, *G. barbadense* possesses two alleles, S and s, together with a series of plus modifiers, and *G. hirsutum* possesses the same alleles of **S** along with a series of minus modifiers.[29]

The concept of modifier genes helps us to understand a case of inheritance of pubescence described by Clausen and Hiesey in *Potentilla glandulosa.* In the coastal race of this species the leaves and stems are densely covered with hairs. The alpine race has herbage with only a few scattered hairs, a condition referred to as glabrate. The F_1 hybrid is pubescent but not as strongly so as the coastal parent. Six grades of pubescence can be recognized in the F_2 generation ranging from glabrate like the alpine parent to very pubescent like the coastal parent. The frequency distribution of the various degrees of pubescence among 970 F_2 individuals is summarized in Table 6.[30]

In order to account for the observed results in the F_1 and F_2 generations, Clausen and Hiesey propose a hypothesis involving the following postulates. First, the difference in pubescence between the parental types is due to five independent multiple genes with additive effects ($G_1 \cdots G_5$). Secondly, the very pubescent parent carries dominant alleles and the glabrate parent recessive alleles for four of the five genes ($G_2 \cdots G_5$), but dominance is not manifested by the interaction between the two alleles of G_1. Thirdly, the five genes form an epistatic series in which G_1 is epistatic or dominant over G_2, G_2

---

[28] *Ibid.*
[29] *Ibid.*
[30] Clausen and Hiesey, 1958, 88–89.

TABLE 6 INHERITANCE OF THE PUBESCENCE IN
Potentilla glandulosa *

Density of Hairs on Herbage	Alpine Race	Coastal Race	F_1 Hybrid	Observed Segregation in F_2	Expected Frequency on Hypothesis of Epistatic Series	Expected Frequency on Hypothesis of One Major Gene and Minus Modifiers
Glabrate	+			0	1	
Glabrescent				1	3	
Fairly glabrescent				195 { 20	11	<242
Fairly pubescent				174	227	
Pubescent			+	599	485	>485
Very pubescent		+		176	242	242

* From Clausen and Hiesey, 1958, 89, with modifications.

over G_3, and so on. The very pubescent parent is thus the top dominant and the glabrate parent the bottom recessive for five genes ex-
hibiting intergenic dominance or epistasis, four of which also exhibit interallelic dominance. The strong preponderance of pubescent
types in the F_1 and F_2 generations and the rarity of glabrate and
glabrescent types is consistent with the foregoing hypothetical assumptions, and indeed the agreement between the observed and the expected frequencies of F_2 phenotypes is very close (Table 6).

One of the assumptions made in this hypothesis is that the allele G_1,
though epistatic over the dominant alleles of four other genes, is not
dominant over its homologous allele g_1 carried in the generally recessive genotype. There is no evidence to support this assumption.

An alternative and simpler hypothesis which is in better agreement
with the breeding data is that the presence or absence of pubescence
in the two races of *P. glandulosa* and their hybrids is due to a single
major gene (**G**) together with a series of modifiers like those found
in Drosophila and Gossypium. No dominance is manifested in the
interaction between the two alleles of this gene carried by the very
pubescent and glabrate parents respectively, and therefore the F_2 offspring of their hybrid segregates into phenotypic classes approximating a 1:2:1 ratio. About one-quarter of the F_2 individuals are like
the very pubescent parent; about two-quarters are like the F_1; and
the remaining one-quarter range from fairly pubescent to glabrescent.

These phenotypic classes would correspond to the following genotypes for the major gene **G**: very pubescent like the coastal race, g_1g_1; pubescent like the F_1, g_1g_2; and glabrate or weakly pubescent, g_2g_2.

The basic $1:2:1$ ratio is altered, however, by the action of the modifiers. The available data can be explained if it is assumed that the modifier genes are hypostatic (viz., subordinate in action) to the allele g_1 but not to g_2, so that the modifiers exert their effects only in the g_2g_2 genotypes. The direction of action of most of the modifier genes is such as to inhibit the effects of the g_2 alleles. Consequently, some F_2 genotypes consisting of g_2g_2 and minus modifiers have the same pubescent phenotype as g_1g_2, while some other g_2g_2 genotypes approach g_1g_2 in their phenotypic expression. The net result of the action of the minus modifiers is an excess of F_2 phenotypes like the F_1 hybrid, and a deficiency of glabrate or glabrescent phenotypes. (See Table 6.)

The varying degree of expression of the pubescence character in the genotypic class, g_2g_2, ranging from glabrate through intermediate stages to fairly pubescent, can be accounted for by the assortment of the modifier genes independently of the gene **G**. Recombination types in the F_2 generation which are homozygous for g_2 and contain a large dose of minus modifiers resemble or approach g_1g_2 in phenotype. F_2 recombination types consisting of g_2g_2 together with a slight dose of minus modifiers are glabrate or glabrescent. Intermediate doses of the minus modifiers in combination with the homozygous condition g_2g_2 produce various intermediate degrees of pubescence.

It should be made clear that neither the foregoing hypothesis of modifier genes, nor the hypothesis of an epistatic series—both of which have features in common—can be regarded as more than provisional at present. The graded series of pubescent types *could* be due to the segregation of one major gene and a series of modifier genes. Whether it actually is or not can only be made clear by future research. As Clausen and Hiesey aptly remark, "An analysis of F_3 and F_4 populations would be required to clarify our understanding of the inheritance of pubescence beyond this point." [31]

We have examined two certain and one probable example in which the expression of a character determined primarily by a major gene is affected by additional modifier genes with relatively small individual effects. Not all individuals of Drosophila carrying the dominant allele D for dichaete bristles have a phenotypic expression of this allele, for some D/d genotypes possess the normal bristle number. The allele

---

[31] *Ibid.*, 89.

D is said to have incomplete penetrance. Since this incomplete penetrance is due to the effects of modifier genes, the latter are called penetrance modifiers. In Gossypium the allele S for petal spots is dominant over the allele s in certain genetic backgrounds but not in other genetic backgrounds. Here the dominance or non-dominance of an allele is conditioned by modifier genes, which are accordingly called dominance modifiers. The distinction between dominance modifiers and penetrance modifiers does not appear to be very fundamental.

It is sufficiently clear that modifier genes have relatively slight effects on the characteristics which they modify. We may ask, however, whether modifying the effects of other genes is the sole function of modifiers. Is the action of a modifier gene limited to influencing in a slight way the action of some major gene? Or does the modifier gene have an important primary function of its own besides its secondary pleiotropic effects on other genes? Is the action of a modifier gene quantitatively slight in an absolute sense, or slight only in relation to some particular characteristic which it affects indirectly?

In cotton (*G. barbadense*) one of the modifiers of the gene S for petal spot turns out on analysis to be the gene Y, which controls the production of yellow pigment in the corolla. The dominant allele S produces much more intensely colored spots when in combination with the allele Y than with y. Similarly, the gene H for hairiness acts as a modifier of leaf shape, the allele H making the leaf lobes shorter in proportion to their length.[32]

POLYGENES

In some cases where it is possible to identify the modifiers, they thus turn out to be major genes in their own right. But is this generally true? Do all modifier genes have a major function of their own? Or does the genotype include a class of modifier genes with minor *primary* actions?

The opinions of different geneticists are not in agreement on this question. Mather and others have suggested that major genes with pronounced phenotypic effects and polygenes with minor effects represent two real categories of genetic factors.[33] Many other students do not accept the idea of minor genes as a special class apart of genetic determinants. Since it is technically difficult to establish the existence

[32] Harland, 1936.
[33] Mather, 1949. Darlington and Mather, 1949, 150 ff.

and nature of genes with small phenotypic effects which are readily overridden by the effects of major genes and environmental conditions, the information needed to answer the question in a decisive way is not available at present, and we will consequently have to content ourselves with an inconclusive discussion here.

The term polygene will be used here, following Mather, to denote a gene with a minute total effect on the phenotype. A modifier gene, as we have already seen, may have a small effect on one character but a large effect on another, or it could have a small total effect. In the first case the modifier would be a major gene with modifying influences on other genes; in the second case it would be a polygene by the definition adopted here. Modifier genes undoubtedly exist. The question before us is whether, in the unanalyzed class of modifiers, there exist also true polygenes.

Let us recall to begin with our earlier discussion of the various routes by which multiple gene systems can produce a precise quantitative effect which is adaptive for the organism. One of the efficient ways of attaining a fine phenotypic adjustment in some quantitative product of gene action is by combinations of major genes with large effects and polygenes with minute overall effects. Variations in the number and dosage of the polygenes can bring the quantity of gene product to any particular level required by the organism.

Now if there is any genetic system which is physically possible and would be useful to organisms, but which has not been exploited by at least some forms of life, biologists have yet to learn of it. In fact, the inventiveness of life is usually well ahead of the imagination of biologists. If, therefore, to reason deductively, the genotypes of organisms did not possess polygenes with minute effects, but would be benefitted by having them, they could be expected to acquire them in their evolution towards a state of better adaptedness. Consequently, if polygenic systems are genetically and physically possible, as seems to be the case, and if they represent a means of producing a finely adjusted quantitative effect, as also seems to be the case, we would expect to find such systems being used by at least some well-adapted organisms.

Polygenes are indeed postulated to exist in *Drosophila melanogaster* on the basis of direct evidence which is quite suggestive though not entirely conclusive. Two strains of this fly, named Oregon and Samarkand after their original provenance, differ in the number of hairs on the underside of two abdominal segments, the Oregon strain having an average of 43.5 hairs per female, and the Samarkand strain an average of 59.2. The hereditary differences in hairiness between the two strains cannot be traced to any particular genes, but segregate as though several or many genes were involved. There are only three large (and one very small) chromosomes in the haploid set of *D. melanogaster* on which the genes controlling the number of abdominal hairs can be located. Each of these chromosomes can be tagged with appropriate genetic markers and followed in the progeny of crosses between the Oregon and Samarkand strains. By using such markers, the influence of each of the three large chromosomes on the density of abdominal hairs was assayed.[34]

In this way it could be estimated that the sex or X chromosome of the Samarkand strain causes about 3.3 more hairs to be formed than does the X chromosome of the Oregon strain; a Samarkand chromosome II gives rise to about 4.2 more hairs than an Oregon chromosome II; a Samarkand chromosome III determines about 8.2 more hairs than an Oregon chromosome III.[35] The three chromosomes combined in the Samarkand strain thus carry several or many factors determining 15.7 more hairs than the homologous factors on the three homologous chromosomes in the Oregon strain. These factors, scattered over three chromosomes and accounting for the phenotypic differences in hairiness of the two strains of flies, can be said to be polygenes.

The density of another type of hair in *D. melanogaster,* the sternopleural bristles, is controlled by a number of genes with individually small effects. The distribution of these genes on the X chromosome was investigated in crosses between the Oregon, Samarkand, and other strains, which differ phenotypically and genetically with respect to this character. The genes controlling the number of sternopleural bristles are located in five separate regions throughout the X chromosome. The two ends of the X chromosome have a maximum effect on the bristle character, and therefore may harbor a high concentration of the bristle-determining genes. At least five, and probably more, genes for the density of sternopleural bristles are thus found on the X chromosome alone. Since the phenotypic effects of all genes combined is slight, the effect of any individual gene is even slighter. The number of sternopleural bristles seems to be controlled by a system of polygenes.[36] A similar polygenic system, consisting of at least five

---

[34] Mather and Harrison, 1949. Darlington and Mather, 1949, 73–77.

[35] Mather and Harrison, 1949. Darlington and Mather, 1949. The figures given here are extrapolations from the authors' data on the average differences in genetic activity between the Samarkand or Oregon chromosomes and the tester stock.

[36] Wigan, 1949.

and probably more polygenes concerned with the number of abdominal bristles, is found on chromosome II of Drosophila.[37]

It has been suggested that the polygenes are mostly located in the heterochromatic regions of the chromosomes, which are the darkly stained regions in the metabolic non-dividing nucleus, whereas the major genes with specialized and often conspicuous phenotypic effects lie in the euchromatic regions, which differ from the heterochromatin in their staining properties.[38] Although heterochromatin does not contain major genes, it does possess a definite though generalized genetic activity.[39] As Darlington and Mather stated: [40]

We can now recognize two types of gene and two types of chromatin. The major genes occur only in euchromatin and heterochromatin contains only polygenes. Euchromatin may well also contain polygenes, perhaps in the euchromatin proper or perhaps lying in segments not distinguishable as heterochromatin owing to their small size or for some other reason.

The genetic activity of heterochromatin in *D. melanogaster* is indicated by various facts. The Y chromosome of the fruitfly is wholly heterochromatic and carries very few major genes. Yet it does exert a generalized and quantitative effect on the characteristics of the flies. Thus different Y chromosomes from different strains influence the number of sternopleural bristles, giving quantitative effects like those produced by polygenes. Similar effects are brought about by the heterochromatic regions of the X chromosome.[41]

Mutant flies with small bristles, and also with blunt wings, weak legs, rough eyes and altered male genitalia, known as "minutes," are due to mutations in any one of numerous regions scattered over all the chromosomes and frequently coinciding with heterochromatic regions.[42] It is remarkable that over 50 chromosomal segments, frequently heterochromatic, carry genetic factors which in a mutant form bring about a very similar group of characteristics.

Homologous alleles of a gene and homologous regions of two chromosomes are attracted together in pairs at meiosis and sometimes also in mitosis. Now if the polygenes represent more or less homologous genes with similar influences on general growth processes, and if they are widely distributed throughout the heterochromatin in different re-

[37] Harrison and Mather, 1950.
[38] Mather, 1944, 1949. Darlington and Mather, 1949, 150 ff.
[39] Mather, 1944. Goldschmidt, 1949; 1955, 74–94.
[40] Darlington and Mather, 1949, 151.
[41] Mather, 1944. Darlington and Mather, 1949, 151.
[42] Schultz, 1929. Goldschmidt, 1955, 72, 85, etc.

gions of different chromosomes, then considering the tendency of homologous genic units to form pairs, we would expect to find evidences of an attraction between different heterochromatic regions. In fact the heterochromatin of different chromosomes does tend to pair unspecifically, and may even unite in dense masses, as in the chromocenters of the salivary gland chromosomes of Drosophila.[43]

---

[43] Goldschmidt, 1949, except as regards the concept and term polygene.

Organization of a
chromosome region

6   The nature of the genic units on the chromosomes has been
revealed to us gradually and in successive stages by breeding
experiments, by cytogenetic studies, by detailed genetic analysis of small chromosome segments, and by biochemical investigations. It would be convenient if the various lines of evidence
regarding the mode of organization of a chromosome region were in
agreement with one another. The agreement between different lines
of evidence is, however, incomplete.

The results of breeding experiments in the nineteenth and early
twentieth centuries were successfully integrated with the results of
cytological investigations during the period from 1900 to the 1930's.
These early studies supported the classical concept of the gene as a
discrete hereditary particle. During the 1940's and since then, however, refined genetic analysis of chromosome segments and biochemical analysis of the genetic material have made the identity of the gene
as a particulate unit questionable. It will be our difficult task in this
chapter to consider the various lines of evidence on which conflicting
concepts of the gene are based and then to attempt to reconcile, in
some measure at least, the generalizations drawn from the different
lines of evidence.

THE CLASSICAL CONCEPT OF THE GENE

Both the chromosomes and the genes possess the property of self-
duplication and the power to control phenotypic characteristics. On

the basis of the combined genetic and cytological data obtained in the early period of modern genetics, the gene could be defined as a region or locus on a chromosome which is separable by crossing-over from adjacent regions, and which controls in a specific way the development of some characteristic.

The discreteness of the gene was believed to be due to the existence of definite points of breakage at intervals along the length of the chromosome. And therefore the gene is a segment of a chromosome bounded by zones of regular breakage; it is, in other words, a unit of crossing-over.

According to classical genetic theory, furthermore, the physical boundaries of the gene as defined by breakage and crossing-over were supposed to coincide with the boundaries defined by functional unity. The gene was the structural and functional atom of genetics, and the chromosome was a string of these discrete entities.

Now the chromosome does present a beaded appearance, consistent with the classical theory, under favorable conditions of microscopic observation. Granular bodies or swellings, known as chromomeres, occur in fixed positions along the length of the chromosomes, and are connected by thin thread-like regions. The chromosome as a whole thus consists of a series of chromomeres and the thread-like connections between them. The number and position of the chromomeres are constant for each chromosome of the complement, the pattern being preserved in chromosome reproduction and reappearing in different nuclei of the species.[1] (See Fig. 24.)

When examined under the electron microscope at magnifications much higher than can be obtained with the light microscope, the chromomeres are seen as localized snarls or coils in the chromosomal thread. A continuous thin thread of chromosomal material presents a densely packed appearance at the sites of the chromomeres and is unravelled in the intervening regions.[2]

The chromomeres were believed by many workers in the early period of genetics to be the cytologically visible loci of the genes.[3] In Drosophila a number of genes were found to be located in the darkly staining bands of the salivary gland chromosomes.[4] These bands are equivalent to the chromomeres in the more usual type of chromosome.

The view of the chromosome as a string of particulate and well-

---

[1] Belling, 1928. Lima-de-Faria, 1952.
[2] Buchholz, 1947. Ris, 1957.
[3] Belling, 1928.
[4] Muller and Prokofyeva, 1935. Lea, 1955, 134–135.

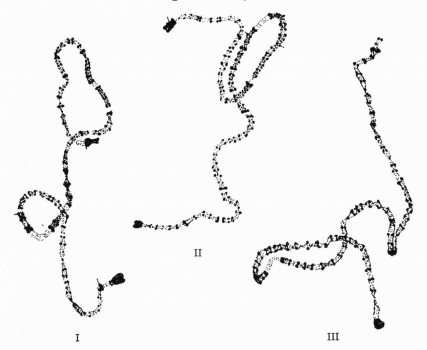

FIG. 24. Three of the seven chromosomes of rye (*Secale cereale*), showing the chromomeres. (From Lima-de-Faria, in *Chromosoma*, 1952, Springer-Verlag, by permission.)

separated genes was arrived at before the phenomenon of pseudo-allelism was discovered, before the significance of position effect was appreciated, and before the chemical nature of the genetic material was known. Many facts discovered since the 1930's have proven difficult to reconcile with the classical gene concept, as we shall now see.

DIVISIBILITY OF THE GENE

Up through the 1930's the gene was regarded as the smallest unit of recombination and as a functional unit. The two definitions were supposed to coincide. And a chromosome region, as noted earlier, was regarded as a string of different genes producing different phenotypic effects and separable from one another by crossing-over.

In the decade from 1945 to 1955 this concept was altered by the discovery of rare crossing-over between genic components that had been described formerly as the members of one allelic series. The phenomenon of crossing-over within the limits of what had been considered a "gene" became known as pseudoallelism.[5] The facts of pseudoallelism, derived from refined cytogenetic analyses in various organisms could be interpreted in two ways. Either the adjacent genes, instead of possessing different functions, have similar and related functions; or else one gene as defined by its functions can be divided into subunits. Either interpretation required a modification of the classical theory of the gene.

The recognition of a hierarchy of structural-functional units in a chromosome region, ranging from small subdivisions of what was formerly considered one gene to larger but closely linked aggregations of these entities, forces a reappraisal of terminology. To which of the several structural-functional units on a chromosome, differing in order of magnitude, does the term gene properly refer? And then how will the other units be designated?

For purposes of communication at this stage in the present chapter it will be sufficient to recognize, provisionally, three broad categories of genic units. The unit of regular and normal crossing-over on the chromosome will be called, following long usage, a "gene" in the strict sense, or to be more explicit, a "Mendelian gene." For the occasionally separable and recombinable parts of a gene, as found in pseudoallelic series, the appropriate term, "subgene," suggested by Raffel and Muller, is adopted here.[6] A closely linked group of genes with similar functions will be called, finally, a "linked serial gene system."

The foregoing three terms will be useful to us in discussing various examples of infragenic and supragenic organization in this and in the following section of this chapter. We will return to the problem of the genic units as such and their definition later in the chapter.

The gene **W** controlling eye color in *Drosophila melanogaster* had been shown in the early period of Drosophila genetics to occupy a specific locus on the X or sex chromosome, and to consist of a series of alleles determining white, apricot, eosin and other colors of the compound eye. The different alleles were inherited as the members of a single gene. In 1952, however, Lewis found that crossing-over occurs rarely between two of these alleles, namely w for white eyes and w^a for apricot eyes, which must, therefore, exist at closely adjacent but separable loci. The distance between the "apricot" and the "white-eosin" allelic series on the genetic map was calculated to be between 0.02 and 0.005 crossover units.[7]

---

[5] For reviews see Symposium, 1955; and Wagner and Mitchell, 1955, Chapter 9.
[6] Raffel and Muller, 1940. The term pseudoallele is synonymous with subgene.
[7] Lewis, 1952.

It will be recalled that a distance of 0.005 crossover units on a genetic map implies that the two loci are so close that crossovers between them occur in only five-thousandths of 1% of the paired chromosome strands. Under these conditions the heterozygote $\dfrac{a_1\ b_1}{a_2\ b_2}$ will produce on the average 99,995 parental type gametes (a_1b_1 and a_2b_2) for every five recombination gametes (a_1b_2 and a_2b_1). Consequently very large numbers of gametes must be tested in order to detect the occurrence of rare crossing-over.

Other genes in Drosophila besides the eye color gene were also found to consist of closely linked but separable and recombinable subgenes. The pseudoallelic components "star" and "asteroid" lie 0.02 crossover units apart on the second chromosome.[8] The "lozenge" gene (**Lz**) on the X chromosome was likewise found to consist of three subgenes in the order, lz^{BS} lz^{46} lz^{g} with intervals between the subunits of about 0.06 to 0.09 crossover units.[9] Recombination has been detected between two components of the "rosy" gene, namely ry^{26} and ry^2, which are calculated to be 0.00026 crossover units or about 40 nucleotide pairs apart.[10] In one of the first cases to be analyzed, the genes "scute" and "achaete" controlling related characters were shown to lie very close together on the X chromosome.[11]

Similar results were obtained in other organisms. The **A** gene in corn (*Zea mays*), governing the formation of anthocyanin pigment in the endosperm of the kernels, was found to be compound, consisting of separable and recombinable subunits about one crossover unit apart on the genetic map.[12] Several genes in the bacterium Salmonella consist of separate neighboring components controlling different biochemical steps in the same process.[13] In the yeast, Saccharomyces, closely linked but separable genic units control different stages in the process of sugar fermentation.[14]

In the bacterial virus T4, numerous mutations determining the ability or inability of the viruses to multiply in the cells of the host

[8] Lewis, 1945.
[9] Green and Green, 1949.
[10] Chovnick, Schalet, Kernaghan, and Talsma, 1962.
[11] Raffel and Muller, 1940.
[12] Laughnan, 1948, 1952.
[13] Demerec, Blomstrand, and Demerec, 1955. Demerec, 1956.
[14] Winge, 1955.

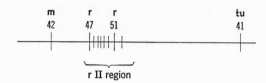

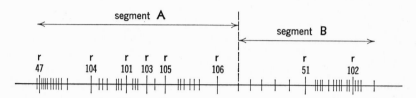

FIG. 25. A portion of the genetic map of the bacterial virus T4, showing the location of the rII mutations. Above, the rII region in relation to the genes **m** and **tu**. Below, the rII region enlarged, showing two genes **A** and **B**, with the locations of the various types of rII mutations as indicated. (Benzer, 1955.)

bacterium, *Escherichia coli,* and hence similar in their functions, were all found to be located in one region of the gene-string, designated rII, between the genes **m** and **tu**. (See Fig. 25.) The region rII as a whole represents a structural and functional unit consisting of two genes, **A** and **B**, which have complementary phenotypic effects.[15] Different individual types of the rII group of mutations can be located, on the basis of recombination data, at different points within either the **A** or the **B** gene, as shown in Fig. 25. Benzer has shown that rII mutations lying as close as 0.02 crossover units apart on the gene-string may become separated and recombined. In terms of molecular structure, this represents recombination between one nucleotide pair and another estimated to lie only two nucleotide units away on the DNA chain.[16]

Numerous instances of pseudoallelism have thus been reported in Drosophila, corn, yeast, bacteria, virus, and other organisms.[17] Indeed, recombination between the members of one allelic series has been found in every organism which has been studied from this point of view, and pseudoallelism is thus a widespread phenomenon.[18] The

---

[15] Benzer, 1955, 1957. **A** and **B** are cistrons in Benzer's (1957) terminology.
[16] Benzer, 1957.
[17] See Komai (1950) and Pontecorvo (1958, 57–58) for additional examples with references.
[18] Pontecorvo, 1953. Glass, 1955.

fact that the functional unit can be broken up by crossing-over into smaller recombinational units suggests that the gene as a unit of inheritance is frequently capable of being subdivided. The atom of classical genetics, in other words, can be split.

THE LINKAGE OF FUNCTIONALLY RELATED GENES

The atom of genetics lost its integrity in another sense. The individual gene is usually a component of a gene system, which functions as a unit in itself. The integration of genes into gene systems may take place on a functional level only, as where different genes working together on the same developmental process are located on different chromosomes. Or this integration may be carried further by the spatial grouping of different genes with related functions.

The linkage maps of Drosophila and corn reveal, at first glance, an apparently haphazard distribution on the chromosomes and throughout the chromosome complement of the genes governing each characteristic. The different genes possessing related functions are often located on separate chromosomes. This mode of arrangement of functionally related genes made possible the identification and factorial analysis of the various types of gene interaction considered in Chapters 4 and 5. On the other hand, a good deal of evidence has accumulated which points to an orderly spatial grouping of the genes controlling similar characters.

In *D. melanogaster*, all of the known mutations which bring about extra wing venation occur in chromosome II, and all of the so-called homeotic mutations which transform wings or antennae into legs, etc., occur in a small region of chromosome III.[19] In the mouse five genes governing the characteristics of the tail lie close together in a segment 8 crossover units long on one chromosome.[20] In tomatoes six out of fifteen seedling mutations that were placed in a linkage group were found to be located on chromosome 2, which represents an unusual concentration on one chromosome of the genes affecting the seedling.[21]

The flower petals of the asiatic cottons (*Gossypium arboreum* and *G. herbaceum*) are yellow or white and in addition may have a red spot at the base. The crossing of a spotted (G S) by a spotless (g s) plant will yield an F_1 hybrid of the constitution $\dfrac{G \quad S}{g \quad s}$, which ex-

---

[19] Dubinin, 1948.
[20] Dunn and Caspari, 1945.
[21] Rick, 1959.

hibits the dominant condition of petal spots, and segregates into spotted and spotless types in the F_2 generation in a 3:1 ratio. The spotless plants will mostly breed true to type. The spotless condition is thus usually inherited as though it is determined by a simple Mendelian recessive allele.

Occasionally, however, the intercrossing of two spotless plants will yield an individual possessing petal spots. The exceptional spotted individuals in the progeny of spotless plants are explained by Stephens as the result of the following chain of events: first, rare crossing-over between G and S in the double heterozygote $\dfrac{G \quad S}{g \quad s}$; second, the formation of the recombination types, $\dfrac{G \quad s}{G \quad s}$ and $\dfrac{g \quad S}{g \quad S}$, both of which are spotless; and thirdly by intercrossing of two such spotless types the formation of their complementary product, $\dfrac{G \quad s}{g \quad S}$, which exhibits petal spots. These exceptional types show that the presence or absence of petal spots is controlled, not by a single gene, but by two closely linked genes.[22]

The two genes **G** and **S** control successive and similar chemical processes leading to the formation of red pigment at the base of the petal. The petal spot is produced only in the presence of the dominant alleles, G and S, of the two genes, both of which are necessary to carry the process of pigment formation through to completion (Fig. 26). Furthermore, the two genes **G** and **S** lie adjacent to one another on a chromosome. Consequently, as Stephens pointed out, they are like two steps on an assembly line in both their functional and positional relationships.[23]

One region on the gene-string of the bacterium *Salmonella typhimurium* is concerned with the synthesis of tryptophane. The synthesis of tryptophane takes place in the following sequence of steps: precursor → anthranilic acid → compound B → indole → tryptophane. Each step in this synthesis is controlled by a different adjacent section of the tryptophane region of the gene-string, as shown in Fig. 27. Furthermore, the linear order of the sections on the genetic map corresponds to the sequence of steps in tryptophane synthesis, as would be expected if these sections were organized for tryptophane production in the manner of an assembly line.[24]   (Fig. 27).

---

[22] Stephens, 1948.

[23] *Ibid.*

[24] Demerec, 1956. Discussions also in Pontecorvo (1958, 58–62); Sinnott, Dunn, and Dobzhansky (1958, 384–386); and Sagar and Ryan (1961, 158–163).

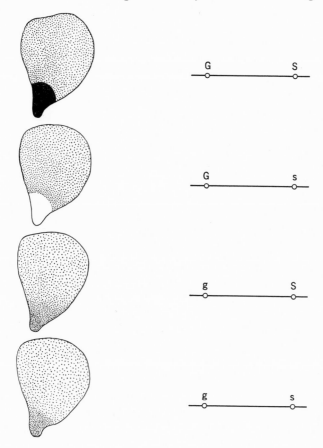

FIG. 26. Phenotypic characteristics of the flower petals of asiatic cotton, and the corresponding genotypic conditions. (Stephens, 1948.)

Closely linked complementary genes are exemplified by the genes **G** and **S** controlling petal spots in asiatic cotton and by **A** and **B** in the rII region of virus T4. In the phenomenon of pseudoallelism in Drosophila, corn, yeast, bacteria, and other organisms, we observe extremely close linkages of subgenic components with complementary effects. The close proximity and linear arrangement of the different genes or subgenes definitely correspond in some of the cases analyzed —in the bacterium Salmonella and in yeast—to the sequence of stages in a biochemical process. The linear order of the genes probably corresponds to a developmental sequence in the other examples in Drosophila and corn. The close functional and spatial relationships can be explained on the hypothesis that the separate genes or subgenes, as

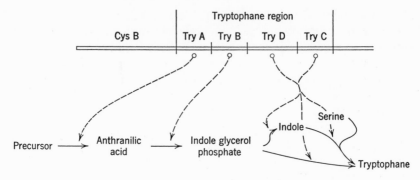

FIG. 27. The linear order of four groups of tryptophane mutants in *Salmonella typhimurium* (above) as correlated with the steps in the biosynthesis of tryptophane (below). Each section on the genetic map controls a different step in tryptophane synthesis, as indicated by the dashed arrows. (Redrawn from *Cell Heredity*, by Sager and Ryan, after Demerec, copyright 1961, John Wiley, New York and London, by permission.)

the case may be, are arranged on the chromosome in the fashion of an assembly line, so as to control the successive steps in a biochemical reaction.[25]

Chromosomes can break and the broken ends can rejoin in new ways so that the linear order and grouping of the genes is altered. If two breaks occur in one chromosome, and if the ends of the broken segment reunite in a new way with the broken ends in the rest of the chromosome, the resulting chromosomal rearrangement is called an inversion. If breaks occur in non-homologous chromosomes, and the broken ends join to give a new combination of chromosome segments, the rearrangement is called a translocation. The arrangement of the genes is strongly altered in either case. If the linear order of the genes in the original chromosome is ABCDEFGHI, a chromosome carrying an inversion might have the gene order ABCGFEDHI. Or if the chromosome with ABCDEFGHI and one with *MNOPQRST* exchange segments or arms, the new translocated chromosomes may be ABCD-*QRST* and *MNOP*EFGHI. The nucleus contains the same genes in the same proportions as before but their spatial relations are different. (See also Chapter 8.)

The vast majority of the inversions and translocations that have been studied in plants and animals have produced no detectable

[25] Stephens, 1948.　Lewis, 1951, and in Symposium, 1955.　Demerec, Blomstrand, and Demerec, 1955.　Demerec, 1956.　Beadle, 1957*a*.

phenotypic effect. This is not always the case however. In a number of cases in Drosophila and in a very few cases in plants the chromosomal rearrangement is associated with a definite change in the visible characteristics of the organism.[26] Such a phenotypic change, dependent upon a change in the spatial relations of the genes, and not on mutational changes in the genes themselves to new allelic forms, or changes in their proportions or dosage, is known as a position effect.

The most probable explanation of position effects starts with the precept that the gene arrangement is not in fact as haphazard as it appears on the genetic map but is orderly over segments of varying length which are subject to occasional breakage. If genes with similar or successive functions are grouped like the parts of an assembly line, a chromosomal rearrangement following a break within the organized region would be expected to disrupt the workings of the system and interfere with production. The result should be apparent in the phenotypic products of gene action, and furthermore should represent a phenotypic change deleterious to the organism. As a matter of fact, position effects are nearly always deleterious and are sometimes lethal.[27] Thus 60% of a large number of translocations produced by X-rays in *Drosophila melanogaster* were lethal in the homozygous condition.[28]

SUPERGENES

Different genes which are not necessarily similar functionally, but which cooperate to produce some adaptive characteristic, are sometimes tightly linked and inherited as a block. Such a group of genes held together mechanically on a chromosome has been called a supergene.[29]

In many of the wild species of Drosophila, such as *D. pseudoobscura* in North America and *D. willistoni* in the American tropics, to mention only two examples, a series of adjacent genes located on a chromosomal segment of moderate length is tied together in a block so that under normal conditions of sexual reproduction they cannot be separated from one another by crossing-over. The block of genes is

---

[26] Goldschmidt, 1938; and Lewis, 1950, for reviews. Some later cases mentioned or reviewed by Grant, 1956*b*.

[27] Muller and Prokofyeva, 1935. Raffel and Muller, 1940. Goldschmidt, 1938. Darlington and Mather, 1949, 331. Lewis, 1950.

[28] Patterson, Stone, Bedichek, and Suche, 1934.

[29] Darlington and Mather, 1949, 334–339. See also Dobzhansky, 1959, 24–26, for a recent discussion.

preserved intact by a special chromosomal mechanism (heterozygosity for inversions), the operation of which will be explained in Chapter 8. The genes contained in these blocks are known from both population analyses in the wild and experimental studies in the laboratory to affect the adaptive characteristics of the flies, as will be mentioned in Chapter 9.[30]

A remarkable series of forms exists in the female sex of the African butterfly, *Papilio dardanus*.   The various forms differ in the color pattern and presence or absence of tails on the wings.   Some females of the type "meriones" have yellow wings with black marks and tailed appendages; the female forms known as "hippocoon" and "hippo-coonides" have brown and white, tailless wings; and the form "tro-phonius" has orange and brown, tailless wings.   Some of these forms mimic other distasteful species of butterflies, thereby gaining some degree of protection from insectivorous animals.

The genetics underlying the morphological variation in *P. dardanus* has been worked out recently by Clarke and Sheppard, who find that the main differences between the various female forms are controlled by two supergenes.   Each supergene contains several genes, some major genes and some modifiers, which are transmitted as a block in inheritance.   One of the two supergenes controls the color pattern of the wing, while the other determines the presence or absence of tailed appendages.   The alternative alleles of the major genes within each supergene act as a switch to determine the development of clearcut alternative wing types.[31]

A third example of a probable supergene is found in the so-called "speltoides" mutants in the cultivated hexaploid wheat, *Triticum vulgare vulgare*, which affect simultaneously a whole complex of characters in the head or spike.

The wheat spike consists of a main axis (rachis) bearing the spikelets, each of which contains at maturity several grains enclosed by two bracts (glumes).   In the cultivated wheats, *T. vulgare vulgare, T. durum, T. carthlicum*, etc., the rachis is tough and the glumes are loose, so that when threshed the grains fall out freely from the head. Such types are called naked wheats.   In the more primitive species and varieties of wheat, wild or early cultivated, the rachis is by contrast brittle and the glumes persistent, so that on threshing the rachis

---

[30] Reviews by Dobzhansky (1951, Chapter 5; 1955); and Grant (1963, Chapter 10).

[31] Clarke and Sheppard, 1959–1960, 1960a, 1960b.

breaks and the grains remain enclosed within the glumes. These types are known as spelt wheats.[32]

Obviously the success of the modern cultivated wheats as grain cereals depends to a large extent on the complex of spike characters determining the response of the heads to threshing. The evolution of the wheat plant under domestication has involved, among other changes, the replacement of the spelt by the naked type of spike.

Now as mentioned at the beginning, the normal type of *T. vulgare vulgare,* which is naked, gives rise occasionally to speltoid mutants, which possess some interesting features. The speltoid mutants comprise a syndrome of characters including the toughness of the rachis, the glumes, the number of fertile grain-bearing spikelets, and others. These characters mutate together, and there is no recombination between them. Furthermore, the mutation always occurs from normal naked *vulgare* to speltoid, and never in the opposite direction.[33]

The foregoing features are explained on the hypothesis that the speltoid mutant is a result of the loss or deletion of a short chromosome segment, designated as Q. This hypothesis has been confirmed by cytological observation of the deletion, which turns out to be located in the long arm of chromosome IX.[34] The presence of the Q segment thus determines the normal *vulgare* phenotype, while the absence of this segment is associated with the speltoid mutant characters. And since the normal and speltoid types of wheat are differentiated in respect to several separate characters, it is likely that the Q segment contains several or many genes and is thus probably a supergene.

Where did the Q supergene in *T. vulgare* come from? Sears has pointed out that Q is present in another and more ancient species of wheat, the tetraploid *T. carthlicum,* and therefore might have arisen in that species and been transferred by hybridization from it to the hexaploid *T. vulgare.*[35] Then how did Q originate in the first place? Bearing in mind that the Q supergene consists of a complex of genic units affecting a variety of characters, one possibility is that Q arose by a reorganization and division of functions within an originally compound gene, while another possibility is that several originally separate genes became assembled by a series of translocations into a single block.[36]

---

[32] Review by Frankel and Munday, 1962.
[33] *Ibid.*
[34] Sears, 1944. Mackey, 1954.
[35] Sears, 1959. Frankel and Munday, 1962.
[36] Frankel and Munday, 1962. These authors favor the first possibility.

CONTINUITY AND DISCONTINUITY
IN THE GENETIC MATERIAL

The obvious question left unanswered by the Watson-Crick model of DNA is where, on a DNA chain containing thousands of nucleotide units, is the individual crossover gene? The same question is posed by the phenomenon of pseudoallelism, wherein crossing-over occurs between the constituents of one gene. It is posed again by position effect, which forces us to view the gene as a subordinate element of a higher functional unit. The atom of genetics is hard-pressed from several sides. First reduced to an elementary component of a gene system, then split into subdivisions of its own, it is now by way of disappearing into a continuous array of nucleotides on a macromolecular chain.

A generalization which is consistent with many of the facts discovered in recent years holds that the chromosome of a higher organism or the gene-string of a bacterium or virus is a continuum of molecular links. The structural pattern resides in, and the physiological action derives from, the chromosome as a whole. The largest genetic unit within the chromosome complement is the individual chromosome. The smallest unit is the individual nucleotide. Recombination could theoretically take place between adjacent nucleotides, and has actually been observed to occur in bacterial virus between one nucleotide pair and another estimated to lie two nucleotide units away on the DNA thread.[37] Between these two extremes, the single nucleotide and the entire DNA chain, any number of segments of varying size can be recognized. The segments of varying length on the DNA chain are associated with genetic functions of different orders of complexity. These segments can be separated and recombined in a multitude of ways.

This picture leaves no place for genes in the sense of discrete units with definite limits. The term gene cannot be related to an objectively demarcated entity on the chromosome and hence cannot be given a precise definition. Consequently, if the word gene is retained at all—which some authors are disinclined to do—it can only be used in an indefinite sense to refer to genetically active regions of varying size and limits on a chromosome.[38]

The evidences for a continuous linear structure of the genetic ma-

---

[37] Benzer, 1957.
[38] Goldschmidt, 1938, 1955. Benzer, 1957. Pontecorvo, 1958.

terial cannot be denied. The facts of pseudoallelism and position effect reveal the lack of discontinuity in the organization of the genetic material within particular regions of the chromosomes or genetic threads. Our present hypothesis of the structure of DNA postulates a continuous chain of nucleotides. The limitations of these lines of evidence must be borne in mind, however, in attempts to generalize from them.

The postulated continuous structure of DNA is hypothetical in itself, and consequently is subject to revision if evidences of discontinuity can be found. The evidence of pseudoallelism and random crossing-over between paired chromosomes refers to *some* segments of genetic material; but whether the distribution of the breakage and crossover points is random in *all* regions of the chromosomes or not is quite another question.

One of the arguments for denying the existence of particulate atomistic genes is based on the occurrence of position effects, which imply a functional and organizational pattern extending beyond the limits of any single gene on a chromosome.[39] The force of this argument must be admitted. It must also be recognized that the argument cuts two ways, for if the functional pattern resides in the chromosome as a whole, and if atomistic genes are lacking entirely, position effects should be a much more common result of chromosome breaks and rearrangements than they actually are. Hundreds of chromosome rearrangements have been studied in plants, but position effects associated with the altered chromosome structures have been found only in special cases in Oenothera and corn.[40] In corn, 64 translocations were all viable in the homozygous condition,[41] and in Drosophila 134 out of 332 translocation homozygotes were viable.[42]

The existence of deleterious position effects is thus consistent with the hypothesis that the genes in *some* regions of the chromosomes are organized structurally to perform their collective function and cannot continue to function well when their pattern of organization is disrupted. But the fact that position effects are not a universal or even a particularly common result of chromosomal rearrangements indicates that many other regions of the chromosomes in which breaks occur frequently do not contain integrated gene systems which are

---

[39] Goldschmidt, 1938, 1955.
[40] Catcheside, 1939. McClintock, 1953.
[41] Anderson, 1935.
[42] Patterson, Stone, Bedichek, and Suche, 1934.

functionally inhibited when broken apart.   In fact, breakage and separation by crossing-over of neighboring chromosome segments is the normal event in meiosis.

A linear sequence of nucleotides occupying a segment on a chromosome and functioning as a whole would have an adaptive value for the organism possessing it.   Wright and Muller have pointed out that the functional unit on the chromosome, if valuable to the organism, would be expected to be protected from disintegration by some structural mechanism causing the breakage points to fall outside the functional unit.[43]   In short, the functional unit requires a structural vehicle for its successful reproduction.   In the evolution of organisms towards a state of better adaptedness, therefore, mechanical devices would be expected to develop so as to hold valuable nucleotide sequences together, and structural units on the chromosomes would thus come to coincide with functional units.

There are various indications that the points of breakage on the chromosomes are not distributed at random but are more or less localized.   Chromosome breaks in the spiderwort (Tradescantia)[44] and in rye (Secale)[45] seem to fall preferentially in certain regions of the chromosomes.   In *Drosophila melanogaster* the exposure of flies to X-rays leads to much breakage in all regions of all chromosomes, with a higher than average frequency of the breaks occurring in certain regions containing heterochromatin.[46]   Chromosome breakage induced by irradiation in a small region of the X chromosome of *D. melanogaster*, the region containing the genes "yellow" and "scute," was studied by Muller and his collaborators, who found that 13 independent breaks did not occur at random throughout this region, but fell into four definite positions, so as to block out just three segments.[47] In another region of the same chromosome, containing the "lozenge" pseudoalleles, Green and Green likewise found that different X-ray-induced and spontaneous breaks occur at definite points demarcating three separate loci.[48]

The chromosomes break normally and regularly, without the agency of radiation, during the process of crossing-over in sexual organisms. If the points of crossing-over were randomly distributed on the chro-

---

[43] Wright, 1959. Muller, 1959.
[44] Sax and others; see Lea, 1955, 216.
[45] Rees and Thompson, 1955.
[46] Patterson, Stone, Bedichek, and Suche, 1934. Kaufman; see Lea, 1955, 366.
[47] Muller and Prokofyeva, 1935. Raffel and Muller, 1940, 11.
[48] Green and Green, 1956. Wright, 1959, 482.

mosomes, a great many if not a majority of them would be expected to fall somewhere in the middle of a functionally useful sequence of nucleotides. Many or most of the crossover products of meiosis would then be deleterious to some degree. The fact that the predicted lowering of viability is not a usual consequence of crossing-over between the chromosomes of a normal breeding population can be taken as indirect evidence that the spontaneous breaks and crossovers do not occur at random but rather in predetermined zones.[49]

As a matter of fact, the chiasmata, which are cytologically visible connections between paired chromosomes believed to represent crossover points, are known from cytological studies in a number of organisms to be localized in particular chromosomal regions.[50] This is the case, for example, in the grasshopper, Bryodema, and in numerous plants such as tomato, rye, Fritillaria, Oenothera, Plantago, Anemone, and Veltheimia.[51]

The chromomeres, as noted earlier, represent regions in which the chromosomal thread is packed or coiled. For mechanical reasons these tightly packed local regions might be expected to remain unbroken when the chromosomal strand is under tension. Consequently, breakage and crossing-over would tend to be restricted to the thin straight regions between the chromomeres.[52]

The restriction of breakage to specific sites could also be achieved by a chemical mechanism. Mazia has suggested that the DNA macromolecule may not be a continuous chain of nucleotides, as originally postulated, but may consist of sections linked together by bonds of calcium or magnesium ions or both.[53] These minerals are known from chemical analyses to be present in the nucleus.[54] The calcium or magnesium bridges could represent sites of preferential breakage in the DNA chain and would thus delimit structural units.[55]

The treatment of salivary gland chromosomes of Drosophila with a chelating agent which binds calcium and magnesium ions (Versene or EDTA), breaks the chromosomes up into segments, some of which

---

[49] Wright, 1959.

[50] Darlington, 1932, 394–398; 1937.

[51] For references to earlier examples see Darlington, 1932, 1937. Later examples are added inter alia by Japha (1939), Coleman (1940), Böcher (1945), Barton (1951), Hyde (1953), White (1954), Böcher, Larsen and Rahn (1955), and Rees and Thompson (1955).

[52] Wright, 1959, 482.

[53] Mazia, 1954.

[54] *Ibid.*

[55] *Ibid.*

are about 4000 A. long.[56]   Individuals of Drosophila reared on media containing this same chelating agent have an increased frequency of crossing-over between certain genes.[57]   The feeding of an excess of calcium to young adult female flies, on the other hand, causes a decrease in crossing-over.[58]

Similar results have been observed in the alga, Chlamydomonas, and in the herbaceous plant, Tradescantia.   Plants of Tradescantia grown under conditions of magnesium deficiency have several times more breakage and fragmentation of the chromosomes than control plants.[59] The frequency of crossing-over in Chlamydomonas is increased by treatment with a chelating agent.   The effect of this agent can be reversed by subsequent incubation of the cells in a high concentration of calcium or magnesium ions.[60]

Kaufman and McDonald have shown that chromosome breakage and gene recombination between the genes **W**, **M**, and **F** in Drosophila can be increased by treatment with the digestive enzyme ribonuclease as well as the chelating agent EDTA.   They conclude that a wide variety of chemical agents with specific or unspecific actions on metallic ions are capable of disturbing the metabolic activity of the nucleus and causing breakage of chromosomes, and therefore the results obtained by Mazia, Levine, and others with chelating agents cannot be taken as proof for the existence of structural units in the chromosomes bounded by metallic ions.   Pontecorvo, in referring to the work of Kaufman and McDonald, has gone on to state that "the original interpretation of Mazia is probably based on a fallacy." [61]

It would be more correct to say that Kaufman and McDonald presented evidence for an interpretation alternative to that of Mazia. Segments of a chromosome could be linked by calcium or magnesium ions, by colloidal nucleoproteins, or by some other material, and the tests have not always discriminated decisively between the various possibilities.   Steffensen has performed new experiments designed to meet these objections.   These experiments indicate that metal ions, particularly calcium, are in fact bound into the structure of the chromosomes of Lilium and of the wasp Habrobracon.[62]

---

[56] *Ibid.*
[57] Levine, 1956.   Colwell and Burdick, 1959.
[58] Levine, 1955.
[59] Steffensen, 1953.
[60] Eversole and Tatum, 1956.
[61] Kaufman and McDonald, 1956.   Pontecorvo, 1958, 47.
[62] Steffensen, 1959.

Some recent attempts to generalize about the organization of the genetic material seem to emphasize certain groups of facts and ignore others. The older generalizations did not have the benefit of the newer findings. By selecting different groups of facts it is possible to derive mutually contradictory generalizations from the same original body of data. Diverse theories of the gene do coexist at the present time.

The facts available at present are derived from studies of the genetics of organisms as different as viruses, fungi, plants, and Drosophilas, and from analyses of the genetic factors in different chromosomal regions of the same organism. If the structure of the genetic material were more or less the same in different parts of the genotype of one organism, and for organisms belonging to different kingdoms, it would be possible to arrive at valid universal generalizations from the sample of information now at hand.

The existence of alternative concepts of the gene, each supported by much evidence but contradicted by other facts, may be taken as an indication of an underlying condition of diversity in the genetic material itself. The genetic material may be organized into units of various types within any single genotype and from one kind of organism to another. If this is so, no single generalization can be formulated which will describe in a satisfactory way all kinds of genetic factors in all kinds of organisms, and the true theory of the gene, yet to be hammered out by future research, will have to be a composite of several different generalizations each of which possesses a limited validity.

Thus the genetic material of viruses and bacteria may consist to a considerable extent of interchangeable nucleotide pairs, while that of plants and animals may be organized to a much greater extent into large structural units.[63] In short, discrete Mendelian genes may be a characteristic element in the genotype of complex organisms, but may be a relatively uncommon feature of the genotype of simple viruses and bacteria. Again, it is quite possible that bead-like genes coextensive with chromomeres may be found in one part of the chromosome of a higher plant or animal, and poorly delimited sequences of genetic material elsewhere in the same chromosome. Both theoretical and factual considerations indicate that the genetic material of higher organisms does not form a continuum throughout the entire length of a chromosome but exists in a discontinuous state in at least some chromosomal regions.

---

[63] Wright, 1959. Muller, 1959. Dobzhansky, 1959.

THE ELEMENTARY GENETIC UNITS

We have seen that a chromosome segment is organized into a hierarchy of functional, mutational, and recombinational units. Over any given length in a DNA chain there may be various levels of physiological action. A genetic function accomplished by one segment of DNA might be the specification of one amino acid in a protein chain; or the function might be the formation of one peptide chain in an enzyme. Again, the synthesis of the whole enzyme could represent the genetic function. Or, finally, the genetic function could be the control of some physiological process involving several enzymatic steps.[64] Clearly the smaller functions will generally be performed by the smaller sequences of nucleotides on the DNA chain, while the more inclusive functions will require the action of larger segments of the macromolecule. Accordingly, there is no such thing as a functional unit per se; rather there is a hierarchy of functions and hence of functional units on an inclusive segment of DNA.

By the same reasoning, a hierarchy of mutational units must exist within the limits of a chromosome segment. For a mutation is an alteration in the structure and functioning of the genetic material which leads to an altered phenotypic effect. Mutations are changes in the function of the genetic material at any functional level. Every functional unit within a chromosome region, from individual nucleotide to linked serial gene system (as well as the larger units consisting of whole chromosomes or chromosome sets), is subject to mutation. Recombination, similarly, takes place between smaller as well as between larger units within a chromosome segment.

The smallest structural-functional unit on the DNA chain is evidently the single *nucleotide unit*. We saw in Chapter 2 that a group of about three adjacent nucleotide units may be able to specify, through an RNA intermediary, the identity of an amino acid in a protein chain. Such a group, known as a *triplet* (or codon [65]), may therefore be a natural organizational unit.

Benzer has defined the muton as "the smallest element that, when altered, can give rise to a mutant form of the organism." He finds in virus T4 that an alteration in five or perhaps fewer nucleotides can bring about a visible mutation.[66] The smallest element that is inter-

---

[64] Benzer, 1957.
[65] Crick, 1962.
[66] Benzer, 1957.

changeable by genetic recombination, but not divisible, is termed a recon, which may be as small as two nucleotide pairs in T4 virus.[67] A muton or recon would be approximately the right size to perform the function ascribed to a triplet. Perhaps it will prove desirable to reduce the terms muton, recon, and codon to synonymy under the term triplet, assuming that the latter corresponds to a fundamental unit.

The conceptual and nomenclatural problem, as regards the more inclusive elementary genetic units centering around what has traditionally been called the gene, is difficult and controversial. In attempting to deal with this problem here, let us begin by recalling the arguments put forward in the preceding section for the existence, within a chromosome region, of functional units bounded by predetermined zones of breakage and crossing-over. If such structural-functional units do in fact exist, as seems likely from the available evidence in higher organisms at least, then we obviously require a name by which to refer to them.

The discrete crossover units have, of course, long been known as genes. But the word, gene, has also been used in a variety of senses to designate hereditary particles of various kinds, and has therefore acquired a certain terminological looseness. In view of this situation, some authors propose to relegate the word, gene, to a limbo of undefined terms, preserving it as a general collective designation perhaps, but replacing it with a wholly new set of terms for use in precise communication.[68] A new term, cistron, has been coined and defined in a special way.[69] The cistron, as defined, is not entirely synonymous with the crossover gene, but in its application in various cases seems to refer to essentially the same unit, with the result that the new term has tended to supplant the old one in a number of recent publications.

In the view of other students, including myself, the deletion or demotion of the long established word, gene, from the vocabulary of genetics is inadvisable. We should continue to refer to the crossover units on the chromosomes as genes. If it is desirable to make a distinction between genes in the strict sense, considered as units of regular crossing-over, and genes in the general collective sense, perhaps we can call the former *Mendelian genes,* since they correspond to the units with which Mendel and the early Mendelian geneticists worked.

---

[67] *Ibid.*
[68] Benzer, 1957, 70 ff.   Pontecorvo, 1958, 28 ff.
[69] Benzer, 1957.

Entities smaller and larger than the Mendelian gene are found in a chromosome region.   The term *subgene* is useful to denote the separable main subdivisions of a Mendelian gene, as found in pseudo-allelic series.[70]   Among supragenic organizational units is the *linked serial gene system*.   We must also recognize that hard and fast distinctions cannot be drawn in every case between subgenes, Mendelian genes, and linked serial gene systems, which form successively more inclusive groupings of the genetic material.   In this respect these elementary genetic units stand in the good company of other biological units which likewise defy absolute definition.   There are, nevertheless, differences between the aforementioned genetic units which justify their recognition.

We saw in Chapter 2 that a gene frequently, if not generally, determines the formation of an enzyme, while a triplet specifies the identity of an amino acid in the peptide chain or chains constituting the enzyme macromolecule.   This suggests that a string of triplets long enough to determine the complete sequence of amino acids, either in a peptide chain [71] or in the whole protein macromolecule, may correspond to a Mendelian gene.   On this basis, a subgene might be a major subdivision of the gene concerned with the production of some major component of the protein macromolecule.   A linked serial gene system, by the same token, would consist of two or more contiguous Mendelian genes which produce two or more species of protein involved in a series of enzymatic steps.

Benzer has proposed a more sophisticated test of the functional integrity of the genetic units based on the so-called *cis-trans* comparison devised by Lewis.[72]   Benzer has developed his concept in relation to viruses and has expressed it in terms of cistrons.[73]   Following various other authors,[74] we will state the same concept here in terms of the diploid condition in higher organisms, and furthermore will attempt to relate it to the gene terminology adopted in this section.

The *cis-trans* comparison depends on the presence in the same cell of two recessive mutations which occur in the same chromosome region and produce the same, usually defective phenotype, together with the dominant normal alleles of the two mutations.   The diploid

---

[70] Raffel and Muller, 1940, 570.
[71] Beadle, 1962.
[72] Lewis, 1951.
[73] Benzer, 1957.
[74] See Pontecorvo, 1958, for an especially good discussion.

cell is, in other words, heterozygous for two independent recessive mutant alleles. In the heterozygote, the mutant alleles may both occur on the same chromosome, thus in the *cis* position $\dfrac{m_1\ m_2}{+\ +}$, or on separate homologous chromosomes in the *trans* arrangement $\dfrac{m_1\ +}{+\ m_2}$. The *cis* arrangement and the *trans* arrangement may or may not produce the same phenotypic effects.

If the *trans* genotype $\dfrac{m_1 +}{+\ m_2}$ does not produce a mutant or recessive phenotype, but on the contrary gives rise to a normal phenotype, it can be concluded that the mutant units m_1 and m_2 are not allelic in the strict sense but belong to separate complementary genes. They form a linked serial gene system, or, in Benzer's terminology, they belong to different cistrons.

It will be recalled from an earlier discussion in this chapter that two genic units, **G** and **S**, control different phases of petal spot formation in asiatic cotton. Two different homozygous recessive mutant genotypes, $\dfrac{G\ s}{G\ s}$ and $\dfrac{g\ S}{g\ S}$, are both spotless, whereas the double heterozygote in the *trans* arrangement, $\dfrac{G\ s}{g\ S}$, is spotted. Therefore, **G** and **S** can be classified as separate but linked complementary genes.

It may turn out, on the other hand, that the *trans* genotype $\dfrac{m_1\ +}{+\ m_2}$ gives rise not to a normal but to a recessive mutant phenotype, whereas the corresponding *cis* genotype $\dfrac{m_1\ m_2}{+\ +}$ gives rise to a normal phenotype. Or, if the phenotypic differences between the *trans* and *cis* configurations are not as qualitative as this, at least the *trans* genotype may be more recessive in phenotype than the *cis* form. The complete or relative recessiveness of the *trans* genotype $\dfrac{m_1\ +}{+\ m_2}$, as the case may be, indicates a lack of complementarity, and hence a high degree of functional integration, between m_1 and m_2. The functional unity of m_1 and m_2 is clearly greater where $\dfrac{m_1\ +}{+\ m_2}$ engenders a recessive mutant phenotype than where it produces a complementary and normal phenotype.

The functional unity of m_1 and m_2 in the case where the *cis* but not the *trans* genotype can produce a normal non-mutant phenotype can be recognized by treating the units m_1 and m_2 as members of the same cistron [75] or, as we would prefer to put it, by treating them as different subgenes of the same Mendelian gene.

In this chapter we have recognized and discussed two categories of small supragenic units, namely linked serial gene systems and supergenes, which differ in the tightness of the linkage and in the functional unity or diversity of the constituent genes. In a *linked serial gene system* the component genes are functionally related and are tied together by linkages of normal intensity. A *supergene,* by comparison, contains several or many genes which are not necessarily related functionally but are tightly linked in a block that is preserved intact by some special device such as heterozygous chromosomal rearrangements or localized chiasmata.

SIZE OF THE MENDELIAN GENE

In the X chromosome of *Drosophila melanogaster* as seen in the salivary glands, where this and the other chromosomes are stretched out with their linear differentiation clearly visible microscopically, a single band is known to contain four genes, namely "yellow," "achaete," "scute," and a lethal next to "scute." [76] The length of the band is about 0.5 microns (= 5000 A.). Assuming, as is likely, that the segment contains only the four genes and no others, the average length of the chromosomal segment occupied by each gene would be 1250 A.[77]

The gene may well consist of a metabolically active central part bounded on both sides by inactive regions of potential breakage and crossing-over. The metabolically active part of the gene in this particular case would then be well less than 1250 A. From considerations such as this, Lea has calculated that the dimensions of a Mendelian gene in Drosophila may be about 1000 A. long.[78]

If the base-pairs occur at intervals 3.4 A. apart on the DNA macromolecule, a segment 1000 A. long would consist of about 300 nucleotide pairs. If, furthermore, a triplet composed of three adjacent bases can specify a single amino acid, then a segment of DNA 1000 A. long consisting of 300 nucleotide units could determine the formation of a protein chain composed of 100 amino acids. Now each polypeptide

[75] Benzer, 1957.
[76] Muller and Prokofyeva, 1935.
[77] Muller, 1935.
[78] Lea, 1955, 135–136.

chain in human hemoglobin, which is controlled by a single gene as noted in Chapter 2, contains 150 amino acids. The direct estimate of the length of a Mendelian gene is thus in reasonably good agreement with an indirect estimate based on the premise that a gene contains enough bases to determine the sequence of amino acids in a protein chain.

Linkage of functional
gene systems, I

7   The exact number of genes is not known for any organism. Since a gene can be recognized as a unit only when it is represented in two or more allelic forms, and since we have no way of knowing when, if ever, all the genes of a complement have mutated, any census of the *known* genes in an organism, even a genetically well-studied one like Drosophila or corn, can give only a minimal estimate of the *total* number of genes. It is a matter of guesswork, moreover, how far short the list of known genes comes of revealing the total number of genes.

By making extrapolations from mutation rates, from the calculated size of genes, and from various other assumptions, which may be only partially valid, it has been estimated that the number of genes in one chromosome of *Drosophila melanogaster,* the X chromosome, is about 1000. The total number of genes for all chromosomes of this organism would then be about five times greater, or of the order of 5000.[1]

The much greater simplicity of bacteria and viruses calls for a simpler genotype. It has been estimated that there are 250 genes in the colon bacterium (*Escherichia coli*), 110 genes in vaccinia virus,[2] and between 20 and 100 genes in bacterial virus T2.[3]

Plants have a simpler structure than insects, but are far more com-

---

[1] Muller and Prokofyeva, 1935. Lea, 1955, 134. Wallace and Dobzhansky, 1959, 41.

[2] Haldane, 1954a, 102.

[3] Beadle, 1962, 209.

plex than bacteria and viruses, and on this basis would be expected to lie between the two groups in number of genes. Belling counted 2000 chromomeres, which could be the sites of Mendelian genes, in the chromosome complement of the tiger lily, *Lilium pardalinum*.[4]

Vertebrate animals have a more complex body than insects and probably require a more complex genotype. Some geneticists have suggested that man, taken as an example of a higher vertebrate, may have about 8300 or even 11,700 genes, which would be about twice the number estimated for Drosophila.[5]

It must be emphasized that these figures are only educated guesses. Reliable estimates of gene number cannot be offered at the present time, because reliable methods of arriving at the true figures have not been devised owing to difficulties of both a technical and conceptual nature. These limitations are recognized by the geneticists who have proposed, somewhat diffidently, the numerical estimates. But until the facts are better known we can proceed on the assumption that the genotype of a higher plant or animal probably consists of several thousand genes.

In any case, whether the gene number is 20 or 10,000, opportunities exist for diverse interactions and linkage relationships between genes. In this and the following chapter we shall consider some types of gene systems and the systems of linkage which provide the physical basis for these gene systems.

MODES OF GENE INTERACTION AT THE ELEMENTARY FUNCTIONAL LEVEL

The modes of gene interaction are varied. During more than half a century of genetics research many different types of gene systems have been discovered. The diversity of the phenomena is reflected in the richness—and confusion—of the terminology: polymery, epistasis, inhibitors, complementary factors, modifiers, polygenes, etc. There is good reason to believe that our understanding of the workings of gene systems is still very far from complete, and that the existing terminology is far from adequate.

A classification of gene systems according to the biochemical and developmental actions and interactions of the component genes is of fundamental importance. Such a classification would reduce to some order the great variety of gene interactions worked out for numerous

---

[4] Belling, 1928.
[5] Frota-Pessoa, 1961.

characters in numerous organisms by numerous geneticists during numerous years of research.

A few authors have undertaken the difficult but necessary task of reducing the array of known and described modes of interaction to a few general types. Thus Darlington and Mather recognize gene interactions with (1) successive actions and epistatic effects, (2) cooperative actions and complementary effects, and (3) competitive actions and quantitative effects.[6] Sirks recognizes polymeric, anisomeric (unequal additive genes), complementary, epistatic, and some other minor categories of gene interaction.[7] Clausen and Hiesey divide gene systems into those composed of (1) additive (or subtractive) genes, (2) epistatic genes, (3) oppositional genes (combinations of positive factors and inhibitors), and (4) complementary genes.[8]

A somewhat different system of classification has been foreshadowed in the outline according to which the various types of gene interactions have been presented in Chapters 4 and 5 of this book. The following classification is thus in a way a summary of much of the material covered in the earlier chapters.

We may draw a distinction in the first place between gene systems composed of genes which work on the same or a similar substrate and elaborate the same or a similar product in quantity, and systems composed of genes which work on successive and different steps in a developmental sequence. Since terminology has not been completely standardized yet, we will adopt the most widely known and/or appropriate terms for each general category of gene system, and assign definite meanings to them in reference to our present discussion. Accordingly, genes with similar actions and generally cumulative and quantitative effects can be denoted as multiple genes, and genes which control different successive steps in a developmental process are called serial genes. The distinction between multiple and serial genes evidently exists in nature, and though it may not always hold true, or may not always be recognizable in practice, it still permits us to sort out many known types of gene interaction into separate general groupings.

Within either general category the component genes may have different relative strengths and directions of action. Accordingly:

1. The different genes produce the same or a similar growth substance or growth regulator, and hence cooperate to bring about a large

---

[6] Darlington and Mather, 1949, 165.

[7] Sirks, 1956, 153–154.

[8] Clausen and Hiesey, 1958, 263.

quantitative effect; the progeny of crosses between parents possessing different alleles of these genes usually show continuous variation—*multiple genes.*

(*a*) The system composed of relatively *few* genes; the primary actions of the genes *equal* in strength and *alike* in direction; their effects cumulative—*polymeric genes.*

(*b*) Relatively *few* genes; primary actions *moderately unequal* in strength, but *alike* in direction; and the effects cumulative—*anisomeric genes.*

(*c*) Relatively *few* genes; their primary actions *antagonistic* and *moderately unequal;* their net effect a summation of the plus and minus individual effects—*oppositional genes.*

(*d*) Relatively *few* genes; the primary actions *extremely unequal* in strength; the actions cumulative or oppositional or a combination of both—*major genes and modifiers.*

(*e*) The system composed of *many* genes; one or several genes with pronounced effects, the majority of the genes with minute individual effects, the various primary actions consequently *extremely unequal;* the actions cumulative, oppositional or both—*major genes and polygenes.*

(*f*) The system composed of *many* genes; these all with *minute individual effects;* the actions cumulative, oppositional, or a combination of both—*polygenes.*

2. The different genes control different steps in a developmental process, and hence produce qualitatively different products; the progeny of parents differing in the alleles of these genes usually show discontinuous variation—*serial genes.*

(*a*) The normal allele of one gene providing the necessary conditions for the action of a gene controlling a subsequent stage in the reaction chain—*complementary genes.*

(*b*) The normal allele of one gene blocking the action of the genes controlling the later stages in the reaction chain—*plus genes and inhibitors or suppressors; oppositional systems.*

(*c*) The normal allele of one gene switching the reaction onto an alternative pathway—*epistatic series* (in the narrow sense of the term epistasis as used in Chapter 4).

In a typical real case the various types of gene systems will be found in combination. Oppositional actions between plus and minus genes, for instance, are found in both multiple gene systems and serial gene systems. In any given case the oppositional actions of multiple genes are likely to be combined with the oppositional actions of serial genes so closely that it is difficult and meaningless to try to separate the two aspects. Again, any complex developmental process will be governed, in one aspect, by polygenic systems, and in another by serial gene systems. The genetic control of development in a real case is a synthesis of many elements. A classification of gene interactions is an analysis which purports to reveal some of these elementary components.

We have assumed in our discussion up to this point that the organism is homozygous for its particular complement of multiple or serial genes. This assumption is unrealistically simple. Many plants and animals are normally heterozygous for a large number of their genes. The complexities of gene interaction are then compounded by the various possible modes of allele interaction discussed in Chapter 3. To take a simple example, the oppositional action of an inhibitor gene (I) might have one quantitative effect when present in the dominant homozygous condition (I/I), and another less drastic effect when present in the heterozygous condition (I/i).

THE CHROMOSOME SET

The nuclear genes which form components of the various types of gene systems do not exist as free and independent particles. They are borne in special groupings on the chromosomes. The number of chromosomes in the complement, the frequency of crossing-over, and the segmental arrangement within the chromosomes determine the linkage relations between the components of a gene system. The effects of the segmental arrangement on linkage will be discussed later in Chapters 8 and 9.

With regard to the other two factors mentioned above, it is evident that a given number of genes dispersed throughout the chromosome set will be more tightly linked in an organism with a low chromosome number or a low frequency of crossing-over than in an organism with the opposite characteristics. Conversely, a high chromosome number and a high frequency of crossing-over promote a relatively free recombination of genes.[9]

Inasmuch as the genes borne on separate chromosomes become recombined by the independent assortment of the chromosomes at meiosis, a greater number of recombinations will arise if these genes are distributed among many chromosomes than if they are borne on few. A diploid organism which possesses N chromosome pairs, and is

---

[9] Darlington, 1939; 1958, Chapter 15.

heterozygous for one gene on each chromosome pair, can produce 2^N classes of gametes.[10] It follows that the addition of one chromosome pair to the complement doubles, and the subtraction of one pair halves, the number of gene combinations which arise by independent assortment, assuming that the various chromosome pairs are all equally heterozygous.

The basic chromosome number varies widely in different organisms, as is well known. The common haploid numbers in higher insects, for example, range from $N = 4$ to 8 in many species of Diptera to $N = 20$–33 in a majority of the Lepidoptera where, however, a few diploid species with 50 or more chromosome pairs are known.[11] In the mammals the typical haploid numbers range from $N = 7$–12 in marsupials to $N = 24$–36 in ungulates.[12] By far the majority of diploid flowering plants have between 7 and 14 chromosomes in the gametic complement; but numerous polyploid species of flowering plants have chromosome numbers ranging from $N = 14$ upwards to $N = 50$ and higher.[13]

MULTIFACTORIAL LINKAGE FOR A
SINGLE CHARACTER

As we saw in Chapter 5, an F_2 progeny segregating for a series of multiple genes with additive effects and no dominance will form a more or less continuous array of phenotypes with a high frequency of intermediate classes and a low frequency of extreme classes. The greater the number of such multiple genes, moreover, as we also saw earlier, the higher the frequency of intermediate phenotypic classes and the lower the frequency of parental types in the F_2 generation. We must now consider the effect of an additional factor. For any large number of such multiple genes segregating in F_2, the frequency of the intermediate types is restricted and the frequency of the parental types is increased by linkage.

Suppose that two parents differ in respect to fifty multiple genes with equal and additive effects, and suppose that the alleles of these genes do not have interactions of dominance. The series of fifty polymeric genes or polygenes, however we wish to refer to them, will

---

[10] The formulation is from Mendel, 1866, as restated in terms of chromosomes by later geneticists.
[11] Makino, 1951.
[12] *Ibid.*
[13] Grant, 1963, 483–488.

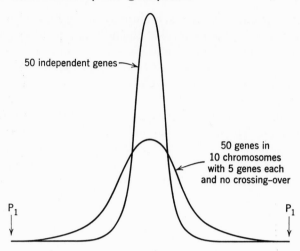

FIG. 28. The frequency distribution of phenotypes in the F_2 generation derived from a cross between two parents differing in fifty multiple genes with equal and additive effects and no dominance, under two conditions of linkage. If the fifty genes segregate independently, as though borne on fifty separate chromosomes, the frequency distribution curve is peaked. If the fifty genes are equally distributed among ten chromosomes with no crossing-over, the frequency curve is normal. (Reprinted from *Introgressive Hybridization*, by Anderson, copyright 1949, John Wiley, New York and London, by permission.)

then segregate in F_2 to produce a preponderance of intermediate phenotypes and a low proportion of extreme phenotypes. Now if the fifty segregating genes are unlinked, the frequency of the intermediate phenotypic classes is very high, and that of the parental types is very low. The frequency distribution curve has a high peak in the intermediate range, as shown in Fig. 28. But if the same fifty genes are equally distributed among ten chromosomes, with no crossing-over between the five genes on each chromosome, the frequency distribution curve of phenotypes will have a much lower peak in the intermediate range and will slope off much more gradually towards the extremes.[14] (See again Fig. 28.)

The effect of linkage, in other words, is to greatly increase the proportion of F_2 individuals which resemble one or the other parent. And some linkage, rather than its complete absence is the normal condition when large numbers of genes are involved.[15]

---

[14] Anderson, 1949, 27–29.
[15] *Ibid.*

In the hypothetical case before us, therefore, the assumption of independent assortment of fifty multiple genes, and the frequency curve of phenotypic classes drawn from that assumption may represent a real possibility in some species of plants and animals with fifty or more chromosome pairs. As applied to the vast majority of plants and animals with chromosome numbers much less than $N = 50$, on the other hand, the foregoing assumption is quite unrealistic; whereas the alternative assumption that the fifty multiple genes are grouped in ten blocks of five genes each, while undoubtedly oversimplified, probably comes closer to representing a typical real situation.

MULTIFACTORIAL LINKAGE FOR TWO OR MORE CHARACTERS

We have been considering the effect of linkage on segregation of multiple genes controlling a single character. Let us next consider the effect of this factor in an F_2 progeny segregating simultaneously for two or more different multifactorial characters. The circumstance that numerous genes must frequently be distributed among few chromosomes then results in restrictions on recombination between the different multifactorial characters, as Anderson has shown.[16]

Lamprecht has resolved the difference between tall and short varieties of the garden pea (*Pisum sativum*) into two multifactorial characters: length of internodes and number of internodes. He finds further that the difference between the tall and short plants in internode length is due to allelic differences in four independent genes, while the phenotypic difference in number of internodes can be attributed to differences in three independent genes. These genes are located in five of the seven linkage groups of the pea, as shown in Table 7.[17]

It is apparent from Table 7 that two of the four genes for internode length are linked with two of the three genes controlling the varietal difference in internode number. Conversely, some components of the multiple gene system governing internode length are independent of some members of the gene system controlling internode number. It would be expected, therefore, that the two characters, internode length and internode number, would be partially, but not completely, correlated in a segregating F_2 progeny derived from the cross between short and tall pea plants.

---

[16] Anderson, 1939*a*, 1939*b*, 1949. See also Dempster, 1949.
[17] Lamprecht, 1962.

138   The architecture of the germplasm

TABLE 7   THE LINKAGE RELATIONS OF CERTAIN
GENES GOVERNING STEM GROWTH IN THE PEA
(*Pisum sativum*) *

Chromosome	I	II	III	IV	V	VI	VII
Genes for length of internodes	Cot	Coe			Coh	Cona	
Genes for number of internodes	Mie				Miu		Min

* Lamprecht, 1962.

The expected loose correlation between the two characters in F_2 is in fact found, as is evident from the data in Table 8. This table shows that the bulk of the F_2 individuals are intermediate in both traits. The few F_2 individuals which approach the short parent in respect to internode length tend to approach that parental type also in respect to internode number. Some recombination between the two charac-

TABLE 8   PARTIAL CORRELATION BETWEEN THE NUMBER
OF INTERNODES AND INTERNODE LENGTH IN THE F_2 PROGENY
OF A CROSS BETWEEN SHORT AND TALL PEA PLANTS *

Number of F_2 Individuals with a Given Number of Internodes	Number of F_2 Individuals with Internodes of a Given Average Length (in mm.)															
	18	22	25	28	31	34	37	40	43	46	49	52	55	58	61	64
30	—	—	—	—	—	—	—	—	—	1	—	—	—	—	—	—
	—	—	—	—	—	1	1	—	2	1	—	—	—	—	—	—
25	—	—	—	—	1	2	1	1	1	3	1	—	—	—	—	—
	—	—	1	—	3	3	8	3	4	—	2	2	—	1	—	—
20	—	—	6	6	18	15	16	24	13	8	4	—	3	—	—	—
	—	2	5	10	10	10	25	14	11	8	7	—	2	1	1	1
15	1	10	8	11	17	15	16	23	14	11	4	5	1	2	1	—
	1	—	—	—	5	5	8	1	5	2	3	—	—	—	—	—
10	2	—	1	—	2	1	2	2	—	1	—	1	—	1	1	—

* Lamprecht, 1962, 36.

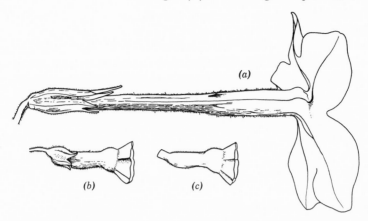

FIG. 29. Flowers of *Nicotiana alata* and *N. langsdorffii.* (*a*) *Nicotiana alata.* (*b*) and (*c*) *Nicotiana langsdorffii.* (Anderson, 1939*b*.)

ters does, however, occur, as exemplified by F_2 individuals with few but long internodes.

Anderson has given a vivid demonstration of the restriction on recombination between different multifactorial characters in the F_2 generation of *Nicotiana alata* $\times$ *N. langsdorffii.* As shown in Fig. 29, the flowers of *N. alata* and *N. langsdorffii* differ in a number of features. We are concerned here with three of these characters: tube length, limb width, and depth of lobing on the limb. *N. alata* has a long corolla tube, broad corolla limb, and deeply lobed limb; while *N. langsdorffii* has a short tube, narrow limb, and shallowly lobed limb. (Fig. 29.)

If these three characters recombined freely in F_2, one would expect to obtain the various extreme recombination types depicted in Fig. 30, (*a*)-(*e*). The most extreme recombination types actually observed in an F_2 generation consisting of 347 plants did not even come close to the ideal extremes, as Fig. 30, (*a'*)-(*e'*) shows.[18]

Anderson proposes to let the three dimensions of a cube represent the three characters. The character combination of one parent is found at one apex of this cube and the character combination of the other parent at the opposite apex. (See Fig. 31.) With complete recombination between the three characters in F_2, every corner of the cube would be occupied. In fact, only a narrow spindle, the so-called recombination spindle, runs through the center of the cube, represent-

---

[18] Anderson, 1939*b.*

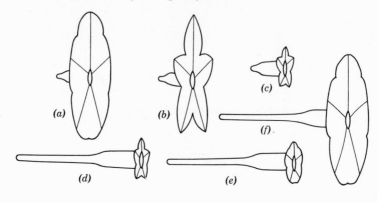

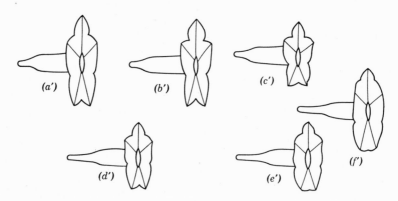

FIG. 30. Recombination between three floral characters in F_2 of *Nicotiana alata* × *langsdorffii*. (*a*)–(*e*) Extreme recombination types expected with free recombination between the three characters. (*a'*)–(*e'*) Extreme recombination types actually obtained in an F_2 progeny of 347 plants. (Anderson, 1939*b*.)

ing a general trend from F_2 types more or less like one parent through types more or less like the F_1 to types approaching the other parent.[19] (Fig. 31.)

It should be noted that genetic linkage is not the only factor involved in the restriction of recombination in the Nicotiana hybrid. Pleiotropy is certainly and selection against the extreme types is possibly a contributing factor.[20]

---

[19] *Ibid*; 1949, 33–34.
[20] Anderson, 1939*b*.

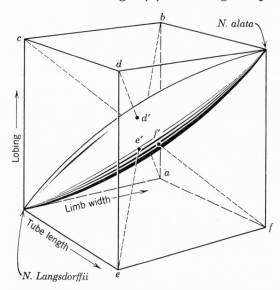

FIG. 31. The recombination spindle for the F_2 of *Nicotiana alata* $\times$ *langsdorffii*. The ideal and actual limits of recombination are designated by the same letters as in Fig. 30. (Reprinted from *Introgressive Hybridization*, by Anderson, copyright 1949, John Wiley, New York and London, by permission.)

The coastal and the alpine races of *Potentilla glandulosa* differ in numerous characteristics of seasonal periodicity, stem and leaf size, pubescence, flower form and color, and seed size, most of which are multifactorial. The minimum number of genes responsible for the character difference between the Santa Barbara and Upper Monarch Lake races in each of fourteen separate characters, as estimated from segregation data, is given in Table 9.[21] This table shows that the interracial differences in three of the fourteen characters could be controlled by a single gene; that the differences in two other characters are controlled by two or three genes each; and that the remaining nine character differences are determined by four or more genes each.

In order to obtain a numerical estimate of the total number of gene differences between the two races for all fourteen characters combined, let us assume arbitrarily, though not unrealistically, that "many" can be equated with "5" in three places in Table 9. Then it can be estimated that in the aggregate at least fifty-one genes, and probably

---

[21] Clausen and Hiesey, 1958, 54–108; but not 109, where the data derived from this and another hybrid combination are pooled.

TABLE 9   ESTIMATED MINIMUM NUMBER OF GENES CONTROLLING THE
DIFFERENCES BETWEEN THE COASTAL (SANTA BARBARA) AND ALPINE (UPPER
MONARCH LAKE) RACES OF *Potentilla glandulosa* IN FOURTEEN CHARACTERS *

Character	Genes	Character	Genes
Winter dormancy	3	Leaflet number	1
Flowering time	many	Seed weight	6
Density of inflorescence	1	Seed color	4
Glandular pubescence	5	Sepal length	5
Anthocyanin	4	Petal width	2
Stem length	many	Petal length	4
Leaf length	many	Petal color	1

* Clausen and Hiesey, 1958, pp. 54–108.   See also our discussion in Chapter 5
of the present book regarding inheritance of pubescence.

many more, determine the interracial differences in fourteen characters.

Now *P. glandulosa* has seven pairs of chromosomes.   Therefore, some linkage is expected to exist between the fourteen characters and between the fifty-one or more genes responsible for these characters.

In the F_2 progeny of the interracial cross, segregating simultaneously for the fourteen characters listed in Table 9, Clausen and Hiesey scored each of about 992 individual plants for each separate character. They then computed the correlation coefficients between the fourteen characters in every possible paired combination.   There are ninety-one such combinations of fourteen characters taken in pairs.   The degrees of correlation between the various characters in F_2 are summarized graphically in Fig. 32.[22]

The correlation coefficient (r) can vary in magnitude from 0 to 1, where 1 indicates perfect correlation and 0 no correlation.   Any given value of r has a certain probability of being due to chance alone, which decreases as the size of the sample increases.   In the present case, where the various paired combinations of characters are represented by a sample of about 992 F_2 individuals for each pair, weak correlations as low as $r = .08$ have a probability of less than 1% of being due to chance alone, while values of r higher than .08 are even more significant statistically.[23]

[22] *Ibid.,* 115.
[23] *Ibid.,* 114–116.

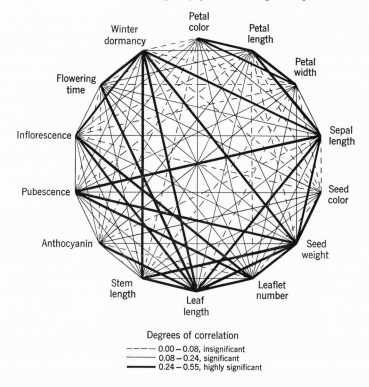

Degrees of correlation
– – – – 0.00 – 0.08, insignificant
——— 0.08 – 0.24, significant
▬▬▬ 0.24 – 0.55, highly significant

FIG. 32. Correlations between fourteen segregating characters in the F_2 progeny of an interracial cross (Upper Monarch Lake × Santa Barbara) in *Potentilla glandulosa*. (From Clausen and Hiesey, 1958.)

The ninety-one correlation coefficients for the different character combinations in the interracial F_2 generation of Potentilla ranged from below .08 to above .7. Of the ninety-one pairs of characters, sixty-seven showed statistically significant correlation. The great bulk of the significant correlation coefficients, moreover, fell in the range $r = .08 - .40$, which represents partial and incomplete correlation.[24]

Correlation coefficients not only vary in numerical value but also in algebraic sign, depending on the direction of the correlation. In the F_2 generation of Potentilla, sixty-one of the sixty-seven significant correlation coefficients had an algebraic sign pointing to correlation in the direction of the parental character combinations.[25]

---

[24] *Ibid.*, 116.
[25] *Loc. cit.*

Correlations in the direction of the parental character combinations could be due to pleiotropy or genetic linkage or both. Pleiotropy would be expected to play a part, and probably a large part, in the correlations between such characters as petal length and sepal length, which are the end products of common or similar growth processes. The correlations resulting from pleiotropy are also likely to be high. The partial correlations observed between developmentally unrelated characters, on the other hand, are best explained as the result of weak or incomplete multifactorial linkage.[26]

It will be recalled that six of the sixty-seven statistically significant correlation coefficients had an algebraic sign pointing away from the parental character combinations. These negative significant correlations do not necessarily imply absence of linkage. The gene systems controlling the various character differences in *Potentilla glandulosa* are composed of multiple genes in some cases, serial genes in others, and mixtures of both in still other cases. Clausen and Hiesey suggest that where one or both characters in a character pair differ with respect to genes with oppositional or complementary interactions, linkage would lead to negative correlations between the characters in F_2, as is actually observed in the six cases.[27]

Referring again to Fig. 32, we see that no character in the interracial F_2 generation of *Potentilla glandulosa* segregates independently of *all* the other characters. On the contrary, each character is partially correlated and probably partially linked with many or most of the other thirteen characters. On the other hand, each character is uncorrelated and may be unlinked with some of the other characters. The various characters, moreover, do not fall into mutually exclusive linkage groups, but rather into overlapping groups. Thus two characters (like sepal length and seed color), which are not correlated inter se, may both be linked independently of one another to a third character (pubescence), and the latter in turn is linked to a fourth character (anthocyanin) which segregates independently of the first (sepal length).

Essentially the same picture of overlapping character correlations has been found in the annual plant, *Gilia capitata*, which has nine pairs of chromosomes. Here, as in *P. glandulosa*, F_2 progenies of interracial crosses segregating simultaneously for several (eight) charac-

[26] Grant, 1950, 293–294. Clausen and Hiesey, 1958, 116.
[27] Clausen and Hiesey, 1958, 117, 122.

ters exhibit partial but significant correlations between characters in a large proportion of the paired combinations.[28]

This picture of an interlocking system of weak linkages probably reflects the following underlying condition in the genotype. The genes (or some of them at least) responsible for each multifactorial character difference between the races are located on different chromosomes. Some of the genes controlling character A are linked with some of the genes for character B. But other genes for character A segregate independently of other genes determining character B. Therefore, characters A and B are only partially correlated in inheritance. Now the genes for character A that are not linked with any genes for character B may occur in the same linkage group or groups with some of the genes controlling character C. Characters B and C then segregate independently of one another. But B and C, while segregating independently of one another, are separately and incompletely linked with A.[29]

The extension of the system of interlocking linkages to characters D, E, etc., eventually ties all the characters together, directly or indirectly, into a loose but coherent complex. Any character that displays continuous variation in F_2 is also likely to display correlations with other such characters. Conversely, no multifactorial character is transmitted in inheritance as a unit separate from the character complex. Recombination between different characters in this character complex is not prevented, to be sure, but is strongly restricted by the conditions of multifactorial linkage.[30]

In plants with relatively low basic chromosome numbers in the range $N = 14$ to $N = 7$ or even lower, the coherence between separate characters which is expected on theoretical grounds is actually found in both hybrid progenies and natural populations, where the variation in one character tends to be correlated with the variation in others. In placental mammals, birds, Lepidoptera, and other animals with relatively high basic numbers, in the range $N = 20$ to $N = 36$ or even higher, on the other hand, one would expect a greater degree of independence between separate characters in inheritance. This expectation is also realized in many actual cases of geographical variation in higher animals. Mayr notes in a discussion of geographical variation in animals that, "The various characters of a species may

[28] Grant, 1950, 290–294.
[29] Grant, 1950, 294; 1956c, 65, 67–68. Clausen and Hiesey, 1958, 116, 266.
[30] *Loc. cit.*

and usually do vary independently. Neighboring populations agree, therefore, in some characters and differ in others." [31] Such independence of characters is contrary to experience in many investigated groups of higher plants.

Genes and gene systems are components of whole genotypes. The organism develops and functions as an integrated whole, and the genotype which determines this development and functional unity must also possess an internal integration. The several thousand genes comprising the genotype of a complex organism must be able to work together harmoniously if that organism is to be successful in life.

The coordination and balance between the genes of a genotype which is expected on theoretical grounds is in fact found on every hand. By far the majority of the mutational changes in any genotype are changes for the worse, the mutant individuals usually being physiologically deficient, physically deformed, inviable or sterile. The loss of a chromosome segment of moderate length, a long deletion, is apt to be lethal even in the heterozygous condition. Small deficiences of chromosomal material, resulting from the deletion of a short segment, may or may not be viable in heterozygotes, but are nearly always lethal as homozygotes.

Nicotiana sylvestris, a wild species related to tobacco, normally possesses twelve pairs of chromosomes. Goodspeed and Avery obtained a series of so-called trisomic types of *N. sylvestris* in which one or the other of the twelve chromosomes of the basic set was represented, not twice as in the normal diploids, but in three doses. If the different individual chromosomes constituting the haploid set are designated A, B, C, D, · · · L, one trisomic type would have an extra A chromosome, and would thus have the chromosomal constitution AAA BB CC DD · · · LL. Another trisomic type would be diploid for all chromosomes except B, which would be present in an extra dose, giving the constitution AA BBB CC DD · · · LL. All of the twelve possible trisomic types were produced, maintained as separate lines, and studied morphologically. For convenience these were designated by

---

[31] Mayr, 1963, 333, 362. Chapters 9 and 10 and other parts of Mayr's important book, *Animal Species and Evolution* (1963), contain discussions of many of the topics dealt with in the present work. Since *Animal Species and Evolution* appeared after *The Architecture of the Germplasm* had gone to the press, it has not been possible to weave Mayr's conclusions into the text of the present book.

TABLE 10   DIMENSIONS OF THE COROLLA IN DIPLIOD
AND TRISOMIC FORMS OF *Nicotiana sylvestris* *

	Average Length of Corolla Tube	Average Diameter of Corolla Limb
Diploid	8.46 cm.	3.78 cm.
Trisomic types		
Compact	6.65	3.53
Stubby	6.76	3.38
Pointed	7.10	3.32
Late	7.45	2.93
Inflated	7.52	4.04
Puckered	7.72	3.71
Narrow	8.11	3.51
Bent	8.81	3.99
Recurved	8.93	3.75
Enlarged	10.83	4.04
Average for all trisomic types combined	7.99	3.62

* Goodspeed and Avery, 1939. The average diameter
of the corolla limb for all trisomics combined is calculated slightly differently here than by the original
authors.

names referring to some conspicuous feature, such as "compact,"
"stubby," and so on.[32]

It was found that each trisomic type deviates from the normal
diploid condition in various morphological characters.   Thus the
average length of the corolla tube in diploid plants of *Nicotiana sylvestris* is 8.46 cm.   The trisomic type "compact" has short corollas
6.65 cm. long, and the trisomic "enlarged" has long corollas 10.83 cm.
long.   The various trisomics deviate from the norm in gross features
of the growth form, the leaves, and the capsules as well as in minute
details of the flowers.   Two accurately measurable dimensions of the
corolla, the length of the tube and the diameter of the petal-like part or
limb, are recorded for ten trisomic types in Table 10.   It will be seen

[32] Goodspeed and Avery, 1939, 1941.

FIG. 33.   Leaves of diploid and five trisomic types of *Nicotiana sylvestris*.   (*a*)
Diploid.   (*b*) Enlarged.   (*c*) Pointed.   (*d*) Puckered.   (*e*) Bent.   (*f*) Stubby.
(From Goodspeed and Avery, 1939; photographs by courtesy of Dr. Goodspeed.)

that some trisomic types differ strongly and others slightly from the diploid in the corolla characters measured, but that all the trisomics differ phenotypically from the diploid in some degree.[33]

The table reveals another significant fact. The average length or breadth of the corolla for all trisomic types combined is close to the condition in the diploid plants. (See Table 10). Not only do the different trisomic types deviate from the norm, therefore, but their individual deviations tend to balance out and give a statistical condition approaching the norm.[34]

The same situation holds true in other organs of the plants besides the corolla. Goodspeed's and Avery's description of the leaf characters in various trisomic types is quoted below and illustrated in Fig. 33.[35]

A character which cannot be subjected to statistical analysis but in which the diploid represents a balance between the variations occurring in trisomic types, concerns distinctions in growth rates of different parts of the leaf expressed in terms of contour and fullness at maturity. Thus the elliptic-ovate rosette leaf of the diploid is relatively flat with the margin slightly erect or reflexed according to age and environmental conditions. In Enlarged, however, the midrib elongates so much more rapidly than the tissue of the leaf blade that the margin and the tips of the leaves are early turned under. In Pointed, on the other hand, it is not the midrib but the leaf-blade tissue bordering the midrib which apparently grows more rapidly so that the leaf blade becomes "fulled in" along the midrib. With Puckered, extra fullness of leaf tissue accumulates not along the midrib as in Pointed but in "puckers" between the veins. In Bent, "blisters" at the outer edge of the veins mark the position of tissue expanding more rapidly than the rest of the leaf. In Stubby, the extra fullness is in still a different location, the leaf tissue being "fulled in" along the veins, instead of along the midrib as in Pointed or between the veins as in Puckered. In this way one can follow the distribution of the control of the rate of development of different parts of the leaf to particular chromosomes of the complement. Many more such comparisons could be made but in all of them the diploid is the centre of the circle of variation.

---

[33] *Ibid.*, 1939.
[34] *Ibid.*, 1939.
[35] *Ibid.*, 452.

Linkage of functional

gene systems, II

8 The spatial relations of the genes within a chromosome are not irrelevant to their modes of action and interaction, as we know from the phenomenon of position effect. Now any given spatial relationship between the genes can be established by one or another of the known types of chromosomal rearrangements. Let us briefly review, therefore, the effects on linkage relations of structural rearrangements of the chromosomes in the homozygous condition.

CHROMOSOMAL REARRANGEMENTS IN HOMOZYGOUS
CONDITION IN RELATION TO LINKAGE

Chromosomes occasionally break, and the broken ends rejoin in new ways, to produce a new segmental arrangement. The main types of chromosomal rearrangements are diagrammed in Fig. 34. These rearrangements bring about new linkage relations between particular genes on a chromosome.

Thus a chromosome with an original or standard segmental arrangement ABCDEFGHI may undergo the loss or deletion of the segment GH, and come to have the new arrangement ABCDEFI, in which case the genes F and I, previously separated, become adjacent. (See Fig. 34-2.) The same original chromosome might, on the other hand, undergo a duplication of the segment GH, which would increase the map distance and the chances of recombination between the genes F and I. (Fig. 34-3.)

1. Terminal deficiency

Std. 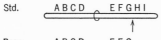 A B C D E F G H I

Rear. A B C D E F G

2. Interstitial deletion

Std. A B C D E F G H I

Rear.  A B C D E F I

3. Duplication

Std. A B C D E F G H I

Rear. 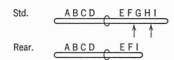 A B C D E F G H G H I

4. Paracentric inversion

Std. 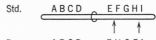 A B C D E F G H I

Rear. A B C D E H G F I

5. Pericentric inversion

Std. A B C D E F G H I

Rear. 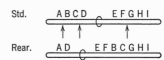 A B G F E D C H I

6. Transposition

Std. A B C D E F G H I

Rear. 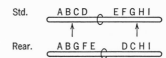 A D E F B C G H I

7. Small reciprocal translocation

Std. A B C D E F G H I   M N O P Q R S T

Rear. 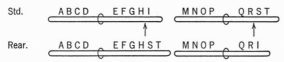 A B C D E F G H S T   M N O P Q R I

8. Whole arm translocation

Std. A B C D E F G H I   M N O P Q R S T

Rear.  A B C D Q R S T   M N O P E F G H I

9. Successive translocations

Std. A B C D E F G H I   M N O P Q R S T   U V W X Y Z

1st Rear. A B C D Q R S T   M N O P E F G H I   U V W X Y Z

2nd Rear. 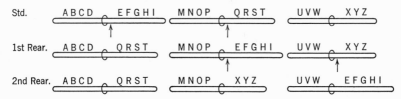 A B C D Q R S T   M N O P X Y Z   U V W E F G H I

FIG. 34. Types of chromosomal rearrangements. The structurally altered chromosome (labeled Rear.) is compared in each case with one and the same standard arrangement (Std.). The small arrows mark the breakage points on the standard chromosome which can give rise to a given structural rearrangement. The centromere is shown as a median or submedian oval.

The duplication and deficiency types could arise from the same event of unequal crossing-over. Suppose that two normal chromosomes pair segment by homologous segment throughout most of their length at meiosis, but that the homologous GH segments are displaced, so that crossovers can occur between them as follows:

Then one of the daughter crossover chromosomes will carry the deletion (being ABCDEFI), and the other will carry the complementary duplication (being ABCDEFGHGHI).

The inversion of a segment lying outside the centromere, that is, a paracentric inversion, can alter the linkage relations between genes on the same arm of a chromosome. In the example shown in Fig. 34-4, the genes **E** and **H**, and **F** and **I**, which were separated before the inversion, come to occupy neighboring loci afterwards. A pericentric inversion places together genes that previously occurred in different arms of the same chromosome (i.e., **B-G** and **C-H**, in Fig. 34-5).

Inversions were first detected as such in Drosophila by the observation of differences in the linear order of genes in the related species *D. melanogaster* and *D. simulans.* The gene order in a region of chromosome III in *D. melanogaster* is "scarlet"-"peach"-"delta." In *D. simulans* Sturtevant observed that the sequence of the homologous genes is "scarlet"-"deltoid"-"peach." This difference could be accounted for by the rotation of the segment containing the genes "peach" and "delta" (or "deltoid").[1] The predicted phenomenon of inversions was of course confirmed later by direct cytological evidence. It will be noted in the above case that the genes "scarlet" and "peach" are closely linked in *D. melanogaster,* lying three map units apart, but are more widely separated—at least 45 units apart—in *D. simulans.*[2]

In a transposition a segment becomes relocated in a new site on the same arm or a different arm of the chromosome (Fig. 34-6). As a result of reciprocal translocations, finally, segments ranging in size from a few genes to a whole arm may become detached from the original standard chromosome and attached to a different chromosome, thus changing greatly the linkage relationships of the genes involved. (Fig. 34-7, 8, and 9.)

---

[1] Sturtevant, 1921. See also Sirks, 1956, 281, for another example of reversed gene order on chromosome III.

[2] Sturtevant, 1921.

PATTERN EFFECT

The most direct relationship of homozygous chromosomal rearrangements to physiological processes, and yet the most recondite one, is that which is manifested as position effect. (See also discussion in Chapter 6.) Any given segmental arrangement or chromosome pattern, by virtue of the spatial relations between genes, may be associated with an ensemble of position effects, or more aptly in this connection, with a pattern effect,[3] which brings about certain physiological and morphological characteristics. Goldschmidt has strongly advocated the view that "chromosomal repatterning . . . is a method of producing new organic reaction systems . . ."[4]

Most known position effects are, to be sure, deleterious to their carriers. Levitan has, however, obtained evidence from studies of inversions in wild populations of *Drosophila robusta* in the eastern United States which indicates that some chromosomal rearrangements are associated with adaptively valuable pattern effects.

The gene order on the left arm of the X chromosome in this fly takes various forms differing by inversions of certain segments, the inversions being designated LS (the standard arrangement), L1, L2. Similarly, the right arm of the X chromosome can carry the standard arrangement RS or the inversions R1 or R2. A female fly carrying two X chromosomes with the segmental arrangement $\frac{\text{LS—RS}}{\text{L1—R2}}$ and a female fly with X chromosomes of the types $\frac{\text{LS—R2}}{\text{L1—RS}}$ have the same representation of genes and segments but a different spatial relation between these elements. It is very interesting, therefore, to learn that the two genotypes differ in adaptive properties. The $\frac{\text{LS—RS}}{\text{L1—R2}}$ types have a higher adaptive value than the $\frac{\text{LS—R2}}{\text{L1—RS}}$ types in some natural environments.[5]

Certain associations of inversions on opposite arms of chromosome II in *D. robusta* likewise have a higher adaptive value than others. Flies of the constitution $\frac{\text{LS—R1}}{\text{L3—RS}}$ for chromosome II are more success-

---

[3] Goldschmidt, 1940, 241.
[4] Goldschmidt, 1938, 1940; quotation from 1940, 249.
[5] Levitan, 1954a, 1954b, 1958.

ful in the populations than flies of the constitution $\dfrac{\text{LS—RS}}{\text{L3—R1}}$, which possess the same inversions in a different spatial relation.[6]

A number of instances have been recorded, as we saw in Chapter 6, where genes or subgenes with related but different functions occur in successive linear order within a chromosome region. It has been suggested, apparently first by Bridges in 1918 [7] and in recent years by Stephens, Lewis, Demerec, and others,[8] that the assembly-line sequence of subgenes or genes could arise from a duplication, in which a single original gene by unequal crossing-over or some other mechanism becomes repeated in two successive segments of the same chromosome. Divergence in the functions of the two originally identical genes could then enable each new component to control related but slightly different processes. The linked serial gene system extending over a duplicated section of a chromosome could carry out more complex activities than any single gene could do.[9]

This hypothesis is favored by considerable cytological evidence indicating that contiguous subgenes and linked serial gene systems are in fact commonly associated with duplicated chromosomal segments. Thus the two adjacent genic elements, "star" and "asteroid," on chromosome II of *Drosophila melanogaster*, are both included in a single doublet, or double band, of the salivary gland chromosome.[10] The subgenes w and w^a for eye color in Drosophila also appear to be located in the same doublet of a salivary chromosome.[11] In the same organism again, two subgenes of the gene "forked" governing the characteristics of the body bristles occur in a region of the X chromosome where a doublet is also found.[12] These doublets are interpreted on cytological grounds as duplications.

It is probable, according to Laughnan, that adjacent subgenes at the **A** locus for endosperm color in corn (*Zea mays*), and according

---

[6] *Ibid.*

[7] Bridges in 1918; see Sinnott, Dunn, and Dobzhansky, 1958, 386.

[8] Stephens, 1948, 1951a, and in Symposium, 1955. Komai, 1950. Lewis, 1951. Demerec, Blomstrand, and Demerec, 1955.

[9] Stephens, 1948, 1951a, and in Symposium, 1955. Demerec, Blomstrand, and Demerec, 1955.

[10] Lewis, 1945.

[11] Lewis, 1952.

[12] Green, 1955.

to Demerec, that several linked serial gene systems in the bacterium Salmonella have also arisen through duplications of original simple genes.[13]

There is evidence in cotton that duplicated genes actually can and do diverge in function.[14] The American cultivated cottons are allo-tetraploids containing 13 chromosome pairs derived from one ancestral diploid species (A) and 13 pairs from another diploid parent (D). The diploid A and D relatives of cotton are known. The gene **R** controlling anthocyanin pigmentation in the plant body occurs in the various diploid and tetraploid species.

In the diploid species A a single **R** gene controls anthocyanin formation. Likewise in the diploid species D there is a single **R** gene. Tetraploid cotton possesses, as expected, two **R** loci, one of which (**R₂**) occurs in the A chromosome set and is homologous with the **R** gene in the ancestral diploid species A, and the other of which (**R₁**) occurs in one of the D chromosomes and is homologous with the **R** gene in the diploid species D.[15]

As Stephens notes, the genes **R₁** and **R₂** were probaby duplicate genes when tetraploid cotton first originated. If they were duplicate factors today, the double heterozygote $\dfrac{R_1}{r_1}\ \dfrac{R_2}{r_2}$ would segregate in a 15:1 phenotypic ratio in F_2. Tetraploid cotton heterozygous for these genes does not, however, segregate in this fashion but instead in the 9:3:3:1 ratio characteristic of independent assortment of two genes, which shows that **R₁** and **R₂** are no longer allelic.[16]

Another pair of duplicated genes, **Cl₁** and **Cl₂**, governing the degree of congestion in the inflorescence, occurs in tetraploid cotton, **Cl₁** being located in the D chromosome set and **Cl₂** in the A set. **Cl₂** is also known in the A type diploid species (but **Cl₁** is not yet known in diploid species D). The two **Cl** genes in tetraploid cotton, instead of giving duplicate factor inheritance, behave as complementary factors. Stephens argues that if, as is probable, **Cl₁** and **Cl₂** were duplicate genes when tetraploid cotton originated, but are complementary genes now, their present differentiation bears witness to the process of divergence in gene function.[17]

---

[13] Laughnan, 1952, and in Symposium, 1955. Demerec, Blomstrand, and De-merec, 1955.

[14] Stephens, 1951*a*.

[15] Stephens, 1951*a*, 1951*b*.

[16] *Ibid.*

[17] *Ibid.*

DUPLICATIONS AND DIVERGENCE IN
GENE FUNCTION

Organisms in the course of evolution towards greater complexity must frequently require the addition of new functions. Gene mutations, as Stephens has pointed out, can alter an original function, but will not bring about a new and additional function. Duplications, however, enable the organism to gain new genes without losing old ones, and the duplicated genes, being relieved of their original functions, can then diverge and acquire new functions.[18]

Small tandem duplications provide a mechanism for the development of compound genes or linked serial gene systems, as described in the preceding section. On a larger scale a functional diversification within the genotype can come about through the establishment of supernumerary chromosome arms or whole chromosomes in the set and the subsequent divergence in function of the extra genes.

Clarkia lingulata ($N = 9$) in the Sierra Nevada of California is closely related to and derived from *Clarkia biloba* ($N = 8$). One arm (designated no. 1) of the ninth chromosome of *C. lingulata,* as will be shown later in Chapter 9, is homologous with an arm of Chromosome 1-2 in *C. biloba,* while the other (no. 4) arm of the ninth *lingulata* chromosome is homologous with an arm of the *biloba* Chromosome 3-4. Evidently, therefore, translocations between the 1-2 and 3-4 chromosomes occurred in the ancestral *C. biloba,* and both the unaltered 1-2 and 3-4 and the translocated 1-4 chromosomes became established in *C. lingulata.* In this way the original population of *C. lingulata* came to possess duplications for two chromosome arms attached to one extra centromere.[19]

Now *C. lingulata* differs from *C. biloba* in a character of the flower petals which is determined by genes located on the extra chromosome.[20] *C. lingulata* of the southern Sierra Nevada also differs from the more northern *C. biloba* in being adapted to more arid conditions. Lewis suggests that the extra genes acquired by *C. lingulata,* perhaps on diverging in function, made possible the ecological and physiological shift from the ancestral mesic to the derived xeric environment.[21]

---

[18] Stephens, 1951*a.*
[19] Lewis and Roberts, 1956
[20] *Ibid.*
[21] Lewis, 1954.

BLOCKS OF LINKED MODIFIER GENES

The two tetraploid species of cotton, *Gossypium hirsutum* and *G. barbadense,* cross readily with one another, and the two diploid cotton species, *G. arboreum* and *G. herbaceum,* likewise cross readily inter se. The F_1 hybrids of *G. hirsutum* × *barbadense* and of *G. arboreum* × *herbaceum* are vigorous and fertile with regular chromosome pairing at meiosis. The level of vigor is much depressed, however, in the F_2 generations, where many inviable or semi-viable individuals appear.

Harland showed, as we saw in Chapter 5, that *G. hirsutum* and *G. barbadense* possess numerous homologous genes (like **S** [22] for petal spots) in common, but differ in their sets of modifiers. Consequently in an intraspecific F_2 progeny, which is uniform for the modifier complex, a heterozygous allele pair (like S/s) segregates into clearcut phenotypic classes in a simple Mendelian ratio; whereas an interspecific F_2 or F_3 progeny which is segregating for the same major gene (**S**), and *also* for the modifier genes, exhibits a semi-continuous array of phenotypes. If, however, the interspecific F_1 hybrid which is heterozygous for the major gene (S/s) is backcrossed to one parental species for several generations, so that the allele (s) derived originally from one parental species is transferred to the background of modifier genes in the other species, the backcross individuals carrying the alien allele s in the constitution S/s segregate in clearcut and simple ratios like those observed in intraspecific progenies. (See Chapter 5.)

Harland's interpretation was that the species of cotton differ mainly in their modifier genes, each species being homozygous for a different set of alleles of the modifier complex. The various genes composing each modifier complex were assumed by Harland to be independently assorting and unlinked, and the complexes were assumed to be independent of any structural rearrangements of the chromosomes as between the species, which indeed were not thought to exist in view of the regular chromosome pairing at meiosis in the interspecific F_1 hybrids.

Stephens later showed by an elegant analysis that Harland's hypothesis in its original formulation of an assemblage of unlinked modifier genes was too simple, but on the contrary, that Harland's

---

[22] The gene **S** in the nomenclature of Harland is synonymous with R_2 in the nomenclature of Stephens.

modifier genes are linked together in blocks. These blocks are co-extensive with chromosome segments which differ structurally as between two related species of cotton.[23] In order to understand Stephens' line of argument it is necessary to realize (as will be shown later in Chapter 9) that the genes borne within small chromosomal rearrangements, either translocations or inversions, do not recombine freely or even at all in individuals heterozygous for those rearrangements. The cotton species, then, on Stephens' view, are homozygous not only for different alleles of the modifier genes but also for different structural arrangements of the segments carrying the modifier genes, whereas the interspecific F_1 hybrids and many of the F_2, B_1, and other later generation progeny of the hybrids are simultaneously structural and genic heterozygotes. In the hybrid generations, consequently, the modifier complexes differentiating the parental species are not broken up by crossing-over and recombination, but tend to be inherited as blocks of linked genes.

Stephens argues that if the cotton species differ in respect to numerous independently assorting modifier genes with minute individual effects, the interspecific backcrosses should exhibit a slow and gradual change from continuous variation to clearcut segregations in successive generations. Actually, sharp segregation into Mendelian ratios appears after only two or three generations of backcrossing. Such a rapid reversion from continuous to non-continuous variation in the backcrosses cannot be explained on the hypothesis of many freely assorting modifiers. A rapid reversion from blurred to sharp segregation would be expected, however, if the modifiers are grouped in blocks corresponding to chromosome segments which have a different segmental arrangement in each parental species.[24]

It was noted earlier that, whereas the F_1 hybrids of *G. hirsutum* $\times$ *barbadense* and *G. arboreum* $\times$ *herbaceum* are vigorous and fertile, the F_2 progenies show much depression of vigor. Now the F_2 types that are viable are those which approach the parental species or the F_1 hybrids. The recombination types in F_2 are inviable. In F_3 and later generations only the types resembling the parents become established.

These facts can be explained on the hypothesis that the parental species are differentiated in respect to small chromosomal rearrangements. The rearrangements being confined to small segments, chromosome pairing would be visibly regular at metaphase of meiosis in

---

[23] Stephens, 1949, 1950.
[24] *Ibid.*

the F_1 hybrids, but crossing-over and segregation of only partially homologous chromosomes would lead to the formation of gametes or F_2 zygotes that are deficient or unbalanced. The most vigorous F_2 segregates would be those carrying the most non-crossover chromosomes and hence those which most closely resemble either parent or the F_1 in phenotype. In later generations further crossing-over would tend to eliminate the types resembling the F_1 and increase the number of segregates approaching one or the other parental species.[25]

Similarly in interspecific backcross progenies the segregation is skewed towards the recurrent parent. In order to demonstrate this skewness, Stephens introduced marker genes on several chromosomes of the two species (*G. hirsutum* and *G. barbadense*), produced the F_1 hybrid which was then heterozygous for these independently assorting markers, backcrossed the hybrid reciprocally to the two parental types, and compared the segregation ratios in the reciprocal backcross progenies. The results are summarized in Table 11.

As shown in this table, the observed ratio differs in nearly every case, and often significantly, from a theoretical 1:1 backcross ratio. In the backcross to *G. hirsutum,* furthermore, there is a consistent excess of *hirsutum* types and deficiency of *barbadense* types for five of the seven marker genes tested. Conversely, in the backcross to *G. barbadense,* the *barbadense* types are more frequent and the *hirsutum* types less frequent than would be expected on the basis of a 1:1 ratio for four of the five genes tested.

It will be noted, furthermore, that the observed segregation ratios for one and the same gene L are skewed in opposite directions in the reciprocal backcrosses. The allele of L derived originally from the *barbadense* parent is represented in far less than the expected 50% of the progeny in the backcross to *G. hirsutum;* whereas the alternative allele of L introduced from the *hirsutum* parent attains the lower frequency in the reciprocal backcross to *G. barbadense.* (See Table 11.) Again, the gene **Cr** segregates to yield a deficiency of *hirsutum* types in the backcross to *G. barbadense,* and the opposite deficiency of *barbadense* types in the backcross to *G. hirsutum.*[26] In short, the skewness of the segregation ratios is reversed when the direction of backcrossing is reversed.

Only in one case is there a significant excess of donor types in a backcross progeny. This case involves the segregation of the alleles

---

[25] Stephens, 1950.
[26] From Table 11 and other data not tabulated there but mentioned by Stephens, 1949, 632.

TABLE 11   SEGREGATION RATIOS FOR SEVERAL INDEPENDENT
MARKER GENES IN THE BACKCROSSES OF *Gossypium hirsutum*
$\times$ *barbadense* TO THE PARENTAL SPECIES *

Direction of Backcross	Marker Gene	Number of Individuals in B_1 Carrying the:	
		Hirsutum Allele	Barbadense Allele
B_1 ($F_1 \times$ hirsutum)	R_1	88	70
	R_2	89	50
	P	78	69
	Y	80	67
	K	47	98
	N	69	77
	L	103	54
B_1 ($F_1 \times$ barbadense)	R_1	40	37
	K	27	42
	N	33	36
	L	19	58
	Cr	26	51

* Stephens, 1949.

K and k of the gene **K** in the backcross to *G. hirsutum*.   The allele k
derived from the *barbadense* parent is more frequent than K from
the *hirsutum* parent in the backcross to *G. hirsutum,* as well as in the
reciprocal backcross to *G. barbadense*.   The reasons for this exception
are unknown.

Considering the seven independent marker genes in the backcross
to *G. hirsutum* altogether, one would expect, on the basis of a 1:1
segregation ratio for each gene and random recombination between
genes, that the frequency of individuals in the B_1 generation with any
given number of marker alleles derived from the *hirsutum* parent
from 0 to 7 would form a symmetrical distribution, as shown by the
heavy line in Fig. 35.   The actual frequency distribution of types
carrying various numbers of *hirsutum* alleles in the backcross to *G.
hirsutum* is not symmetrical, however, but is skewed away from the
donor parent and towards the recurrent parent.   (See Fig. 35.)   In
the reciprocal backcross to *G. barbadense* the frequency distribution
of individuals carrying various numbers of *hirsutum* alleles for all five

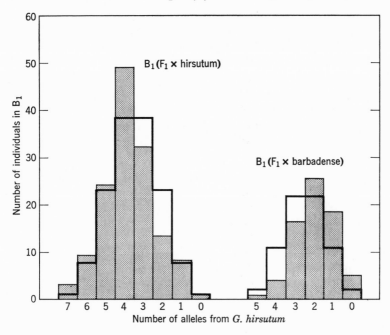

FIG. 35. Frequency distributions of plants carrying the alleles of *Gossypium hirsutum* for various numbers of independent marker genes in backcross progenies of the hybrid *G. hirsutum* × *barbadense*. The frequency distributions for the two reciprocal backcrosses are shown by separate histograms. In each histogram, the expected frequency on the basis of a 1:1 ratio for each independently segregating gene is outlined with a heavy black line, while the observed frequency is shown as a shaded area enclosed by a thin line. (Stephens, 1949.)

marker genes combined is skewed in the opposite direction, which represents again a deficiency of the donor parent genotype and an excess of the recurrent parent genotype.[27] (See again Fig. 35.)

The skewness of the backcross ratios towards the recurrent parent is evidence for a selective elimination of the donor parent genotype in the backcrosses. The question then arises as to where in the life cycle this selective elimination takes place.

In later backcross generations the deviations from the normal 1:1 ratio tend to disappear. Thus in successive backcross generations of the F_1 hybrid to *G. hirsutum*, the ratio between individuals carrying the allele derived from the *hirsutum* parent and those carrying the *barbadense* allele was as follows:

[27] Stephens, 1949.

in B_1,   166 hirsutum types: 98 barbadense types

B_2,   27   24

B_3,   186   172

B_4,   9   10

Only in the B_1 generation is the class containing the allele from the donor parent significantly deficient.[28]   This narrows the process of selective elimination down mainly to the reproductive structures, either gametes or zygotes, produced by the F_1 hybrid.

The backcross of the F_1 hybrid to one and the same parental species can be made either by using the species as the female parent or by using the hybrid as female parent.   When the species is used as female parent for the backcross, only a negligible proportion of abortive seeds is produced.   The proportion of abortive seeds is about the same as that produced normally when the same species is selfed.   Therefore, little or no selective elimination is apparent in the B_1 zygotes.   On the other hand, when the F_1 hybrid is used as the female parent in making a backcross, around 8 to 10% abortive seeds are formed, which may be due to the elimination of some female gametes produced by the hybrid.[29]

The skewness of the backcross ratios was compared as between B_1 (*hirsutum* ♀ $\times$ F_1) and B_1 (F_1 ♀ $\times$ *hirsutum*), and again between *barbadense* ♀ $\times$ F_1 and F_1 ♀ $\times$ *barbadense*.   The deviations from 1:1 ratios for all genes tested were generally the same independently of the direction in which a given backcross was made.   Thus for the R_2 gene, the backcross ratio in B_1 (F_1 ♀ $\times$ *hirsutum*) was 50 individuals carrying the *hirsutum* allele to 38 individuals with the *barbadense* allele, while the reciprocal backcross B_1 (*hirsutum* $\times$ F_1 ♂) exhibited a ratio of 39 *hirsutum* types to 12 *barbadense* types.[30]

The deficiency of donor parent genotypes in the first-generation backcross progeny of F_1 ♀ $\times$ donor species A agrees with the evidence of ovule abortion presented earlier in indicating a selective elimination of F_1 gametes on the female side.   The similar deficiency of donor parent genotypes in the first-generation progeny of the reciprocal backcross of donor species A $\times$ F_1 ♂ indicates a selective elimination of F_1 male gametes in similar proportions.[31]

---

[28] Stephens, 1950.
[29] Stephens, 1949.
[30] *Ibid.*
[31] *Ibid.*

The selective elimination of the donor parent genotype in the interspecific backcrosses, therefore, appears to occur mainly in the gametes produced by the F_1 hybrid. This elimination, moreover, affects both the male and female gametes of the hybrid more or less alike. The gametes thus selected against could well be those which contain chromosomes carrying a block of genes introduced from the donor species.[32]

Direct genetic evidence for the differentiation of Gossypium species with respect to blocks of linked genes which are probably coextensive with small chromosomal rearrangements is provided by several cases encountered in cotton breeding programs. It was desirable, for instance, to introduce increased fiber strength from the wild species *Gossypium thurberi* into the cultivated *G. hirsutum*. The cross can be made successfully by first producing the F_1 hybrid between *G. hirsutum* (which is tetraploid) and a synthetic tetraploid derivative of *G. thurberi* (which is normally diploid), and then backcrossing the F_1 hybrid to *G. hirsutum*. In this way the fiber strength allele of *G. thurberi* was introduced into *G. hirsutum*.[33]

Along with the fiber strength allele, however, came an allele for low yield. The linkage between the two genes was too strong to be broken by repeated breeding attempts. Similar situations have been found in breeding for other characters (like disease resistance) in other species crosses, such as *G. hirsutum* × *barbadense*. In each case hybridization and selection for a single gene resulted in the transfer of a block of genes. The strong linkage of the genes in blocks could be explained on the hypothesis that the separate genes are borne in each case on a chromosome segment which has a different structural arrangement in the two parental species.[34]

If the species of cotton differ by small rearrangements in their chromosomes, as postulated by Stephens, then the species hybrids, being structural heterozygotes, could be expected to undergo reduced pairing and crossing-over within the structurally differentiated chromosome region. This effect could be detected by comparing the crossover values between linked genes borne on the chromosomes in question in interspecific backcrosses with the crossover values obtained for the same genes in intraspecific progenies. Within *Gossypium arboreum* the crossover value between the genes **Lc** and **L** (for lint color and leaf shape respectively) is 28.7%. In the backcrosses of the

---

[32] *Ibid.*
[33] Stephens, 1950.
[34] *Ibid.*

interspecific hybrid, *G. arboreum* × *herbaceum,* the crossover value
between these genes is 24.5%. The crossover value between the "lint
color" and "crinkle" genes is 10% within *G. hirsutum,* but only 5% in
the interspecific backcrosses of *G. hirsutum* × *barbadense.* The observed lowering of the crossover values in the interspecific crosses
supports the idea that the chromosomes of the parental species are
differentiated structurally.[35]

Although the differential chromosome segments separating the cotton
species are, by assumption, too small to give rise to visible aberrations
of meiosis in the F_1 hybrids, so that cytological evidence for their
existence cannot be obtained by direct observation with ordinary
techniques, there is indirect cytological evidence indicating that the
chromosomes of *G. hirsutum* and *G. barbadense* are in fact structurally different, and that the chromosomes of *G. arboreum* and *G.
herbaceum* are likewise differentiated structurally. This evidence
is based on the fact that the closeness of chromosome pairing in an
F_1 hybrid gives a relatively crude measure of the degree of structural
homology. The presence or absence of preferential pairing of chromosomes in a polyploid derivative of the F_1 hybrid in question provides a more sensitive test.

Suppose that the A chromosome is completely homologous structurally in two species, so that one species has the chromosomal constitution A_1A_1 and the other species is also A_1A_1. Suppose next that
two other species differ by small rearrangements in their A chromosome, one species being A_1A_1 and the other A_2A_2. In either the first
or the second case the A chromosomes pair in bivalents in the F_1
hybrid. The bivalents composed of completely homologous chromosomes (A_1-A_1) formed by the F_1 in the first case, moreover, may not
be distinguishable cytologically from the semi-homologous bivalents
(A_1-A_2) formed in the second hybrid.

But the cytological behavior of the A chromosomes in the two cases,
which is indistinguishable in the F_1 hybrid, may differ in the polyploid derivatives of these hybrids. If the chromosome number of the
hybrid A_1A_1 is doubled, the polyploid will have four completely
homologous A_1 chromosomes, which will tend to form quadrivalents
(A_1-A_1-A_1-A_1) at meiosis. The four A chromosomes in the polyploid
derivative of the hybrid A_1A_2, on the other hand, will consist of two
identical pairs (A_1, A_1, A_2, A_2). The two A_1 chromosomes, being completely homologous, will tend to pair preferentially with one another

[35] *Ibid.*

at meiosis in the polyploid, and so will the two A_2 chromosomes. The polyploid derivative of the hybrid A_1A_2 will have a greater tendency than the polyploid derivative of the hybrid A_1A_1 to form bivalents at meiosis.

The F_1 hybrid of *G. hirsutum* $\times$ *barbadense* has 26 bivalents at meiosis. Its polyploid derivative forms an average of 15.2 quadrivalents per cell (out of a possible 26). The polyploids derived from the parental species, *G. hirsutum* and *G. barbadense,* have 17.5 and 18.1 quadrivalents per cell on the average. Therefore, the polyploid of *G. hirsutum* $\times$ *barbadense,* with fewer quadrivalents and more bivalents than the norm for the polyploid derivatives of the parental species, apparently exhibits some preferential pairing. Again, the polyploid derived from the F_1 hybrid of *G. arboreum* $\times$ *herbaceum* forms more bivalents and fewer quadrivalents than the polyploid derivatives of either parental species. Hence some preferential pairing evidently occurs also in the polyploid of *G. arboreum* $\times$ *herbaceum*. This preferential pairing indicates, in turn, that the F_1 hybrids from which the polyploids were derived are structurally heterozygous to some extent.[36]

All these lines of evidence point to the conclusion that the species of cotton, despite regular bivalent pairing in the interspecific hybrids, differ by small chromosomal rearrangements; and that the modifier genes, which according to Harland constituted the essential difference between the species, are borne in linked blocks on these rearranged segments.[37]

BALANCED POLYGENIC SYSTEMS

The ability of an organism which is well adapted to its environmental conditions to breed true to type, and to multiply the numbers of individuals carrying its favorable genotype, is advantageous to it in evolution, and this selective advantage is the basis of the conservative aspects of the hereditary mechanism. But the ability to engender variable progeny is also selectively valuable to organisms living in a world subject to environmental changes. Organisms may be confronted then, as Darlington, Mather, and others have noted, with opposing demands for constancy and variability in reproduction, for immediate fitness versus long-range flexibility.[38]

---

[36] *Ibid.*
[37] Stephens, 1949, 1950.
[38] Darlington, 1936. Mather, 1943.

As Mather states: [39]

Heritable variability is necessary for adaptive change, but, in that it implies some individuals departing from the optimum, it lowers present fitness; for . . . departure from the optimum must be correlated with reduction in fitness. In the same way response to fluctuating environmental changes reduces the heritable variability upon which depends adaptation to environmental trends. The success of any organism, in competition with its contemporaries, must depend on the extent to which it reconciles these needs. Failure to achieve an adequate balance spells either its own doom, on the one hand, or that of its descendants, on the other. Existing organisms must, therefore, have descended from those which had most adequately balanced the advantages of fitness and flexibility in the past. The organisms of the future will equally be descended from those which, to-day, best reconcile the needs of fitness and flexibility, the rest dying out sooner or later.

Mather also distinguishes between free and potential variability. Free variability is that which is manifested by the phenotypes in a population and which is, therefore, exposed to the action of selection. Potential variability, on the other hand, is not manifested in the phenotypes, and hence is not exposed to selection in any given generation, but can become manifested in later generations on passing from the potential to the free state.[40]

The conflicting demands for fitness and flexibility can be partly reconciled by having variability stored in a potential state. Now potential variability is present in heterozygous genotypes. A homozygote gives rise to genotypically identical progeny; however great its fitness, its potential variability is nil and its flexibility slight. A heterozygous genotype, on the other hand, may possess the potential variability and flexibility which is wanting in homozygotes, and have the same degree of immediate fitness too. Thus individuals of the constitution Aa and AA may be alike phenotypically (assuming dominance of A over a); but whereas AA breeds true to type, Aa can engender phenotypically dissimilar progeny of the constitution aa. The AA and Aa individuals possess the same degree of immediate fitness resulting from their phenotypic manifestation of A, that is, from their free variability; but the Aa individuals possess in addition future flexibility associated with their potential variability.[41]

The Aa individuals on intercrossing or selfing produce offspring, one quarter of which are unlike their parents. The potential varia-

[39] Mather, 1943.
[40] *Ibid.*
[41] *Ibid.*

bility for the trait controlled by the gene **A** is thus released in a high proportion of the progeny arising in every generation. The system composed of heterozygotes for a single gene can be said to be unstable. The stability of a system of potential variability will be increased if the character is determined, not by a single gene, but by a set of multiple genes or polygenes with certain properties to be discussed next.[42]

The favorable condition of a character such as size, for example, may be a resultant of the actions of plus polygenes for increased size and minus polygenes opposing the former. Assuming for simplicity two genes on one chromosome, one with plus and the other with minus effects, there are two types of zygotes which have the same balance of gene effects, and at the same time possess potential variability, namely $\frac{+\ +}{-\ -}$ and $\frac{+\ -}{-\ +}$. The first kind of zygote, like the single gene heterozygote Aa, is highly unstable, whereas the second kind is stable. Most of its progeny are either $\frac{+\ -}{-\ +}$, $\frac{+\ -}{+\ -}$, or $\frac{-\ +}{-\ +}$, all of which have the same net size. But it can also release new variability more or less slowly by crossing-over. Crossovers between the two genes on the chromosome can lead to $\frac{+\ +}{}$ and $\frac{-\ -}{}$ gametes, which can produce $\frac{+\ +}{+\ +}$ and $\frac{-\ -}{-\ -}$ individuals with a greater or smaller than normal size.[43]

A gene system controlling some character may thus retain potential variability, yet achieve a high degree of stability in the release of this variability, by possessing the following combination of properties. The system should be heterozygous for linked multiple genes or polygenes with oppositional interactions and with a spatial arrangement on the chromosome such that neighboring polygenes have opposing directions of action. Such a system of plus and minus polygenes balanced in two ways, first from allele to allele of each gene in heterozygous condition, and secondly from gene to neighboring opposing gene, according to the generalized scheme $\frac{+\ -\ +\ -}{-\ +\ -\ +}$, is referred to by Mather as a balanced polygenic system.[44]

If each chromosome is internally balanced in this way for its com-

---

[42] *Ibid.*
[43] Thoday, 1958.
[44] Mather, 1943.

plement of polygenes, and if the polygenic system extends over two or more chromosomes, then the products of independent assortment of chromosomes will also be balanced.[45]

A balanced polygenic system has, as Mather puts it, a statistical stability like the pressure of gas. It contains a great deal of potential variability stored in the heterozygous state. It releases this variability by small increments as a result of crossing-over and recombination between linked polygenes. And the slow and gradual conversion of the variability from the potential to the free state can continue generation after generation.[46]

The density of bristles on the abdomen of *Drosophila melanogaster* is apparently controlled by a set of polygenes, as we saw in Chapter 5. There is evidence that the polygenes comprising this system are in a balanced heterozygous condition. In experimental populations when the individual flies with a greater than average number of bristles are selected as parents of the next generation, and when this selection is carried out systematically during many successive generations, new genetic variations making for greater hairiness continue to appear generation after generation. Selection for a reduced number of bristles has the same results. This gradual and continual release of genetic variability can be accounted for by crossing-over between many linked heterozygous polygenes, giving rise in every generation to new recombination types with a greater than average action in the plus or minus direction. The slow and steady response of the population to selection for a polygenic character is consistent with the hypothesis that the polygenes involved are linked, heterozygous, and oppositional; in other words, that the polygenic system is balanced.[47]

---

[45] *Ibid.*
[46] *Ibid.*
[47] Mather, 1943.   Mather and Harrison, 1949.   Harrison and Mather, 1950.

Linkage of adaptive gene combinations

9 Gene interactions can be considered at the elementary functional level, in which case we can recognize various types of multiple gene systems and serial gene systems, as discussed in preceding chapters, or again at the level of phenotypic expression. At a level in the developmental process far removed from the primary gene action, some combinations of alleles may have antagonistic effects, and other allele combinations synergistic effects, on the viability or fertility of the organism.

ADAPTIVE PROPERTIES OF GENE INTERACTIONS

Timofeeff-Ressovsky compared the average viability of two different mutant types of *Drosophila funebris* with the viability of the double mutant under uniform conditions. The mutant type "abnormes" has a viability 89% of that of normal non-mutant flies; the mutant "lozenge" also has a lowered viability, expressed as 74% of the normal viability for the parental strain of flies. But when the two mutant alleles are combined in the same individual flies the viability is only 59% under the same environmental conditions. The interaction between the two mutant alleles in the double mutant type "abnormes lozenge" thus reduces the viability more than does either allele singly.[1]

A particular combination of alleles may also produce phenotypic

---

[1] Timofeeff-Ressovsky in 1935; see Dobzhansky, 1951, 83–84.

effects more favorable to the organism than those produced by the individual genes taken separately. In *D. funebris* again, the mutant type "miniature" has a viability of 69%. The mutant "bobbed" also has a lowered viability of 85%. But the viability of the allele combination "miniature bobbed" is about normal (97%) and is significantly higher than that engendered by either mutant allele alone.[2]

The two species of willow herb, *Epilobium hirsutum* and *E. luteum*, differ in both their chromosomal genes and their cytoplasmic genes. Certain combinations of the two categories of genetic factors have synergistic effects. Thus plants with chromosomal genes of *E. hirsutum* in the cytoplasm of *E. luteum* produce up to twice as much vegetative growth under certain environmental conditions as plants with the same chromosomal genes in *E. hirsutum* cytoplasm. Again, the chromosomal genes of a strain of *E. hirsutum* from Jena, Germany, form a growth-stimulating combination with the cytoplasm of South African strains of *E. hirsutum*, but not with the cytoplasms of some sixteen other strains of the same species.[3]

Whether the gene interaction brings about synergistic effects or not depends on the relation between the phenotypic characteristics produced by the particular gene combination and the environment in which the phenotype lives. The luxuriance and adaptedness of a phenotype and of the genotype which determines that phenotype are in the last analysis a function of the organism-environment interrelationship. The forms of primary gene action and interaction are somewhat beside the point in regard to the luxuriance or adaptedness of the final phenotypic product. A synergistic interaction between genes, like a heterotic interaction between alleles, can arise as an outcome of different modes of gene action. From the standpoint of vigor and adaptedness, gene combinations must be judged by their fruits.

In short, just as functionally related genes may or may not produce an adaptive phenotype, depending on the particular alleles represented in the functional gene system, so may a combination of functionally unrelated genes give rise to either adaptively superior or adaptively inferior phenotypic products according to the alleles involved. Again, as is the case with functional gene systems, a phenotypic product possessing superior adaptive properties may be engendered by a gene combination in either the homozygous or the heterozygous condition.

----

[2] *Loc cit.*
[3] Michaelis, 1951.

The purpose of the following sections of this chapter is to consider various systems by which adaptively valuable combinations of alleles are linked together in inheritance.

HETEROZYGOUS INVERSIONS IN
RELATION TO LINKAGE

In Chapter 8 we referred to the changes in the spatial relations of genes produced by inversions or translocations in individuals which are homozygous for the altered chromosomes. Inversions and translocations have another effect on linkage in the heterozygous condition. In the inversion or translocation heterozygote, the genes in the inverted or translocated segment, or at least some of them, tend to be transmitted to the gametes in a block, or supergene.

In the following paragraphs we will discuss the complex linkage relations in inversion and translocation heterozygotes in terms of a series of hypothetical cases. We will use for the various cases the same structural rearrangements as were presented in Fig. 34-4, 7, 8, and 9 in the previous chapter. For each of these cases in turn a new diagram illustrating the particular heterozygous combination is presented here. Then with the aid of these diagrams we can proceed to consider the linkage relations between certain selected genes under different conditions of crossing-over.

Crossing-over is shown in the diagrams between single strands of the paired chromosomes in the structural heterozygote. In actuality a larger number of strands, namely four, would be involved. It is not necessary for our present purpose to consider more than one pair of crossover strands at a time; whereas it is desirable, on the other hand, to keep the diagrams as simple as possible, by reducing the number of possible events to a minimum, so that we can focus our attention on the particular genetic effects with which we are primarily concerned in this discussion.[4]

---

[4] For a review of the cytological behavior and sterility effects of inversions and translocations in heterozygotes, the reader is referred first to general genetics texts, such as Sinnott, Dunn, and Dobzhansky (1958, Chapter 15), and Srb and Owen (1952, Chapter 10); and then to cytogenetics texts, i.e., Sturtevant and Beadle (1939, Chapters 8, 9, 11), and Swanson (1957, Chapter 6). An advanced and definitive treatment of the subject is given by Darlington (1937, Chapters 5, 7, 9). For a most valuable comprehensive review of translocations in plants see Burnham (1956). The following account of linkage relations in structural heterozygotes, particularly in translocation heterozygotes, is an attempt to fill a need which I at least have felt, both in my teaching and in my own thinking, for

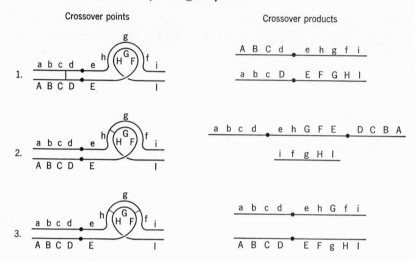

FIG. 36. The genetic consequences of crossing-over in an inversion heterozygote. (1) Crossover outside the inverted region. (2) Single crossover within the inversion. (3) Compensating double crossover within the inversion. Further explanation in text.

Let us consider first a heterozygote containing one standard chromosome and one chromosome with a paracentric inversion, as shown in Fig. 34-4 and again in Fig. 36. At meiosis in this heterozygote, the paired chromosomes form a characteristic loop configuration in the inverted region. (Fig. 36.) Crossing-over within the inversion then leads to the formation of crossover chromosomes which are deficient for some segments and duplicate for others. Thus in Fig. 36-2, one crossover product carries a deficiency for I and a duplication for **ABCDE**, while the other crossover type has a deficiency for **ABCDE** and a duplication for I. Furthermore, the first crossover strand has two centromeres and the second has none. (See again Fig. 36-2.) The products of meiosis—the daughter nuclei or gametes—which carry the deficiency-duplication chromosomes with two or no centromeres are generally non-functional.[5]

The functional gametes produced by this inversion heterozygote are mainly those in which no crossing-over occurred within the inverted

a more detailed and complete explanation than is usually given in treatments of this subject.

[5] Sturtevant and Beadle (1936) and Carson (1946) as regards the mechanism of gamete elimination in flies.

region, as in Fig. 36-1. To be sure, compensating double crossovers may occur within the inversion, as between **F** and **G** and again between **G** and **H**, as shown in Fig. 36-3. Such double crossovers also produce balanced crossover chromosomes and hence functional gametes. However, compensating double crossing-over within an inversion, particularly a short one, will occur only rarely, since one crossover tends to suppress the formation of others in the same immediate vicinity.

With these restrictions in mind, let us now consider the possibilities for effective recombination between different genes on the structurally heterozygous chromosomes. Any two genes lying outside the inverted region can recombine. Thus the genes **C** and **D** form the recombinations Cd and cD in balanced crossover chromosomes and hence in functional recombination gametes in Fig. 36-1. Likewise a gene outside the inversion (**C**) and one inside the inversion (**H**) can become recombined following crossing-over in an intervening structurally homologous region to form the balanced and functional crossover products Ch and cH. (Fig. 36-1.)

But two genes within the inversion like **G** and **H** do not ordinarily form the recombinations Gh and gH in viable products of meiosis. (Fig. 36-2.) These crossover types (Gh and gH), if they arise at all, are products of compensating double crossing-over within the inversion, which is a rare event. (Fig. 36-3.)

It can be shown that the net genetic effects of crossing-over within a heterozygous pericentric inversion, as shown in Fig. 34-5, are the same in principle as those discussed above for a paracentric inversion. The chromosomes resulting from crossing-over within a pericentric inversion in a structural heterozygote possess one centromere each, and not two or none respectively as is the case in the crossover products of a heterozygote for a paracentric inversion (Fig. 36-2), but otherwise carry deficiencies and duplications for particular segments. In plants as typified by corn (*Zea mays*) these deficiency-duplication types are eliminated in the gametic or gametophytic stage, and most stringently in the pollen.[6] In animals like Drosophila the deficiency-duplication gametes may function [7] but then produce inviable zygotes.

The effective recombination between the genes within an inverted region in an inversion heterozygote is thus in general restricted to the exceptional products of compensating double crossing-over inside the inversion loop. Therefore, the genes in the inverted region form a closely linked block or supergene in the inversion heterozygote. In

[6] Russell and Burnham, 1950. Rhoades and Dempsey, 1953.

[7] See Sturtevant and Beadle, 1939, 182–183; and Swanson, 1957, 176.

the setup shown in Fig. 36, the alleles FGH comprise one such linked block and the alleles fgh another.

In corn (*Zea mays*) the recombination value between two genes, **Lg** and **A**, on chromosome 3 is 28% in normal stocks. In other words, the heterozygote $\frac{Lg\,A}{lg\,a}$ normally produces the recombination type gametes (Lg a and lg A) in the average frequency of 28%. But where the alleles Lg and A were included in an inversion, and the genic heterozygote was simultaneously an inversion heterozygote, $\frac{inv\ Lg\,A}{std\ lg\,a}$, the recombination between the two genes in the pollen mother cells was only 0.5%. This small amount of recombination in the inversion heterozygote is attributed to occasional double cross-overs within the inverted segment.[8]

In *Drosophila robusta* Carson has found that a heterozygous inversion suppresses crossing-over in the structurally homologous as well as in the inverted regions of a chromosome.[9] A further unexpected discovery is that inversion heterozygosity in one chromosome pair of the complement is associated with an increase in the amount of crossing-over in other non-homologous chromosome pairs. Heterozygous inversions do not drastically change the total frequency of recombination within a nucleus in Drosophila, therefore, since suppression of crossing-over in one chromosome is accompanied by increase in another.[10]

HETEROZYGOUS TRANSLOCATIONS IN RELATION TO LINKAGE

Let us next consider certain selected aspects of the breeding behavior of an individual heterozygous for a small reciprocal translocation. The rearrangement shown in Fig. 34-7 is illustrated again in Fig. 37. The standard and the translocated chromosomes are structurally homologous throughout most of their length, being different only in the short translocation segments, and therefore they will usually form bivalents at meiosis in the heterozygote, as shown in Fig. 37. The independent assortment of the two pairs of chromosomes then leads to four classes of daughter nuclei or gametes. Two of

---

[8] Rhoades and Dempsey, 1953.
[9] Carson, 1953. See also Novitski and Braver, 1954.
[10] Carson, 1953.

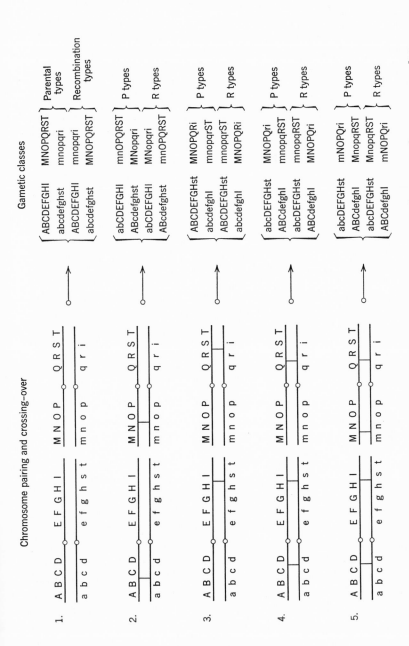

FIG. 37. The products of meiosis in an individual heterozygous for a small translocation under various conditions of crossing-over. The gametic products are classified as parental or recombination types with respect to the translocation.

these classes are parental types and two are recombination types with respect to the segmental arrangement.

The constitution of the meiotic products in respect to the segmental arrangement can be seen most clearly in Fig. 37-1, where the simplifying assumption of no crossing-over is made. One type of gamete contains the standard structural arrangement for both chromosomes of one parent, and another gametic class has the two translocation chromosomes as found in the other parent. The third and fourth meiotic products are recombinations of the standard and translocation chromosomes. One of these recombination types carries a deficiency for the segment **ST** and a duplication for **I**; the other recombination type is deficient for **I** and duplicate for **St**. (See Fig. 37-1.)

In plants where the immediate products of meiosis must develop into functioning gametophytes, pollen or embryo sac, the recombination nuclei which are deficient in some genes and duplicate in others are normally eliminated before the stage of fertilization. In Drosophila the deficiency-duplication gametes may function in fertilization but then the deficiency-duplication zygotes are inviable. In one stage or another, therefore, the recombinations of the two parental chromosomes, and of the genes borne on the translocated segments of these chromosomes, are eliminated.

A gene borne on the structurally homologous part of one chromosome pair and a gene in a homologous part of the other chromosome pair, as for example **A** and **M**, can recombine effectively to produce the new allele combinations Am and aM following crossing-over at the appropriate points and independent assortment of the crossover chromosomes. In most of the setups shown in Fig. 37, to be sure, the gene recombinations Am and aM are associated with deficiencies and duplications, and hence are eliminated from reproduction. But the appropriate conditions for the production of the gene recombinations Am and aM are found in the setup diagrammed in Fig. 37-4.

Again, crossing-over between two genes on structurally homologous arms of one chromosome pair, like **A** and **D** on the first chromosome pair in Fig. 37, will give rise to the gene recombinations Ad and aD in viable products of meiosis. Such recombinations of **A** and **D** are produced in the setups shown in Fig. 37-2, 4, and 5.

Or consider a pair of genes **A** and **I**, one of which occurs in a structurally homologous region and the other in a translocated segment. Crossing-over at the points indicated in Fig. 37-2 and 3 leads to the formation of the gene recombinations Ai and aI in balanced daughter nuclei.

But the genes within the translocation segments are not separable by crossing-over in the structural heterozygote. Thus the genes **S** and **T** in one translocated segment form only the parental allele combinations ST and st in viable products of meiosis. And **ST** is likewise linked with **I** on a different chromosome. The translocation heterozygote does not produce the non-parental combinations of alleles Ist or iST. (See Fig. 37.)

In a heterozygote for a transposition, like that shown in Fig. 34-6, the genes in the transposed segment will be linked in the same manner.

The linkage relations are somewhat different in an individual heterozygous for a large translocation, as shown in Fig. 34-8 and again in Fig. 38. Here the homologous segments on separate chromosomes can pair at meiosis to form an association of four chromosomes. This association has the form of a four-armed figure in early stages of meiosis, when pairing and crossing-over take place (Fig. 38), and later opens out into a ring or chain of four chromosomes in preparation for the movement of the chromosomes to the poles, which become the daughter nuclei.

The separation of the chromosomes to the daughter nuclei can occur in various ways. If adjacent chromosomes on the ring go to the same pole, the two daughter nuclei both inherit a deficiency for one large segment and a duplication for another. There are two modes of adjacent disjunction, depending on the orientation of the chromosome ring or chain prior to chromosome movement, but either mode leads to large deficiencies and duplications in the daughter nuclei, as shown in Fig. 38-1. The deficiency-duplication nuclei give rise to inviable gametophytes, gametes, or zygotes. The only balanced products of meiosis are those resulting from the migration of alternate chromosomes in the ring or chain to the same pole, or in other words, from alternate disjunction. (See again Fig. 38-1.)

The types of gene recombinations recovered in the progeny of this translocation heterozygote depend on the points of crossing-over between chromosomes that become distributed to the poles by alternate disjunction. The allele combinations resulting from crossing-over at various points, making the simplifying assumption of one or two crossovers per chromosome association, and from alternate disjunction of the crossover chromosomes, are shown in Fig. 38-2, 3, 4, and 5.

The genes **A** and **D** in the same unrearranged arm of one chromosome can form the recombination products Ad and aD, as in Fig. 38-2 and 3. Similarly the genes **F** and **I** occurring together in a translocated segment produce the recombinations Fi and fI in the setup shown in Fig. 38-3. And **A** and **I** occurring in unrearranged

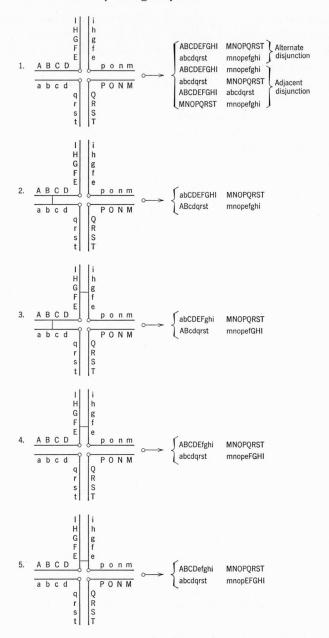

FIG. 38. The products of alternate disjunction in an individual heterozygous for a whole arm translocation under various conditions of crossing-over. The products of adjacent disjunction are also shown in diagram 1. Further explanation in text.

and translocated arms respectively form the new allele combinations Ai and aI in Fig. 38-2. The same is true of I and T which lie on two separate translocated segments, and recombine as It and iT in Fig. 38-3. In none of these cases are the parental allele combinations held together in the progeny of the translocation heterozygote.

However, the pairing between chromosome regions lying close to the translocation breakage points, which happen to be near the centromeres in the example before us, is reduced in the translocation heterozygote as a result of mechanical difficulties. Crossing-over in the neighborhood of the breaks is, therefore, also reduced or inhibited. The genes in such regions consequently tend to be linked in the structural hybrid.[11]

Thus the genes E and F, both of which lie on the same side of and close to a breakage point, will form the new allele combinations Ef and eF in proportion to the frequency of crossing-over in this region of the chromosomes. The requisite crossovers as shown in Fig. 38-4 may occur only rarely. Likewise the genes D and E on opposite sides of the break can be recombined only by crossovers at a point like that indicated in Fig. 38-5. Pairing and crossing-over in this region may occur rarely or not at all. Then the parental allele combinations DE and de will be linked to the same degree in the translocation heterozygote. Furthermore, the alleles d and e which occur on separate chromosomes are as tightly linked in the heterozygote as the alleles D and E which occupy neighboring loci.

In Drosophila the gene Bl (for bristle) occurs on chromosome II and D (dichaete) on chromosome III. Normally, the double heterozygote Bl/bl D/d produces four classes of gametes (Bl D, Bl d, bl D, bl d) in equal frequency. Male flies heterozygous for a translocation between chromosomes II and III, and for the genes Bl and D, however, produced all Bl d or bl d gametes, the recombination classes being absent.[12]

By successive overlapping translocations, the system of linkage can be extended to other chromosomes of the complement. The heterozygote for two successive reciprocal translocations affecting three chromosomes shown in Fig. 34-9 is presented again in Fig. 39-2. Chromosome pairing and crossing-over between the structurally homologous arms will typically occur as shown in Fig. 39-2. Alternate

---

[11] Dobzhansky, 1931. Darlington, 1937, 286.
[12] Experiment of Dobzhansky; from summary by Sturtevant and Beadle, 1939, 181. Some crossing-over and a reduced amount of recombination between Bl and D would be expected in female flies heterozygous for the same translocation.

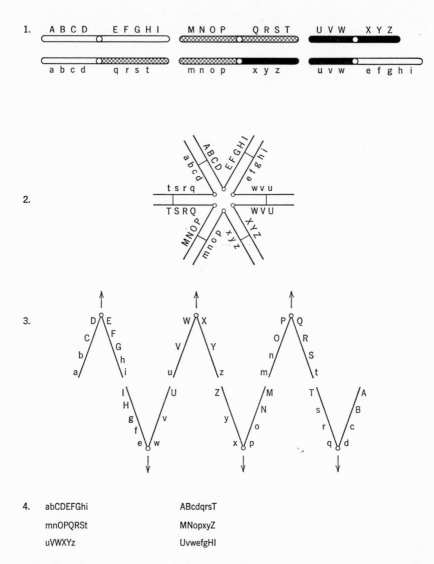

FIG. 39.   The course of meiosis in an individual heterozygous for two successive translocations.   (1) Chromosomal and genic constitution of the heterozygote. (2) Chromosome pairing and crossing-over at meiosis.   (3) Alternate disjunction at meiosis.   (4) Genic constitution of the two balanced products of meiosis.

disjunction of the crossover chromosomes, as in Fig. 39-3, will then produce the two classes of balanced daughter nuclei seen in Fig. 39-4.

It will be noted that the genes located on the arms at some distance from the breakage points can cross over and recombine frequently in the translocation heterozygote. Thus the parental allele combinations RT and rt give rise to the viable recombination gametes Rt and rT in Fig. 39.

But genes located close to the breakage points cross over and recombine more rarely, or not at all in the case of some such genes, in the structural hybrid. As a consequence, the alleles of genes which entered the heterozygote from one parent on three separate chromosomes, but near the translocation breaks on those chromosomes, are linked in transmission by the heterozygote to future generations. Although the genes **E**, **Q**, and **X**, for example, are located on separate chromosomes, the parental allele combinations EQX and eqx are normally preserved in the progeny of the translocation heterozygote, as shown in Fig. 39.

PERMANENT INVERSION HETEROZYGOTES
IN NATURE

In Chapter 3 we saw that a superior adaptive fitness probably can be produced by heterozygosity for a single gene. Undoubtedly, more complex adaptive properties can be engendered by heterozygosity for clusters of genes than by the interactions between a single pair of alleles. Now any given heterozygous gene combination, however valuable adaptively, will be broken up in a sexual organism if the genes involved are subject to the normal processes of crossing-over and independent assortment. Thus the heterozygote Aa Bb Cc, on reproducing sexually, gives rise to numerous progeny of the constitution AA Bb cc, aa Bb Cc, and so on, in which the particular phenotypic effects resulting from heterozygosity in all three genes together are lacking.

But if these three genes are associated with a chromosomal rearrangement, so that one allele combination (ABC) occurs in one inverted segment or in one small translocated segment or near the breakage points of a large translocation, and the other allele combination (abc) occurs on the corresponding segment(s) of the other structurally different chromosome(s), then the genic heterozygote $\frac{ABC}{abc}$, being simultaneously a structural heterozygote, produces by sexual means only the two classes of gametes (ABC and abc) and hence a high proportion of completely heterozygous progeny.

If the genes **A**, **B**, and **C** in the heterozygote Aa Bb Cc recombine at random, and if the resulting eight classes of gametes unite at random, the complete heterozygous type will appear in only 12.5% of the progeny in the next generation. By comparison, the random union of the two gametic classes produced by the structural hybrid with the same genic constitution $\left(\dfrac{ABC}{abc} \right)$ enables that hybrid to reconstitute its heterozygous genotype in 50% of its offspring.

Let us suppose now that the particular heterozygous gene combination in question determines phenotypic traits of superior adaptive value. In that case it will be selectively advantageous to the population if the complete heterozygotes breed as true to type as possible for their heterozygous constitution. This result is achieved by the location of the alternative allele combinations ABC and abc in heterozygous inversions or translocations. The formation of adaptively inferior zygotes (such as AA BB CC and aa bb cc) is not prevented, to be sure, but is minimized by this system of balanced supergenes.

The wild populations of *Drosophila pseudoobscura* in western North America and Mexico consist of individuals homozygous or heterozygous for various inversions on chromosome III. The sixteen known inversion types, designated ST, AR, CH, PP, etc., occur in varying frequencies in different parts of the distribution area of the species. In California populations of *D. pseudoobscura*, for example, the ST, AR, and CH inversion types comprise a majority of the third chromosomes present. (Fig. 40-*a*, *b*.) These chromosomes are combined in the larval and adult flies constituting such populations in the various structurally homozygous and heterozygous genotypes (ST/ST, AR/AR, CH/CH, ST/AR, ST/CH, AR/CH). (Fig. 40*c*, *d*.)

Dobzhansky and his school have demonstrated by repeated experiments with laboratory populations of the flies, and by extensive studies of natural populations, that certain inversion heterozygotes (i.e., ST/CH) are adaptively superior to either structural homozygote (ST/ST or CH/CH) under certain environmental conditions.[13]

The relative frequencies of the ST and CH forms of chromosome III in a population of flies can be determined by appropriate test crosses and cytological examination of the F_1 larvae. Knowing the frequencies of ST and CH in the gamete pool in any generation, it is possible to calculate the frequencies of the homozygous and heterozygous genotypes (ST/ST, CH/CH, ST/CH) that would be expected

---

[13] For reviews with references, see Dobzhansky (1951, Chapter 5; 1955), da Cunha (1955), and Grant (1963, 244–257).

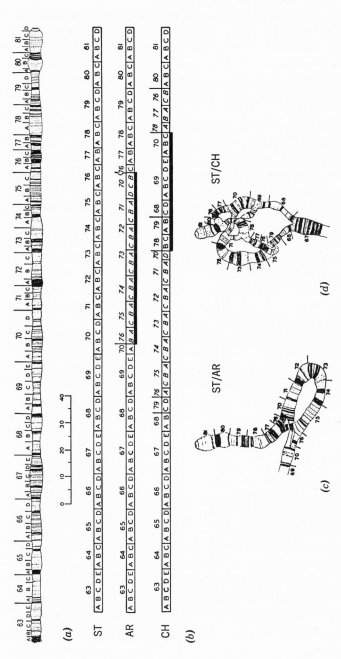

FIG. 40. Chromosome III of *Drosophila pseudoobscura* as seen in salivary glands. (*a*) The standard gene order (ST), with the arbitrary subdivisions into numbered sections and lettered subsections shown. The 40 micron scale indicates the magnification. (*b*) The length and position of the inversions AR and CH in relation to the sections of the ST chromosome. (*c*) Chromosome pairing in the inversion heterozygote ST/AR. (*d*) Chromosome pairing in the inversion heterozygote ST/CH. (From *The Origin of Adaptations*, by Grant, after Dobzhansky, Sturtevant, and Epling, copyright 1963, Columbia University Press, New York.)

to arise in the next generation as a result of the random union of these gametes. It has been shown in certain experiments with laboratory populations that samples of F_1 eggs consist of structural homozygotes and heterozygotes in the expected ratios. But samples of adult flies in the same generation exhibit a significant deficiency of the homozygous classes and a corresponding excess of the inversion heterozygote ST/CH as compared with the expected numbers. This skewing of the ratios between the egg stage and the adult stage indicates that the inversion heterozygotes survive better than the homozygotes under the given experimental conditions.[14]

Similar relationships are found in natural populations where, in some seasons of the year at least, flies heterozygous for inversions are more frequent than would be expected on the basis of the union of the alternative types of gametes in proportion to their relative numbers in the gamete pool.

The properties of the heterozygote ST/CH which give it a fitness superior to that of either homozygous class have been identified in laboratory populations. Moos found that at 25°C. the ST/CH individuals developed more rapidly, were more viable in the larval stage, were longer lived, and laid more eggs than the ST/ST or CH/CH flies.[15] These superior adaptive properties of the heterozygote, as noted by various workers, are manifested under certain environmental conditions and not under others. The inversion heterozygotes are adaptively superior under conditions of overcrowding and competition, at warm temperatures, and when fed on certain types of food yeasts.[16]

The adaptive properties of the ST/CH heterozygotes are not due to the chromosomal structural changes in themselves, but evidently to the gene combinations carried in the heterozygous inversions. This is shown by the fact that an ST chromosome from one region does not usually interact in a heterotic way with a CH chromosome from another geographically remote population.

The ST chromosomes occurring in different geographical races of *D. pseudoobscura* are alike structurally but different in their genic contents. Similarly, the CH chromosomes differ genically but not structurally in different areas. The combination of any ST chromosome with any CH chromosome may or may not produce heterotic effects, and most likely will not, in the appropriate environment. Such heterotic effects are brought about by the combinations of ST and CH

[14] Dobzhansky, 1947.
[15] Moos, 1955.
[16] Levine, 1952.   Wright and Dobzhansky, 1946.   Da Cunha, 1951.

chromosomes coexisting in the same population and carrying co-adapted genes. The function of the heterozygous inversions, then, is to preserve these gene combinations intact.[17]

PERMANENT TRANSLOCATION HETEROZYGOTES IN NATURE

The classical example of a permanent translocation heterozygote is *Oenothera lamarckiana* and related members of the *Oe. hookeri—biennis* species group (Onagraceae). The remarkable breeding behavior of these annual or biennial plants has been elucidated by a long series of studies by DeVries, Renner, Darlington, Cleland, and many others.[18]

The *Oenothera hookeri—biennis* group has a widespread distribution in North America, and is represented in parts of Europe by introduced forms such as *Oe. lamarckiana* itself. The plants are diploid with $2N = 14$ chromosomes. The chromosomes are structurally homologous in the western American *Oe. hookeri* which consequently forms seven bivalents at meiosis. In most other species of the group the plants comprising the natural populations are heterozygous for whole arm translocations between four or more of the fourteen chromosomes, which pair in rings of various size.

Individual plants belonging to this species group in the southwestern United States, *Oe. irrigua* for example, may exhibit rings of four, six, or eight chromosomes, the remaining chromosomes being paired in bivalents.[19] In Europe *Oenothera lamarckiana* regularly forms a ring of twelve chromosomes and one bivalent at meiosis.[20] The east-

---

[17] Dobzhansky and Levene, 1951.

[18] As in the case of *Drosophila pseudoobscura*, I have not attempted to give anything like a complete review of Oenothera cytogenetics here, but am presenting only some selected aspects that are relevant to our present discussion. Good general reviews of Oenothera genetics, or rather of parts of this very large subject, are given by Emerson (1935), Cleland (1936), Darlington (1937, Chapter 9), Stebbins (1950, Chapter 11), and Tischler (1951–1953, II, 601–605, III 400–413). See also Cleland (1950) for a collection of papers containing more recent findings with references to earlier literature. In the following paragraphs where original papers are not cited specifically I have based my account on the reviews of Cleland and Tischler primarily. For clarity of exposition, I am letting the Oenothera story unfold here in a sequence which is largely the reverse of the historical order of discovery.

[19] Cleland, 1940; 1949; 1950, 218.

[20] Dr. P. A. Munz informs me that the correct taxonomic name for the plant widely known as *Oe. lamarckiana* is *Oe. erythrosepala* Borbas.

TABLE 12   END ARRANGEMENTS OF THE CHROMOSOMES IN THE TWO HAP-
LOID SETS IN SEVERAL SPECIES OF THE *Oenothera hookeri—biennis* GROUP *

Species	Haploid Sets	End Arrangements of the Seven Chromosomes						
Oe. hookeri, standard race	set I	1–2	3–4	5–6	7–8	9–10	11–12	13–14
	set II	1–2	3–4	5–6	7–8	9–10	11–12	13–14
Oe. hookeri, Johansen race	set I	1–2	3–4	5–6	7–10	9–8	11–12	13–14
	set II	1–2	3–4	5–6	7–10	9–8	11–12	13–14
Oe. lamarckiana	velans	1–2	3–4	5–8	7–6	9–10	11–12	13–14
	gaudens	1–2	3–12	5–6	7–11	9–4	8–14	13–10
Oe. parviflora (= *muricata*)	curvans	1–14	3–2	5–13	7–12	9–8	11–10	4–6
	rigens	1–2	3–4	5–6	7–11	9–10	8–14	13–12
Oe. grandiflora	acuens	1–4	3–2	5–6	7–10	9–8	11–12	13–14
	truncans	1–13	3–7	5–2	4–6	9–14	11–10	8–12

* Cleland and Hammond, 1950, 31, 54. Catcheside and Cleland have independently assigned different arbitrary numbers to the chromosome arms in certain
cases. The slight difference in formulas does not affect the conclusions regarding
chromosomal relationships. The system of designation of Cleland is used consistently here.

ern North American *Oe. biennis, grandiflora, parviflora* [21] and other
species possess rings of fourteen chromosomes. [22]   These plants are
thus heterozygous for successive translocations involving all or nearly
all of the chromosomes in the complement.

The homologies of the chromosome arms in any species or race of
the *Oenothera hookeri—biennis* group can be expressed in terms of
a standard arrangement. A few of the many known chromosomal
relationships are tabulated in Table 12. It will be noted that two
races of *Oe. hookeri* are both structurally homozygous, but differ ra-
cially in a single reciprocal translocation involving the 8-arm of one
chromosome and the 10-arm of another. The arm arrangement in the

---

[21] *Oenothera parviflora* is often referred to in the genetics literature by the name
Oe. muricata, which is a later synonym according to Dr. Munz.
[22] For tabular summaries of the ring-forming behavior of the various species see
Darlington (1937, 344–345), and Tischler (1953, 405–406).

first race of *Oe. hookeri* is the arbitrary standard with which other races and species can be compared. The arrangement in the second race (Johansen) is now known to be more widespread and more probably reflects the ancestral condition.[23]

Now consider *Oe. lamarckiana* in the table. Both of its haploid sets, designated "velans" and "gaudens," differ by translocations from the standard arrangement in *Oe. hookeri*. Furthermore, velans and gaudens differ between themselves by successive translocations involving all but the 1-2 chromosomes. Consequently, at meiosis in *Oe. lamarckiana*, the 1-2 chromosomes pair in a bivalent, while the other twelve chromosomes pair end to end in a ring as follows:

```
velans   3–4        9–10        13–14       8–5       6–7        11–12        3–4
               \      /      \      /      \      /      \      /      \      /      \      /      \
gaudens        4–9        10–13       14–8       5–6        7–11        12–3
```

(See Fig. 41*a*.) The two haploid sets making up *Oe. parviflora*, and the two sets in *Oe. grandiflora*, differ for whole arm translocations on all chromosomes, so that pairing between homologous arms leads to rings of fourteen chromosomes at meiosis.

The chromosomes in the ring regularly undergo alternate disjunction. As a result, in *Oe. lamarckiana*, *all* the gaudens chromosomes go to one pole and *all* the velans chromosomes to the other, so that two classes of gametes, gaudens and velans, are produced. (See Fig. 41*b*.) The formation of deficiency-duplication gametes, which would result from the segregation of some velans and some gaudens chromosomes to the same daughter nucleus, is avoided by this mechanism of regular alternate disjunction.

Most ring-forming members of the *Oe. lamarckiana* group reproduce by self-pollination to give rise exclusively to ring-forming progeny. With rare exceptions the plants breed true for their structurally heterozygous constitution. The expected structurally homozygous classes do not appear in the sexual progeny of translocation heterozygotes. Thus *Oe. lamarckiana*, which has the constitution velans/gaudens, and produces velans and gaudens gametes, gives rise by union of these gametes to all velans/gaudens offspring, the velans/velans and gaudens/gaudens types being absent.

The absence of the homozygous classes is due to the association of a balanced system of complementary lethal factors $\left(\dfrac{+\ l_2}{l_1\ +} \right)$ with the alternative haploid chromosome complements. The constitution

---

[23] Cleland and Hammond, 1950, 55.

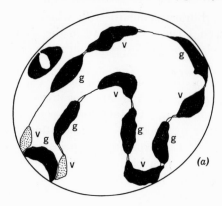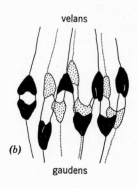

FIG. 41.   Chromosome configurations at meiosis in *Oenothera lamarckiana*.   The chromosomes lying in the upper optical plane are shown black, while those lying in an optical plane below are stippled.   (*a*) Pairing in a ring of twelve chromosomes and a bivalent at diakinesis.   (*b*) Orientation on the spindle for alternate disjunction at anaphase.   (From Emerson, 1935, after Cleland.)

of *Oe. lamarckiana,* taking the lethal genes into consideration, is $\dfrac{\text{velans} + l_2}{\text{gaudens } l_1 +}$.   The velans/velans structural homozygote, being homozygous also for the alleles $l_2 l_2$ which exert a lethal effect in the zygote, does not survive; nor for the same reason does the $\dfrac{\text{gaudens } l_1}{\text{gaudens } l_1}$ homozygote.   But the lethal alleles are unexpressed in the genic and structural heterozygote, which is consequently viable.   The action of the lethal genes, which occurs in the zygote stage in *Oe. lamarckiana,* takes place earlier—in the gametes—in some other species such as *Oe. parviflora,* with the same net effect in suppressing the segregation of homozygous types.

Hybridization experiments indicate that the ring-forming Oenotheras are heterozygous for various genes affecting visible phenotypic characteristics as well as for the chromosome arm arrangement and the lethal factors.   Although a structurally heterozygous Oenothera produces only one phenotypic class of offspring on selfing, except for a certain low proportion of "mutant" types to be mentioned later, and thus breeds true to type phenotypically as well as chromosomally, it yields two or more phenotypic classes of offspring on outcrossing to another Oenothera species.   The cross *Oe. lamarckiana* $\times$ *grandiflora,* for example, gives rise to four sorts of phenotypes in the F_1 generation. These four phenotypes correspond to the four diploid combinations between the gametes of *Oe. lamarckiana* (gaudens and velans) and those of *Oe. grandiflora* (acuens and truncans), namely gaudens/acuens, gaudens/truncans, velans/acuens, and velans/truncans. The observed phenotypic differences between these genotypes show that the respective chromosome sets transmitted through the gametes differ in their genic contents.

Thus one chromosome set in *Oe. biennis I* carries genes determining broad thin smooth leaves, while the other set carries genes for thick hairy leaves.[24] The genes **R** and **P** governing the color of the midribs of the leaf and the papillae respectively have the following heterozygous linkage relationships in two species. *Oenothera parviflora* has the constitution $\dfrac{\text{rigens} \quad \text{P} \quad \text{R}}{\text{curvans p} \quad \text{r}}$; and *Oe. lamarckiana* the constitution $\dfrac{\text{velans} \quad \text{P} \quad \text{R}}{\text{gaudens p} \quad \text{r}}$. In the nearly complete translocation heterozygote, *Oe. lamarckiana,* **P** is linked with the structurally differentiated chromosome sets, but **R** is independent, being located in the bivalent-forming 1-2 chromosomes. Neither **R** nor **P** is independently assorting in the complete translocation heterozygote, *Oe. parviflora.*[25]

The homologous arms of translocated chromosomes in Oenothera pair and cross over in their terminal regions at meiosis. Genes located in the terminal pairing segments can consequently recombine more or less freely. The brevistylis gene **Br** in *Oe. lamarckiana,* for example, which in alternative allelic forms (Br or br) determines normal or short styles, is located near the end of the 12-arm. This arm belongs to the 11-12 chromosome in the velans set and to the 3-12 chromosome of the gaudens set. (See Table 12.) Pairing between the terminal regions of the 12-arms belonging to the two structurally differentiated chromosome sets permits one allele, say br, on chromosome 11-12 to cross over into the gaudens set, and the other allele (Br) on chromosome 3-12 to cross over into the velans set with a high frequency.[26]

The chromosomal regions in the neighborhood of the translocation breakage points, which are also the regions near the centromeres in Oenothera, on the other hand, are not normally able to pair and form crossovers. Therefore, as Darlington argues, the heterozygous gene combinations for which an Oenothera normally breeds true, both the lethal factors and the genes determining various morphological char-

---

[24] Cleland, Preer, and Geckler, 1950, 239; and Munz, oral communication.

[25] Renner, 1928. Emerson and Sturtevant, 1932, 394–396. Cleland 1936, 323.

[26] Emerson and Sturtevant, 1932. Catcheside, 1954.

acters, must be located in the non-pairing or differential segments.[27]

The alleles of a gene located close to a differential segment may pair and cross over rarely. A heterozygous parent thereupon produces some exceptional homozygous progeny which deviate from type. These exceptional homozygous crossover types are one of the sources of "mutations" in Oenothera.

Oenothera lamarckiana, which generally breeds true for tall stature, gives rise to a certain low frequency of dwarf or nanella segregates. Stature is determined by a gene **N** located in the 4-arm of the 3-4 chromosome of the velans set and in the homologous 4-arm of the gaudens set. This gene is represented by a dominant allele N for normal stature and a recessive allele n for nanella stature in *Oe. lamarckiana.* The heterozygote N/n is tall owing to dominance of the normal allele, and yields predominantly tall progeny owing to the linkage of **N** with the gaudens and velans lethals. This linkage is not complete however. Crossing-over occurs rarely between **N** and the lethal genes. Then a plant of the constitution $\frac{\text{velans}\ \ N}{\text{gaudens}\ n}$ produces exceptional progeny $\frac{\text{velans}\ \ n}{\text{gaudens}\ n}$ which exhibit the nanella phenotype and breed true for the nanella condition thereafter.[28]

A line may become homozygous, not merely for a single gene, but for a large block of genes, following the occurrence of new translocations within the chromosome set. The new translocation, by changing the end arrangement, is likely to break up a ring of 14 or 12 chromosomes into an array of smaller rings and bivalents. The same result follows from outcrossing between one translocation heterozygote and another different one. The chromosomes in some of the newly formed rings and bivalents will be separated from the balanced lethal genes. Consequently progeny can arise which are homozygous for whole chromosomes and for the genes on them.

The rare separation of a large proportion of the genes from the balanced lethal factors, by unusual crossovers or new translocations or hybridization, and the subsequent segregation of individuals which are structurally and genically homozygous to a large degree, make it possible to compare the homozygotes and the heterozygotes in Oenothera with respect to their vigor.

A homozygous and bivalent-forming derivative of *Oe. lamarckiana*

---

[27] Darlington, 1937, 350.

[28] Emerson and Sturtevant, 1932. Emerson, 1935.

known as "blandina" is distinguished from the normal heterozygous plants by pale yellowish-green seedling leaves, slender rosettes, slow growth, and reduced fruit formation.[29] According to Renner, the flavens/flavens homozygote obtained from *Oe. suaveolens* (albicans/flavens), by hybridization in one case and in another by selfing and crossing-over between the gene complex and the lethals, is difficult to keep alive.[30] A homozygous segregate of *Oe. pratincola* containing the pollen-transmitted chromosome set in double dose, so that seven bivalents are formed at meiosis, is an inviable dwarf which blooms only rarely.[31] Plants of the homozygous constitution curtans/curtans derived from *Oe. cockerelli* (curtans/elongans), again forming seven bivalents at meiosis, are weak.[32]

Normal vigor and fertility in all these cases is associated with heterozygosity for a large block of genes, and is lost when these genes become homozygous. The heterozygous gene combination in a ring-forming Oenothera evidently has heterotic effects. By virtue of the peculiar genetic system of these plants, consisting of heterozygosity for successive translocations, balanced lethal genes and self-pollination, any particular heterozygous gene combination which is adaptively valuable can be reproduced exactly and multiplied indefinitely.

Permanent translocation heterozygotes occur in other sections of Oenothera, in other members of the family Onagraceae, as in the genera Clarkia and Gaura, and again in unrelated plant genera such as Rhoeo (Commelinaceae), Trillium (Liliaceae), Hypericum (Guttiferae), Datura (Solanaceae), and Paeonia (Paeoniaceae).[33] The case of *Paeonia californica* presents some especially interesting features and will be briefly described here.

Paeonia californica is a perennial herb which occurs in a sage scrub vegetation in the foothills and coastal plain of central and southern California. The plants reproduce sexually by seeds and are diploid with $2N = 10$ chromosomes. In 1939 Stebbins and Ellerton reported

---

[29] DeVries, 1917.

[30] Renner, 1941.

[31] *Ibid.*

[32] Oehlkers and Harte, 1943.

[33] See Stebbins (1950, 432 ff.) for brief review with references. Since 1950 a number of additional studies have appeared but it will have to suffice here to call attention to only a few of these. See Haga and Kurabayashi (1954) regarding structural heterozygosity in Trillium. Two recent interesting papers on translocations in populations of Clarkia have been published by Mooring (1958) and Snow (1960). The Datura story has been discussed recently by Wallace (1959) and Snow and Dunford (1961).

that six individuals from a locality in the northern part of the range of the species were all heterozygous for translocations, forming chromosome rings of various size at meiosis.[34]   Walters thereupon examined the meiotic configurations in numerous plants throughout the entire range of the species, finding that translocation and inversion heterozygotes are of widespread occurrence.[35]

In his valuable paper of 1942 Walters demonstrated that a diverse array of structurally homozygous and heterozygous types exists in *P. californica*. With respect to translocations, some individual plants regularly form five bivalents at meiosis, and are thus translocation homozygotes, while other plants exhibit single rings of 4, 6, 8, or 10 chromosomes, or combinations of two independent small rings.   In many parts of the distribution area of the species the ring-forming types outnumber the bivalent-forming individuals.   Thus in a sample of ten individuals from a local population near Pasadena (southern California), nine were translocation heterozygotes and one a translocation homozygote; and in a second colony in the same region ten randomly selected individuals were all translocation heterozygotes.[36] In another colony near Claremont to the east of Pasadena, 25 plants, representing nearly the entire population, were all heterozygous for two independent translocations, and no structural homozygotes at all could be found.[37]   The peonies throughout their distribution area are also heterozygous for paracentric or pericentric inversions in a high proportion of the individuals examined.[38]

It was at first assumed, on plausible indirect evidence, that *P. californica* is outcrossing.[39]   Taking this premise as a point of departure, I set out to observe several colonies near Claremont in the spring of 1952 in order to determine the identity of the agent of cross-pollination and hence the agent responsible for producing the structural heterozygotes.   Surprisingly, these peonies turned out to be habitually self-pollinating.   The plants bloom in the cool rainy weeks of early spring when few insects are on the wing, and the flowers observably receive few or no insect visitations.   The floral mechanism, on the other hand, brings about self-pollination, and this selfing leads to seed formation as shown by tests with bagged flowers and with caged plants.   The field

---

[34] Stebbins and Ellerton, 1939.

[35] Walters, 1942.

[36] *Ibid.*

[37] Grant, 1956*b*, and unpublished.

[38] Walters, 1942, 1952.

[39] Walters, 1942, 274. Stebbins, 1950, 433.

observations and caging tests were repeated in 1953 and 1954 with identical results.[40] Walters reached the same conclusion on the basis of observations and bagging tests in a different part of the distribution range.[41]

It will be recalled that a Claremont population of Paeonia, which is predominantly self-fertilizing, is composed exclusively of translocation heterozygotes. The effect of the breeding system in itself would be to change the constitution of the population from a high frequency of heterozygotes to a preponderance of homozygotes in a few sexual generations. The persistence of structural heterozygotes in the face of this strong tendency points to the operation of some force counteracting the effects of self-fertilization.

The maintenance of a high frequency of translocation heterozygotes in the populations, under conditions of self-fertilization, can be explained most readily by the hypothesis that the structurally homozygous segregates are wholly or largely eliminated by natural selection, whereas the heterozygous classes have a strong selective advantage.[42] The reproductive biology of *Paeonia californica* is such as to afford ample opportunity for a strong selective elimination in the seed and seedling stages. In the formation of a typical fruit only a few, frequently one to three, of the numerous seeds reach maturity, the others petering out at various stages of development. A further loss of zygotes occurs at the time of seed germination. Among the seedlings, again, there is a high rate of mortality.

It is not known whether the observed high elimination of seeds and seedlings in these peonies has a selective component or not. Attempts to verify experimentally the hypothesis that the elimination is selective have so far been unsuccessful due to technical difficulties in growing the plants. All that we can say at present is that the slow-breeding peonies, in their relatively stable scrub community, suffer a very high loss of zygotes between successive generations, and that these conditions are favorable for the operation of strong stabilizing selection. The translocation heterozygotes, if adaptively superior to the corresponding homozygous types in consequence of their heterozygous allele combinations, could be maintained at high frequencies in the populations by stabilizing selection alone.

---

[40] Grant, 1956*b*, 96.

[41] Walters, personal communication.

[42] This interpretation has been stated by Walters (1952, 150) with reference to heterozygous pericentric inversions in *Paeonia californica*, and by Grant (1956*b*, 97), following discussions with Drs. Walters and Stebbins, with reference to the heterozygous translocations.

DIFFERENCES BETWEEN SPECIES IN THE SEGMENTAL
ARRANGEMENT OF THE CHROMOSOMES

The meiotic behavior of parental species and their F_1 hybrids in numerous plant and animal groups indicates that related species frequently possess chromosome sets which differ with respect to homozygous translocations, inversions or other rearrangements. Several cytogenetically well-analyzed cases of chromosomal repatterning between species will be presented in the next two sections as a basis for a discussion of the significance of this phenomenon in the final part of this chapter.

The two lily species, *Lilium martagon album* and *L. hansonii,* both possess $2N = 24$ chromosomes which form 12 normal bivalents at meiosis. Two of the 12 chromosomes in the haploid complement of each species are large and have a submedian centromere with slightly unequal arms, while the other ten chromosomes are shorter and have a subterminal centromere with very unequal arms. The former are designated M_1, M_2, the latter $S_1 \cdots S_{10}$. In the interspecific hybrid the M and S chromosomes of *L. martagon* pair with their partial homologues from *L. hansonii* in configurations indicating that the parental species differ for several inversions.[43]

By an ingenious cytogenetic analysis of the hybrid Richardson was able to deduce the probable number, position, and size of the inversions. The inversion configurations were associated with the two M and four of the S chromosomes. Therefore, the two lily species differ by inversions on six of their chromosomes. Since the chromosomes resulting from crossing-over within the inversion had respectively two and no centromeres, rather than one centromere each, it could be concluded that the inversions are located in an arm outside the centromere, in other words, are paracentric. (See Fig. 36-2 and the accompanying discussion regarding the alternative types of crossover products from paracentric and pericentric inversions for a clarification of the reasoning involved in this point.) The absence of certain configurations expected from double crossing-over within an inversion (as in Fig. 36-3), furthermore, indicates that the inverted segments are probably relatively small in all cases.[44]

Which of the two chromosome arms carries the inversion, and the position of the inversion in an arm relative to the centromere, can be

---

[43] Richardson, 1936.
[44] *Ibid.*

inferred from still other cytologically observable features of the pairing configuration. On the basis of these features Richardson concluded that the six small paracentric inversions differentiating the two lily species are located in the following positions in their respective chromosomes: [45]

M_1 near distal end of short arm.
M_2 near centromere in long arm.
S_1 near distal end in short arm.
S_2 near distal end in long arm.
S_3 near centromere in long arm.
S_4 near centromere in long arm.

The closely related species, *Nicotiana alata*, *N. langsdorffii*, and *N. bonariensis*, possess nine pairs of chromosomes each. The chromosomes comprising the complements can be distinguished by size, position of the centromere, and other morphological features. As shown in Fig. 42, the A chromosomes are long with median centromeres; the B chromosomes long with subterminal centromeres and satellites; the C chromosomes are like the B's but without satellite; the D chromosomes short with subterminal centromeres; and the E chromosomes are short with median centromeres.[46]

In the three possible hybrids between the three Nicotiana species, as analyzed cytogenetically by Avery, the mode of pairing between particular chromosomes belonging to the parental complements indicates that the species differ by successive translocations.[47]

The F_1 hybrid of *N. alata* × *N. langsdorffii* exhibits at meiosis six bivalents, a chain of five chromosomes, and a single unpaired chromosome. The chain is composed of the following chromosomes: $D_{alata}–A_{lang}–A_{alata}–B_{lang}–B_{alata}$. The unpaired chromosome is the D_{lang} which could presumably pair with the two ends of the chain to complete a ring of six chromosomes. (See Fig. 42.) The differentiation of the chromosome sets of *N. alata* and *N. langsdorffii* thus involves two successive translocations between the A, B, and D chromosomes in one or the other of these species.

If the chromosome arm arrangement of *N. alata* is taken as standard, and numbered consecutively from 1 to 18 as shown in Fig. 42 and Table 13, the chain-forming A, B, and D chromosomes of *N. alata* will be 1-2, 5-6, and 11-12 respectively. Then the *langsdorffii* A, B, and D

---

[45] *Ibid.*
[46] Avery, 1938.
[47] *Ibid.*

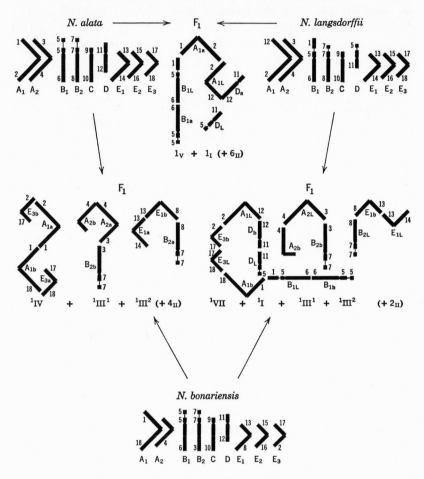

FIG. 42. The chromosomes of three species of Nicotiana and their hybrids. The form of the nine chromosomes comprising the haploid set of each species is shown diagrammatically, and the individual chromosomes are designated by letters and numerical subscripts. The arm arrangement of the nine chromosomes in *Nicotiana alata* is taken as standard and numbered accordingly. The pairing configurations of the structurally differentiated chromosomes in the F_1 hybrids are shown for each hybrid combination. The parental source of a given chromosome in the hybrids is identified by a letter subscript (a, b, or L). The arm arrangements in the two non-standard parental species, *Nicotiana langsdorffii* and *N. bonariensis*, as inferred from the pairing configurations in their hybrids with *N. alata* and with one another, are as indicated. (Avery, 1938.)

TABLE 13 END ARRANGEMENTS OF THE CHROMOSOMES
OF THREE SPECIES IN THE Nicotiana alata GROUP *

	A_1	A_2	B_1	B_2	C	D	E_1	E_2	E_3
N. alata	1–2	3–4	5–6	7–8	9–10	11–12	13–14	15–16	17–18
N. langsdorffii	12–2	3–4	1–6	7–8	9–10	11–5	13–14	15–16	17–18
N. bonariensis	1–18	14–4	5–6	7–3	9–10	11–12	13–8	15–16	17–2

* From Avery, 1938, with minor simplifications; see also Fig. 42.

chromosomes which pair with them in the chain must have the end arrangements 12-2, 1-6, and 5-11 respectively. (See Fig. 42.) The change from the *alata* to the *langsdorffii* arrangement could have taken place in two successive steps as follows: [48]

	A_1	B_1	D
N. alata	1–2	5–6	11–12
↓			
intermediate	5–2	1–6	11–12
↓			
N. langsdorffii	12–2	1–6	11–5

The formation of one chain of four chromosomes and two chains of three chromosomes in the hybrid of N. *alata* × *bonariensis*, representing a potential ring of four and ring of six respectively, indicates that these species differ by successive translocations on five chromosomes. The arm arrangement of N. *bonariensis* relative to the standard arrangement in N. *alata* is, therefore, as shown in Fig. 42 and Table 13.

If N. *langsdorffii* differs from N. *alata* by two successive translocations involving (among others) the A_1 chromosome, and if N. *bonariensis* differs from N. *alata* by two successive translocations one of which also involves the A_1 chromosome, and by a third independent translocation, then N. *langsdorffii* and N. *bonariensis* should differ by five rearrangements. The maximum association possible between their chromosomes in the hybrid should be a ring of eight, a ring of four, and two bivalents. Although a ring of eight was not actu-

[48] *Ibid.*

ally seen, a chain of seven and an unpaired chromosome, representing an approach to the predicted maximum association, were formed in the hybrid, and the expected chain of four and two bivalents were also formed [49] (Fig. 42).

The three interrelated species of the *Nicotiana alata* group, in diverging from their common ancestor, have come to differ, therefore, not only in their genes affecting flower size and other characters, as mentioned in Chapter 7, but also in the arm arrangement of seven of the nine chromosomes.[50]

A third well-analyzed case of two closely related species, *Drosophila pseudoobscura* and *D. miranda* ($N = 5$), which differ in chromosome structure is summarized diagrammatically in Fig. 43. The diagram shows that the chromosomes of the two species differ by inversions, translocations, and undefined rearrangements in a large portion of the chromosomal material.[51]

DIFFERENCES BETWEEN SPECIES IN THE
NUMBER AND SEGMENTAL ARRANGEMENT
OF THE CHROMOSOMES

Related species of diploid organisms frequently differ in chromosome number as well as in chromosome structure. If the ancestral condition preserved in one species is $2N = 12$ chromosomes, the derived condition found in a related species may be either $2N = 14$ or $2N = 10$.

Decreases in the basic chromosome number are initiated by unequal reciprocal translocations. If chromosome I and chromosome II exchange segments of very unequal length, all of the genetically active material previously on chromosome I may become translocated onto chromosome II, while the latter delivers in exchange a small inert segment to chromosome I. Chromosome I can then be lost eventually in some nuclear division and thereafter disappear from the complement without a corresponding loss of genes—and thus without detrimental effects to the organism. In this way the chromosome number may be reduced by one pair (as from $2N = 12$ to $2N = 10$).[52]

---

[49] *Ibid.*

[50] *Ibid.*

[51] Dobzhansky, 1951, 240–242.

[52] The mechanism of chromosome number reduction is explained more fully by Stebbins (1950, Chapter 12), and Swanson (1957, Chapter 13).

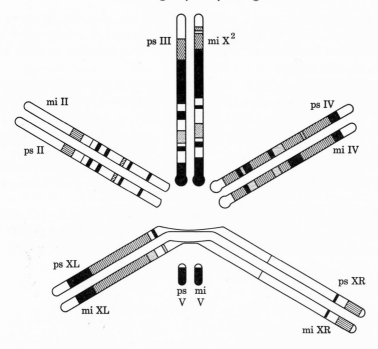

FIG. 43. Comparison of the gene arrangements in five chromosomes of two closely related species of Drosophila, *D. pseudoobscura* and *D. miranda*. The chromosomes of *D. pseudoobscura* are labelled ps; the partially homologous chromosomes of *D. miranda*, mi. The five chromosomes comprising the haploid complement of each species (II, III, IV, V, X), and the two arms of the X chromosomes (XL and XR), are shown side by side. Sections of these chromosomes having the same gene arrangement in the two species are white. In the non-white regions the two species are differentiated with respect to inversions (cross-hatched), translocations (stippled), or undetermined rearrangements (black). (From *Genetics and the Origin of Species,* by Dobzhansky, after Dobzhansky and Tan, copyright 1951, Columbia University Press, New York.)

Crepis neglecta and *C. fuliginosa* differ in the number as well as the form of the chromosomes. As shown in Fig. 44*a* and *b*, *C. neglecta* possesses four pairs of chromosomes, while *C. fuliginosa*, which is derived phylogenetically from an ancestor close to *C. neglecta*, has only three pairs. The chromosomes comprising the complements of each species are few enough in number and distinct enough in form to be recognizable individually in either somatic or meiotic cells and in either parental or hybrid individuals (Fig. 44). By careful cytological study, Togby was able to demonstrate that two of the chromosomes in

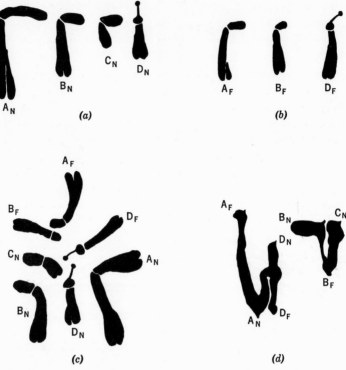

FIG. 44. Chromosomes of two species of Crepis and their hybrid. (*a*) *Crepis neglecta,* haploid set as seen in a somatic cell. (*b*) *Crepis fuliginosa,* haploid set of somatic chromosomes. (*c*) F_1 hybrid, diploid set of somatic chromosomes. (*d*) F_1 hybrid, chromosomes paired at metaphase I of meiosis. (Tobgy, 1943.)

the haploid set of *C. neglecta* (B and C) are represented by only one chromosome (B) in *C. fuliginosa,* the C chromosome being absent from the complement of the latter species.[53] (Fig. 44*b*.)

Not all of the chromosomal material of C is lacking in *Crepis fuliginosa* however. At meiosis in the F_1 hybrid, the B and C chromosomes of *C. neglecta* pair with the B of *C. fuliginosa* in such a way as to indicate that these chromosomes differ with respect to an unequal reciprocal translocation. As Tobgy states: [54]

Phylogenetically the B_N and C_N may be assumed to have given rise to the B_F through a reciprocal translocation between the distal segment of the long arm

[53] Tobgy, 1943.
[54] *Ibid.,* 107.

of the B_N and one arm of the C_N. Of the two chromosomes resulting from this translocation, the one with the C_N centromere is genetically inactive and is lost, while the other with the B_N centromere corresponds to the B chromosome of *C. fuliginosa*.

The B chromosome of *C. fuliginosa*, in other words, is homologous with the B of *C. neglecta* throughout most of its length, but has in addition, on the end of its long arm, a segment that occurs on the C chromosome in *C. neglecta*. Consequently, one part of the B_F pairs with the B_N and another part with the C_N at meiosis in the F_1 hybrid (Fig. 44d).

Other pairing configurations in this hybrid indicate that the parental species are differentiated in respect to several other chromosomal rearrangements. The A and D chromosomes of *C. fuliginosa* differ from the comparable chromosomes of *C. neglecta* by one unequal reciprocal translocation (Fig. 44d). And the long arms of the A, B, and D chromosomes in *C. fuliginosa* carry segments that are inverted relative to the homologous regions in *C. neglecta*.[55]

In the genus Drosophila the ancestral haploid number is believed to be $N = 6$. Many homologous genes are known in different species of Drosophila as a result of mutation studies. It is further found that these homologous genes in many cases cohere in linkage groups which persist in species after species. In the more primitive members of the genus, such as *Drosophila virilis*, six such groups of linked genes occur on six separate chromosomes in the haploid set. In various derived species, essentially the same linkage groups are condensed onto five, four, or three chromosomes. Thus the gene groups which occur on chromosomes IV and V in *D. virilis* are borne on the left and right arms respectively of chromosome II in *D. melanogaster*. Again, the linkage groups associated with chromosomes II and III in *D. virilis* occur on opposite arms of the same chromosome III in *D. melanogaster*.[56]

Since the chromosomes of *D. virilis* are rod-like with subterminal centromeres, while chromosomes II and III of *D. melanogaster* are both **V**-shaped, with two long arms attached to a median centromere in each case, the cytological evidence agrees with the genetic evidence in pointing to a special type of whole arm translocation (called centric fusions) as responsible for the observed changes. Two independent translocations or centric fusions of this sort, one between the

---

[55] *Ibid.*
[56] Sturtevant and Novitski, 1941. Patterson and Stone, 1952, 161.

original chromosomes IV and V (in *D. virilis*) to produce one of the derived chromosomes of *D. melanogaster*, and the other involving the original chromosomes II and III to produce the other derived chromosome, would be sufficient to reduce the haploid chromosome number from the ancestral $N = 6$ to the derivative condition of $N = 4$ as found in *D. melanogaster*.[57]

Increases in the basic chromosome number by increments of one in diploid organisms (as from $2N = 12$ to $2N = 14$) may take place in various ways. The duplication of a whole chromosome or at least of a centromere-containing fragment of a chromosome is usually involved, and translocations are frequently involved, in the change to a higher basic number.

The centromere, a compound structure, may rarely divide crosswise instead of in the longitudinal plane, so that two half-centromeres arise each of which retains the ability to move to a spindle pole during nuclear division. If this misdivision of the centromere occurs in a V-shaped chromosome with a median centromere, two I-shaped or rod chromosomes with subterminal centromeres will be formed. Most of the species of Fritillaria, as well as the related genus Lilium, have 12 pairs of chromosomes, including 10 I + 2 V chromosomes, and this number and arrangement are presumably ancestral. But one species, *Fritillaria pudica*, has 13 chromosome pairs, consisting of 12 I + 1 V chromosome. It is likely, as Darlington has suggested, that the phylogenetic increase in basic number in this case is a consequence of the replacement of 1 V chromosome in the ancestral complement by 2 I chromosomes in the derived set of *F. pudica*.[58]

Or, to consider another mechanism of chromosome number increase, an extra chromosome may be added to the complement as a result of some irregularity in nuclear division. The extra centromere thus furnished may then accumulate new chromosomal material from other members of the complement by translocations. In this way the genes previously borne by N centromeres now become attached to $N + 1$ centromeres.[59]

The ancestral chromosome number in the genus Clarkia, as in the related and more primitive genus Oenothera, is $2N = 14$. There are some morphologically and ecologically advanced, diploid species of Clarkia with 8 and 9 chromosome pairs. Lewis and Roberts made a

---

[57] Patterson and Stone, 1952, Chapter 4.
[58] Darlington, 1932, 80; 1956, 95; 1948, 91.
[59] Darlington, 1937, 559–560.

detailed study of a closely related pair of species, *Clarkia biloba* ($N =$ 8) and *C. lingulata* ($N = 9$). *C. lingulata* is believed on good circumstantial evidence to be derived from *C. biloba*. The pairing behavior of the chromosomes in the interspecific hybrid shows that the chromosome sets of the two species are generally homologous in segmental arrangement, although they differ by one inversion and two independent translocations.[60]

The ninth chromosome of *C. lingulata* forms a chain of five chromosomes with two *biloba* chromosomes and two other members of the *lingulata* complement at meiosis in the hybrid. The extra *lingulata* chromosome is apparently the middle member of the chain, being paired in one arm with one *biloba* chromosome and in another arm with another *biloba* chromosome. This configuration indicates that the ninth chromosome of *C. lingulata* differs from two of the *C. biloba* chromosomes by a translocation.[61]

Evidently in the origin of the ninth chromosome, two *biloba* chromosomes with the end arrangement 1-2 and 3-4 exchanged arms to produce a new chromosome (1-4). Both the original and the translocation chromosomes then became established in the homozygous condition in the ancestor of *C. lingulata*. The latter with the diploid constitution $\dfrac{1\text{-}2 \quad 3\text{-}4 \quad 1\text{-}4}{1\text{-}2 \quad 3\text{-}4 \quad 1\text{-}4}$ consequently possesses one more chromosome pair than *C. biloba*.[62]

Related species in many plant genera differ in the segmental arrangement of their chromosomes. Interspecific differences in chromosome structure are common in herbaceous plants, and particularly in annuals, which grow in open habitats or weedy places, as exemplified by such genera as Brassica, Clarkia, Crepis, Elymus, Galeopsis, Gossypium, Gilia, Layia, Madia, and Nicotiana. Related species of long-lived plants inhabiting closed communities, on the other hand, do not differ greatly (and frequently do not differ detectably at all) in chromosome structure. The segmental arrangement of the chromosomes is similar in such genera of perennial herbaceous plants as Aquilegia, Delphinium, and Iris, and in woody genera like Ceanothus, Quercus, and Pinus.[63]

---

[60] Lewis and Roberts, 1956.
[61] *Ibid.*
[62] *Ibid.*
[63] Stebbins, 1950, 234–236; 1958a, 186–188. Grant, 1956b; 1958, 352–355. References to the original papers on the various plant genera mentioned here are given by Stebbins and Grant.

CHROMOSOME NUMBER REDUCTION AND LINKAGE

As noted in Chapter 7, the reduction of the basic chromosome number greatly increases the amount of linkage between genes. Those rearrangements, particularly unequal reciprocal translocations, which lead to a decrease in the basic chromosome number as between ancestral and descendant species, therefore, must bring about important changes in the intensity of gene linkages.

In the preceding section we examined the derivation of $N = 3$ in *Crepis fuliginosa* from $N = 4$ in an ancestor close to the existing *Crepis neglecta* by means of unequal translocations and loss of an inert centromere. This process of chromosome number reduction may continue step by step from a high basic number in a more remote ancestral species to a considerably lower number in the ultimate derived species. The phylogenetic reduction from $N = 4$ to $N = 3$ in the *Crepis neglecta-fuliginosa* group is a part of a larger trend within the genus Crepis and the tribe Cichorieae (Compositae) to which it belongs. The original basic number in the tribe Cichorieae is probably $N = 9$, as is found today in many of the most primitive genera. From this condition phylogenetic decreases in chromosome number have taken place repeatedly in the different generic lines: in Youngia, for instance, from $N = 8$ to $N = 5$, and in Crepis from $N = 6$ to $N = 3$.[64]

Now the primitive species of Cichorieae with high basic chromosome numbers are perennial herbs occurring in relatively stable meadow and forest habitats. The populations of these long-lived plants contain a great deal of stored variability, which is released by recombination generation after generation, but kept within the limits of adaptive fitness by stabilizing selection. The advanced species with low chromosome numbers, on the other hand, are annuals of open habitats which produce more uniform progeny. An adaptive allele combination is held together in the annual species by linkage and other components of the genetic system.[65]

In several other plant groups high basic chromosome numbers are known to be associated with a perennial habit and relatively free gene recombination; while, conversely, low chromosome numbers are correlated with an annual habit, occupation of open habitats, and a genetic system promoting uniformity in reproduction. A trend from the one combination of features to the other contrasting combination

---

[64] Babcock, Stebbins, and Jenkins, 1937.   Stebbins, 1950, 447–458.   Stebbins, Jenkins, and Walters, 1953.
[65] Stebbins, 1950, 449; 1958*b*.

is found, for example, in Eriophyllum and allied genera (Compositae), where the basic numbers range from $N = 8$ in perennial species to $N = 3$ in some annuals.[66] A parallel trend occurs in Phacelia sect. Phacelia (Hydrophyllaceae) from $N = 11$ in the perennial herbaceous *P. magellanica* group to $N = 9$, 8, and 7 in some annual species.[67] The same trend is found again in the Polemonium tribe of the Polemoniaceae from $N = 9$ in the perennial herbaceous genus Polemonium to $N = 7$ and 6 in two highly reduced annual groups, Microsteris and Gymnosteris.[68]

The trends towards a reduced chromosome number in the annual members of these and other plant groups are probably best explained, as Stebbins has suggested, by selection for increased gene linkage, and hence for greater uniformity in reproduction, in pioneering annuals of open habitats, which, having a well-adapted genotype, must replicate that genotype and build up a population of equally well-adapted individuals in a relatively short time.[69]

THE SIGNIFICANCE OF CHROMOSOME
REPATTERNING IN SPECIATION

The taxogenetic evidence available for many plant genera indicates that the chromosomes remain similar in segmental arrangement during speciation in some plant groups but undergo structural rearrangements during speciation in others. What is the significance of these facts? What is the primary role played by chromosomal repatterning in the life of the species concerned? In the preceding section we have dealt with the case of species differing in both segmental arrangement and basic chromosome number. Here we will attempt to analyze the case, even more difficult to explain in terms of linkage, of species which possess different segmental arrangements but the same chromosome number. We will consider three possible explanations.

The first function of species-specific chromosome patterns to be considered here is hybrid sterility. It is well known that chromosome structural differences between species lead to irregular chromosome behavior at meiosis in the hybrids and hence to the formation of inviable gametes.[70] Now the sterility of hybrids is certainly an im-

[66] Carlquist, 1956.

[67] Cave and Constance, 1947.

[68] Grant, 1956b; 1959, 187–188.

[69] Stebbins, 1950, 177, 458.

[70] For reviews see Stebbins (1950, Chapter 6), and Dobzhansky (1951, Chapter 8).

portant feature in the life histories of those species which are potentially capable of hybridizing or actually hybridize. But the sterility barrier resulting from structural differentiation of the chromosomes in the parental species, important and real though it may be, is probably to be regarded as a secondary effect or by-product of the segmental rearrangements, and not as their primary or original function.[71]

Hybrid sterility, whether chromosomal or otherwise, is from theoretical considerations a by-product of evolutionary divergence wherever it occurs.[72] The problem before us concerns species which are intersterile as a result of having already diverged in chromosome structure. And our task is to search for an explanation of the function performed by the chromosomal rearrangements in the course of divergence culminating in chromosomally differentiated and hence intersterile species.

The second hypothesis to consider is that a particular segmental arrangement of the chromosomes affects the phenotypic characteristics of its carriers directly by means of its pattern effect, as discussed in Chapter 8. According to this hypothesis as advocated by Goldschmidt especially, the chromosome pattern in each species produces a pattern effect, which in turn brings about physiological and morphological characteristics adapting that species to its particular place in nature. And as the morphological and physiological characteristics differ from species to species, so do the segmental arrangements of the chromosomes.[73]

The hypothesis of direct pattern effects is probably true to a considerable extent. In Chapter 8 we examined a concrete case in *Drosophila robusta*. Among others, I have espoused the hypothesis of pattern effects more or less as stated in the foregoing paragraph [74] without following Goldschmidt on various other questions related thereto. Lewis and Raven, in a most stimulating discussion of the possible origin of chromosome pattern differences in Clarkia as a result of gene-induced chromosomal mutations,[75] do not elaborate on the probable genetic function of the rearrangements, but evidently consider that the rearrangements function through their pattern effects.[76]

The hypothesis of direct pattern effects, however, while providing

[71] Grant, 1956b, 102–103.
[72] Grant, 1963, 439–441, 504.
[73] Goldschmidt, 1940.
[74] Grant, 1956b, 101, 104.
[75] Lewis and Raven, 1958. Lewis, 1962.
[76] Lewis and Raven, 1958, 333.

a partial explanation of the function of chromosomal rearrangements in species biology, leaves some important groups of facts unexplained. Chromosomal rearrangements are not always accompanied by position effects, as we saw in Chapter 6. In plants particularly, chromosomal rearrangements have been investigated in numerous cases, whereas position effects have been found only very rarely. Furthermore, as noted in an earlier section of this chapter, structural differentiation of the chromosomes is not closely correlated with the development of different phenotypic traits when a large sample of plant groups is considered. Widely distant species of Quercus or Delphinium or Aquilegia with very different morphological and ecological characteristics, for example, may possess structurally homologous chromosomes; while closely related species of Gilia or Clarkia which differ with respect to numerous chromosomal rearrangements may be rather similar in morphology and ecology. It is necessary, therefore, to consider other possible genetic functions of species-specific chromosome patterns.

The third possibility is that chromosomal repatterning is a means of linking together an adaptive gene combination. It will be recalled from earlier discussions in this chapter that a particular combination of alleles of genes that are not related in their primary gene actions, or in other words, the alleles of genes that do not belong to one and the same functional gene system, may produce adaptively valuable phenotypic effects. We saw further that, given such an adaptive allele combination, a mechanism for holding it together as a block in inheritance will also be advantageous and will be favored by selection. Finally, we know that inversions and translocations in heterozygous condition are such agents of block inheritance, for they can link together the genes on or near the rearranged segments, and do actually function in the linkage of adaptive gene combinations in various cases of natural-occurring structural hybrids. We are led by all these considerations to inquire whether the differentiation of species in respect to homozygous chromosomal rearrangements may not also be related to the linkage of adaptive gene combinations.[77]

But now we come up against certain theoretical difficulties which rule out any simple extrapolation from the premise of gene linkage in structural heterozygotes to the deduction of a similar function in structural homozygotes. The first difficulty is that the conditions under which chromosomal rearrangements can operate as vehicles

---

[77] As suggested and considered probable by Darlington (1936, 1940), Darlington, and Mather (1949, 322–323), and Stebbins (1950, 244–247).

of gene linkage in a structural heterozygote cease to exist in its structurally homozygous segregates. The second difficulty is that the adaptive value of the structural heterozygote depends upon an associated genic heterozygosity, which is lost in the structurally homozygous segregates. Thirdly, related species with different structurally homozygous chromosome sets are in fact frequently heterozygous for many of the genes borne on these chromosomes. The hypothesis that species-specific chromosome patterns serve an adaptively valuable function of gene linkage must account satisfactorily for these difficulties.

The foregoing difficulties place several restrictive conditions on the hypothesis that species-specific chromosome patterns function as agents of gene linkage. We will next proceed to examine these conditions.

Let us consider the first difficulty mentioned above. If the different structurally homozygous chromosome patterns found in related species are concerned with the linkage of gene combinations, but do not exercise that function of linkage under normal existing conditions of intraspecific crossing, then they must do so under exceptional conditions, existing or pre-existing.

Natural hybridization between chromosomally differentiated species is an existing situation which can lead to the appearance of structural heterozygotes, in the progeny of which gene recombination will be strongly restricted by the sheltering effect of heterozygous rearrangements.[78] This situation and this effect are real enough. But as with the associated phenomenon of hybrid sterility, discussed earlier in this section, the linkage function of heterozygous rearrangements in hybrids between species which have already diverged chromosomally is to be considered as a by-product of their divergence and not as an explanation of the original function of the chromosomal divergence.

The only other possibility is that the differences in chromosome pattern between the species performed their function of linkage under previous conditions when the species originated. Those previous conditions, moreover, must have included the presence of alternative segmental arrangements associated with alternative allele combinations in a variable or polymorphic ancestral population.[79]

The difficulty of ascribing a function of linkage to structural arrangements which, though differing as between species, are constant and homozygous within each

---

[78] Grant, 1956*b*, 92, 103.
[79] *Loc. cit.*

species may . . . be resolved by the hypothesis that the structural changes are related to former rather than to present conditions of the population. The existing genomes, being established in the homozygous state within each species, do not prevent gene recombination during regular cross-breeding in the population. Their existence may represent instead [a] vestige from a previous period in the history of the species when the formation of structural heterozygotes was commonplace.[80]

Species with segmentally dissimilar but structurally homozygous chromosome sets, by this reasoning, must have been born in a chromosomally polymorphic population; and the specific chromosome pattern which no longer locks up an adaptive gene combination in intraspecific crossings, but persists as a remnant from an earlier period of species formation in the ancestral chromosomally polymorphic population when it did perform a function of linkage, can thus be regarded as "the umbilical cord of the species." [81]

The requisite chromosomal and genic polymorphism may be present in the ancestral population as a result of a gradual build-up during many previous generations. Populations of Drosophila and of various plant species the world over exemplify a state of permanent chromosomal polymorphism which, under certain conditions, could serve as a starting point for the formation of new species.[82] Or the chromosomal polymorphism may arise suddenly and sporadically from interspecific hybridization, as is known to occur in many plant groups.[83] The chromosomal polymorphism, whether permanent in a balanced polymorphic population or transitory in a hybrid swarm, acts to preserve alternative allele combinations intact within the population where they can segregate out in any generation as new chromosomal and genic homozygotes. The allele combination in any new structural homozygote is then protected by its particular segmental arrangement from disintegration as a result of outcrossing with other individuals in the population. It is thus protected from the very beginning and is afforded a chance to multiply as an intact unit.[84]

In order to discuss the second and third difficulties mentioned in an earlier paragraph, we will consider separately and in turn two somewhat different models. The first model to be considered concerns

---

[80] Grant, 1956*b*, 92. Reprinted with the permission of Academic Press, Inc., New York.
[81] *Ibid.*, 103.
[82] Darlington, 1936. Darlington and Mather, 1949, 322–323. Wright, 1949, 385. Stebbins, 1950, 246–247. Mayr, 1954. Carson, 1959. White, 1959.
[83] Grant, 1956*b*, 92–93, in this particular context.
[84] *Ibid.*, 93.

the divergence of a new structurally homozygous species from a chromosomally polymorphic ancestral population.

In a previous section of this chapter we assumed that a heterozygous allele combination Aa Bb Cc produces phenotypic effects of superior adaptive value. On the basis of this assumption we saw further that the location of the genes **A**, **B**, and **C** on a heterozygous inversion or translocation, by linking the alternative alleles in blocks, would also be selectively advantageous. But crossing-over between the genes **A**, **B**, and **C** is not suppressed mechanically in the structural homozygotes. And furthermore, the structurally homozygous segregates will have the genic constitution AA BB CC or aa bb cc, which is not adaptively superior by our stated assumptions. How, then, can a structural and genic heterozygote $\dfrac{A \quad B \quad C}{a \quad b \quad c}$ be used as a model to explain the occurrence of different structurally homozygous chromosome arrangements in related species with the same chromosome number? The difficulty is great enough if the structurally homozygous species are also genically homozygous (AA BB CC and aa bb cc); it is even greater if, as is commonly the case, the species are structurally homozygous but genically heterozygous (Aa bb Cc, Aa Bb cc, etc.).

It is necessary, in the first place, to postulate a change in the relative adaptive values of different gene combinations such as to favor a homozygous type over the ancestral heterozygotes under the conditions that permit the divergence and multiplication of the new species. In terms of our hypothetical model, the homozygous allele combination aa bb cc which was inferior to Aa Bb Cc in the permanently polymorphic ancestral species, or else the latter would have been replaced, must be assumed to acquire a high adaptive value in some new environment which is successfully occupied by the derivative species aa bb cc. It is of course a well-established principle that the adaptive value of any gene combination is a function of the environment, from which it follows that aa bb cc might well be inferior under one set of conditions but superior under others.

By the same process, under different environmental conditions, other structural and genic homozygotes such as AA BB CC, differing structurally as well as genically from aa bb cc, could segregate out of the same polymorphic ancestral population, giving rise to a diversity of chromosomally differentiated species.

To account for the fact that related species possessing different homozygous chromosome patterns are frequently heterozygous genically, we must postulate that since their origin as structural and genic homozygotes, and probably during their later period of expansion, these species have accumulated many new alleles by mutation and/or gene flow from other species, and have stored the new variability in a derived state of heterozygosity. This necessary postulation is not improbable. On the basis of other evidence, and independently of the line of reasoning presented here, several students have suggested that speciation may occur as a cyclical process in many cases, with new species beginning as homozygous segregates from a polymorphic ancestral population, becoming polymorphic themselves in the course of time, and then giving rise in their turn to new homozygous off-shoots.[85]

Our second model concerns the divergence of a new species from a hybrid swarm. The ancestral species are assumed to differ with respect to homozygous chromosomal rearrangements and a combination of genes located on the rearranged segments.[86]

Let one parental species have the genic constitution AA BB CC and the other aa bb cc. (Genic homozygosity is not necessary so long as the species possess different alleles but is assumed here for the sake of simplicity in discussion.) And let the genes **A** and **B** be associated with one homozygous structural rearrangement, say a translocation, differentiating the two species, and the gene **C** be associated with another independent rearrangement. The structural and genic hybrid ABC/abc will now segregate four structurally homozygous classes of progeny. Two of these are the parental types which do not interest us further here. There are, in addition, two homozygous recombination types (AA BB cc, aa bb CC) which differ structurally and genically from either parental species and from one another.

Either recombination type, aa bb CC for instance, can breed true within the line, but will form structural heterozygotes on backcrossing to F_1's or outcrossing to other F_2 types within the hybrid swarm. The effect of heterozygous rearrangements on gene linkage will come into play in these later generation hybrids and cause them to reconstitute once more the allele combination aa bb CC in their fertile progeny.

If the new allele combination has a high adaptive value, it can multiply, first within the hybrid swarm, and later in a larger area of its own. In its later stage of expansion and maturity it may, like an

---

[85] Mayr, 1954. Carson, 1959. White, 1959. Grant, 1963, 456–459, 550 ff.
[86] For a more complete statement with references of the following hypothesis, which has been worked out successively and in stages by Müntzing, Gerassimova, Stebbins, and myself, see Grant, 1963, 469–481.

originally genically homozygous species derived from a permanently polymorphic population, come to acquire new genic heterozygosity on its structurally homozygous chromosomes.

The hypothesis that chromosome pattern differences between species are related to linkage of adaptive gene combinations in the stage of species formation is supported by a comparison of the types of plants which exhibit interspecific chromosomal differences with those which do not. It was pointed out previously that chromosome pattern differences are characteristically absent between related species of oaks, pines, columbines, Iris, etc., in contrast with genera like Clarkia, Gilia, and Nicotiana in which such differences are characteristically present between species. It can be safely assumed that related species differ in adaptive properties determined by different allele combinations in both long-lived plants and in annuals. But the mode of fixation and stabilization of new adaptive allele combinations, and the requirements for linkage of such gene combinations, appear to differ in the two life-form classes of plants.

The adaptive fitness of woody or perennial herbaceous plants is maintained, in the first place, by their long life as individuals. A well-adapted genotype, once formed, may persist at least for many years and perhaps for many centuries. Given the power of vegetative reproduction, which is widespread in trees, shrubs, and perennial herbs, the carrier of a particular adaptive allele combination can, moreover, multiply its numbers and spread over a territory of considerable size.[87]

Those long-lived woody or herbaceous plants which occur as dominant or subdominant members of more or less stable temperate forest or woodland communities produce, by outcrossing and recombination, an excessive number of genetically different zygotes year after year, the vast majority of which are eliminated in the seed or seedling stage. This process of elimination has a selective component. The selective elimination of the less fit genotypes in each generation is, then, a further means by which an adaptive allele combination is maintained in many perennial plants.[88]

The continual process of stabilizing selection favors different gene combinations in the environments prevailing in different geographical areas. Consequently the population systems of many dominant or subdominant perennial plants, such as oaks, pines, Irises and others, exhibit much geographical variation in their morphological and ecological characteristics. Hybridization between genetically well-dif-

---

[87] Wright, 1949, 381. Stebbins, 1950, 184–186.
[88] Grant, 1958, 349–350.

ferentiated races or species at some point of contact leads occasionally to the formation of an array of new gene combinations. If an environment exists which is favorable for the establishment of some of the hybrid derivatives, the genetic variability becomes stabilized again in time by environmental selection. Allele combinations, in short, are formed and reformed by the sexual process, and are held together in any given area not so much by linkage as by stabilizing selection.[89]

Gene linkage may, indeed, be loosened up in such plants in favor of the ability to produce an increased number of recombination types. In a sample of nearly 12,000 species of Dicotyledons for which chromosome numbers are known,[90] the most common basic numbers in the subsample of herbaceous species, both annual and perennial, proved to be $N = 7$, 8, or 9, whereas the modal basic numbers in the subsample of woody Dicotyledons fall in the range $N = 11$ to $N = 14$.[91] Although it was not feasible in this survey to determine the modal chromosome numbers separately for annual herbs and for perennial herbs, we know from other evidence as noted in the preceding section, that evolutionary trends in chromosome number within a herbaceous group frequently run from high-number perennials to low-number annuals. What is of most interest to us here, however, is the indication that woody Dicotyledons as a whole tend to have higher diploid chromosome numbers, and hence less gene linkage, than herbaceous plants.

The demands on the reproductive system of annual plants are quite different from those facing long-lived perennials. A well-adapted genotype in an annual herb is dependent wholly on its seedling progeny to perpetuate it from one year to the next. This factor in itself favors the development of a genetic system enabling the plant to breed relatively true to type.

Furthermore, among annual herbs which colonize weedy places or open natural habitats in Mediterranean or desert regions, the colonizing individuals, on reaching and becoming established in a new unoccupied habitat for which they are adapted, must build up a population of equally well-adapted individuals as quickly as possible. The allele combination on which the adaptive fitness for the new habitat is based may exist already in the colonizing individuals; or it may arise de novo by hybridization and recombination between pre-

---

[89] *Loc. cit.*

[90] Darlington and Janaki-Ammal, 1945. Darlington and Wylie, 1955.

[91] Grant (1958, 339–340; 1963, 483–486), confirming an earlier survey by Stebbins (1938).

existing genotypes.   In either case, if the population is to take the best advantage of its ecological opportunities, any given allele combination of high adaptive value, once formed, must be capable of rapid and true replication by the genetic system without the wastage of zygotes which accompanies a selective elimination of poorly adapted recombination types.[92]

The function of preserving and multiplying a favorable allele combination is not left to stabilizing selection in the case of pioneering annual plants, but is carried out by the genetic system including, no doubt, the linkage system.   And such plants, significantly, are commonly and generally differentiated into species on the basis of chromosomal rearrangements that could have performed a function of linkage during speciation.

On the hypothesis of direct pattern effects it is not evident why related species should possess different chromosome segmental arrangements in some plant groups but not in others.   The observed differences between plant genera in the distribution of chromosomal rearrangements can, on the other hand, be explained on the hypothesis of linkage of adaptive gene combinations.

---

[92] Stebbins, 1950, 177.   Grant, 1958, 350–351.

Bibliography

Adams, M. W. and D. B. Shank. 1959. The relationship of heterozygosity to homeostasis in maize hybrids. *Genetics*, **44**:777–786.

Allard, R. W. 1960. *Principles of Plant Breeding.* New York and London.

Allfrey, V. G. and A. E. Mirsky. 1961. How cells make molecules. *Scientific American,* September 1961.

Allison, A. C. 1956. Sickle cells and evolution. *Scientific American,* February 1956.

Anderson, E. 1939a. The hindrance to gene recombination imposed by linkage: an estimate of its total magnitude. *Amer. Nat.,* **73**:185–188.

———. 1939b. Recombination in species crosses. *Genetics,* **24**:668–698.

———. 1949. *Introgressive Hybridization.* New York.

Anderson, E. G. 1935. Chromosomal interchanges in maize. *Genetics,* **20**:70–83.

Avery, O. T., C. M. Macleod, and M. McCarty. 1944. Studies on the chemical nature of the substance inducing transformation of Pneumococcal types. *Jour. Expt. Medicine,* **79**:137–158.

Avery, P. 1938. Cytogenetic evidences of Nicotiana phylesis in the *alata*-group. *Univ. Calif. Publ. Bot.,* **18**:153–194.

Babcock, E. B., G. L. Stebbins, and J. A. Jenkins. 1937. Chromosomes and phylogeny in some genera of the Crepidinae. *Cytologia,* Fujii jubilee vol., 188–210.

Barton, D. W. 1951. Localized chiasmata in the differentiated chromosomes of the tomato. *Genetics,* **36**:374–381.

Beadle, G. W. 1953. Heterosis. *Jour. Heredity,* **44**:88.

———. 1955. The gene: carrier of heredity, controller of function and agent of evolution. *Nieuwland Lectures* (Notre Dame), **7**:1–24.

———. 1957a. The role of the nucleus in heredity. In, *The Chemical Basis of Heredity,* ed. Wm. D. McElroy and B. Glass. Baltimore.

———. 1957b. *The Physical and Chemical Basis of Inheritance.* Univ. Oregon Press, Eugene.

———. 1960. Physiological aspects of genetics. *Annual Rev. Physiol.,* **22**:45–74.

———. 1962. Structure of the genetic material and the concept of the gene. In, *This Is Life,* ed. W. H. Johnson and Wm. C. Steere. New York.

Beadle, G. W. and E. L. Tatum. 1941. Genetic control of biochemical reactions in Neurospora. *Proc. Nat. Acad. Sci.,* **27**:499–506.

215

Belling, J. 1928. The ultimate chromomeres of Lilium and Aloe with regard to the number of genes. *Univ. Calif. Publ. Bot.*, 14:307–318.

Benzer, S. 1955. Fine structure of a genetic region in bacteriophage. *Proc. Nat. Acad. Sci.*, 41:344–354.

———. 1957. The elementary units of heredity. In, *The Chemical Basis of Heredity*, ed. Wm. D. McElroy and B. Glass. Baltimore.

Böcher, T. W. 1945. Meiosis in *Anemone apennina* with special reference to chiasma localisation. *Hereditas*, 31:221–237.

Böcher, T. W., K. Larsen, and K. Rahn. 1955. Experimental and cytological studies on plant species. III. *Plantago coronopus* and allied species. *Hereditas*, 41:423–453.

Brink, R. A. 1956. A genetic change associated with the R locus in maize which is directed and potentially reversible. *Genetics*, 41:872–889.

———. 1958. Paramutation at the R locus in maize. *Cold Spring Harbor Symposia Quant. Biol.*, 23:379–391.

Buchholz, J. T. 1947. Chromosome structure under the electron microscope. *Science*, 105:607–610.

Burnham, C. R. 1956. Chromosomal interchanges in plants. *Bot. Rev.*, 22:419–552.

Carlquist, S. 1956. On the generic limits of Eriophyllum (Compositae) and related genera. *Madroño*, 13:226–239.

Carson, H. L. 1946. The selective elimination of inversion dicentric chromatids during meiosis in the eggs of *Sciara impatiens*. *Genetics*, 31:95–113.

———. 1953. The effects of inversions on crossing over in *Drosophila robusta*. *Genetics*, 38:168–186.

———. 1959. Genetic conditions which promote or retard the formation of species. *Cold Spring Harbor Symposia Quant. Biol.*, 24:87–105.

Caspari, E. 1948. Cytoplasmic inheritance. *Advances in Genetics*, 2:1–66.

Catcheside, D. G. 1939. A position effect in Oenothera. *Jour. Genetics*, 38:345–352.

———. 1954. The genetics of brevistylis in Oenothera. *Heredity*, 8:125–137.

Cave, M. S. and L. Constance. 1947. Chromosome numbers in the Hydrophyllaceae: III. *Univ. Calif. Publ. Bot.*, 18:449–465.

Chovnick, A., A. Schalet, R. P. Kernaghan, and J. Talsma. 1962. The resolving power of genetic fine structure analysis in higher organisms as exemplified by Drosophila. *Amer. Nat.*, 96:281–296.

Clarke, C. A. and P. M. Sheppard. 1959–1960. The genetics of *Papilio dardanus*, Brown. I–III. *Genetics*, 44:1347–1358; 45:439–457; 45:683–698.

———. 1960a. Evolution of mimicry in the butterfly *Papilio dardanus*. *Heredity*, 14:163–173.

———. 1960b. Super-genes and mimicry. *Heredity*, 14:175–185.

Clausen, J. 1926. Genetical and cytological investigations on *Viola tricolor* L. and *V. arvensis* Murr. *Hereditas*, 8:1–156.

———. 1951. Stages in the Evolution of Plant Species. Ithaca, New York.

Clausen, J. and Wm. M. Hiesey. 1958. Experimental studies on the nature of species. IV. Genetic structure of ecological races. *Carnegie Inst. Washington Publ. 615*.

Clausen, J., D. D. Keck, and Wm. M. Hiesey. 1940. Experimental studies on the nature of species. I. Effect of varied environments on western North American plants. *Carnegie Inst. Washington Publ. 520*.

Cleland, R. E.   1936.   Some aspects of the cyto-genetics of Oenothera.   *Bot. Rev.*, 2:316–348.

——.   1940.   Analysis of wild American races of Oenothera (Onagra).   *Genetics*, 25:636–644.

——.   1949.   Phylogenetic relationships in Oenothera.   *Hereditas*, suppl. vol. 1949, 173–188.

——, ed.   1950.   Studies in Oenothera cytogenetics and phylogeny.   *Indiana Univ. Publ.*, science series, 16.

Cleland, R. E. and B. L. Hammond.   1950.   Analysis of segmental arrangements in certain races of Oenothera.   *Indiana Univ. Publ.*, science series, 16:10–72.

Cleland, R. E., L. B. Preer, and L. Geckler.   1950.   The nature and relationships of taxonomic entities in the North American Euoenotheras.   *Indiana Univ. Publ.*, science series, 16:218–254.

Coleman, L. C.   1940.   The cytology of *Veltheimia viridifolia*, Jacq.   *Amer. Jour. Bot.*, 27:887–895.

Colwell, R. R. and A. B. Burdick.   1959.   Uptake and effect on crossing-over of ethylenediamine-tetraacetic acid (EDTA) in *Drosophila melanogaster*.   *Nucleus*, 2:125–130.

Comstock, R. E.   1955.   Theory of quantitative genetics: synthesis.   *Cold Spring Harbor Symposia Quant. Biol.*, 20:93–102.

Crick, F. H. C.   1954.   The structure of the hereditary material.   *Scientific American*, October 1954.

——.   1962.   The genetic code.   *Scientific American*, October 1962.

Da Cunha, A. B.   1951.   Modification of the adaptive values of chromosomal types in *Drosophila pseudoobscura* by nutritional variables.   *Evolution*, 5:395–404.

——.   1953.   A further analysis of the polymorphism of *Drosophila polymorpha*.   *Nature*, 171:887.

——.   1955.   Chromosomal polymorphism in the Diptera.   *Advances in Genetics*, 7:93–138.

Darlington, C. D.   1932, 1937.   *Recent Advances in Cytology*.   1st and 2nd ed., London.

——.   1936.   The limitation of crossing over in Oenothera.   *Jour. Genetics*, 32:343–351.

——.   1939, 1958.   *The Evolution of Genetic Systems*.   1st and 2nd ed., Cambridge and New York.

——.   1940.   Taxonomic species and genetic systems.   In, *The New Systematics*, ed. J. Huxley.   London.

——.   1956.   *Chromosome Botany*.   London.

——.   1958.   (See under 1939.)

Darlington, C. D. and E. K. Janaki-Ammal.   1945.   *Chromosome Atlas of Cultivated Plants*.   London.

Darlington, C. D. and K. Mather.   1949.   *The Elements of Genetics*.   London.

Darlington, C. D. and A. P. Wylie.   1955.   *Chromosome Atlas of Flowering Plants*.   London.

Demerec, M.   1956.   A comparative study of certain gene loci in Salmonella.   *Cold Spring Harbor Symposia Quant. Biol.*, 21:113–121.

Demerec, M., I. Blomstrand, and Z. E. Demerec.   1955.   Evidence of complex loci in Salmonella.   *Proc. Nat. Acad. Sci.*, 41:359–364.

Dempster, E. R.   1949.   Effects of linkage on parental-combination and recombination frequencies in F_2.   *Genetics,* **34:**272–284.

DeVries, H.   1917.   *Oenothera lamarckiana* mut. *velutina. Bot. Gazette,* **63:** 1–24.

Dobzhansky, Th.   1931.   The decrease in crossing-over observed in translocations, and its probable explanation.   *Amer. Nat.,* **65:**214–232.

——.   1947.   Genetics of natural populations.   XIV. A response of certain gene arrangements in the third chromosome of *Drosophila pseudoobscura* to natural selection.   *Genetics,* **32:**142–160.

——.   1951.   *Genetics and the Origin of Species.*   3rd ed., New York.

——.   1955.   A review of some fundamental concepts and problems of population genetics.   *Cold Spring Harbor Symposia Quant. Biol.,* **20:**1–15.

——.   1959.   Evolution of genes and genes in evolution.   *Cold Spring Harbor Symposia Quant. Biol.,* **24:**15–30.

Dobzhansky, Th. and H. Levene.   1951.   Development of heterosis through natural selection in experimental populations of *Drosophila pseudoobscura. Amer. Nat.,* **85:**247–264.

——.   1955.   Genetics of natural populations.   XXIV. Developmental homeostasis in natural populations of *Drosophila pseudoobscura. Genetics,* **40:** 797–808.

Dobzhansky, Th. and B. Wallace.   1953.   The genetics of homeostasis in Drosophila.   *Proc. Nat. Acad. Sci.,* **39:**162–171.

Dubinin, N. P.   1948.   Experimental investigation of the integration of hereditary systems in the processes of evolution of populations.   *Zhurn. Obshch. Biol.,* **9:**203–244.   (Transl., Univ. Calif. Dept. Genetics.)

Dunn, L. C. and E. Caspari.   1945.   A case of neighboring loci with similar effects.   *Genetics,* **30:**543–568.

Dunn, L. C. and J. Suckling.   1955.   A preliminary comparison of the fertilities of wild house mice with and without a mutant at locus T.   *Amer. Nat.,* **89:**231–233.

East, E. M.   1916.   Studies on size inheritance in Nicotiana.   *Genetics,* **1:**164– 176.

Emerson, R. A. and E. M. East.   1913.   The inheritance of quantitative characters in maize.   *Bull. Agric. Expt. Station Nebraska,* Research Bull. 2.

Emerson, S. H.   1935.   The genetic nature of DeVries's mutations in *Oenothera lamarckiana. Amer. Nat.,* **69:**545–559.

——.   1952.   Biochemical models of heterosis in Neurospora.   In, *Heterosis,* ed. J. W. Gowen.   Ames, Iowa.

Emerson, S. H. and A. H. Sturtevant.   1932.   The linkage of certain genes in Oenothera.   *Genetics,* **17:**393–412.

Eversole, R. A. and E. L. Tatum.   1956.   Chemical alteration of crossing-over frequency in Chlamydomonas.   *Proc. Nat. Acad. Sci.,* **42:**68–73.

Falconer, D. S.   1960.   Introduction to Quantitative Genetics.   Glasgow and New York.

Fraenkel-Conrat, H.   1956.   Rebuilding a virus.   *Scientific American,* June 1956.

Fraenkel-Conrat, H., B. A. Singer, and R. C. Williams.   1957.   The nature of the progeny of virus reconstituted from protein and nucleic acid of different strains of tobacco mosaic virus.   In, *The Chemical Basis of Heredity,* ed. Wm. D. McElroy and B. Glass.   Baltimore.

Frankel, O. and A. Munday. 1962. The evolution of wheat. In, *The Evolution of Living Organisms*. Symposium, Royal Society, Victoria.

Frota-Pessoa, O. 1961. On the number of gene loci and the total mutation rate in man. *Amer. Nat.*, 95:217–222.

Glass, B. 1947. Maupertuis and the beginnings of genetics. *Quart. Rev. Biol.*, 22:196–210.

———. 1955. Pseudoalleles. *Science*, 122:233.

Goldschmidt, R. B. 1938. *Physiological Genetics*. New York.

———. 1940. *The Material Basis of Evolution*. New Haven.

———. 1949. Heterochromatic heredity. *Hereditas*, suppl. vol. 1949, 244–255.

———. 1955. *Theoretical Genetics*. Berkeley.

Goodspeed, T. H. and P. Avery. 1939. Trisomic and other types in *Nicotiana sylvestris*. *Jour. Genetics*, 38:381–458.

———. 1941. The twelfth primary trisomic type in *Nicotiana sylvestris*. *Proc. Nat. Acad. Sci.*, 27:13–14.

Gowen, J. W., ed. 1952. *Heterosis*. Ames, Iowa.

Grant, V. 1950. Genetic and taxonomic studies in Gilia. I. *Gilia capitata*. Aliso, 2:239–316.

———. 1956a. The development of a theory of heredity. *Amer. Scientist*, 44: 158–179.

———. 1956b. Chromosome repatterning and adaptation. *Advances in Genetics*, 8:89–107.

———. 1956c. The genetic structure of races and species in Gilia. *Advances in Genetics*, 8:55–87.

———. 1958. The regulation of recombination in plants. *Cold Spring Harbor Symposia Quant. Biol.*, 23:337–363.

———. 1959. *Natural History of the Phlox Family*. The Hague.

———. 1963. *The Origin of Adaptations*. New York.

Green, M. M. 1953. The beadex locus in *Drosophila melanogaster*: Genetic analysis of the mutant Bx^{r49k}. *Zeitschr. Abstammungs- u. Vererbungslehre*, 85:435–449.

———. 1955. Phenotypic variation and pseudo-allelism at the forked locus in *Drosophila melanogaster*. *Proc. Nat. Acad. Sci.*, 41:375–379.

Green, M. M. and K. C. Green. 1949. Crossing-over between alleles at the lozenge locus in *Drosophila melanogaster*. *Proc. Nat. Acad. Sci.*, 35:586–591.

———. 1956. A cytogenetic analysis of the lozenge pseudoalleles in Drosophila. *Zeitschr. Abstammungs- u. Vererbungslehre*, 87:708–721.

Haga, T. and M. Kurabayashi. 1954. Genom and polyploidy in the genus Trillium. V. Chromosomal variation in natural populations of *Trillium kamtschaticum* Pall. *Mem. Fac. Sci. Kyusu Univ.*, E, 1:159–185.

Hagberg, A. 1953. Heterozygosity in erectoides mutations in barley. *Hereditas*, 39:161–178.

Haldane, J. B. S. 1954a. *The Biochemistry of Genetics*. London.

———. 1954b. The statics of evolution. In, *Evolution as a Process*, ed. J. Huxley. London.

Harland, S. C. 1936. The genetical conception of the species. *Biol. Rev.*, 11: 83–112.

Harrison, B. J. and K. Mather. 1950. Polygenic variability in chromosomes of *Drosophila melanogaster* obtained from the wild. *Heredity*, 4:295–312.

220   Bibliography

Heimans, J. 1962. Hugo de Vries and the gene concept. *Amer. Nat.*, **96**:93–104.
Hoagland, M. B. 1959. Nucleic acids and proteins. *Scientific American*, December 1959.
Horowitz, N. H. 1950. Biochemical genetics of Neurospora. *Advances in Genetics*, **3**:33–71.
Horowitz, N. H. and U. Leupold. 1951. Some recent studies bearing on the one gene—one enzyme hypothesis. *Cold Spring Harbor Symposia Quant. Biol.*, **16**:65–72.
Hyde, B. B. 1953. Differentiated chromosomes in *Plantago ovata*. *Amer. Jour. Bot.*, **40**:809–815.
Ingram, V. M. 1956. A specific chemical difference between the globins of normal human and sickle-cell anaemia haemoglobin. *Nature*, **178**:792–794.
Japha, B. 1939. Die Meiosis von Oenothera. II. *Zeitschr. Bot.*, **34**:321–369.
Jinks, J. L. 1955. A survey of the genetical basis of heterosis in a variety of diallel crosses. *Heredity*, **9**:223–238.
Kaufman, B. P. and M. R. McDonald. 1956. Organization of the chromosome. *Cold Spring Harbor Symposia Quant. Biol.*, **21**:233–246.
Kihlman, B. A. 1961. Biochemical aspects of chromosome breakage. *Advances in Genetics*, **10**:1–59.
Komai, T. 1950. Semi-allelic genes. *Amer. Nat.*, **84**:381–392.
Lamprecht, H. 1962. Studien zur Vererbung des Höhenwachstums bei Pisum sowie Koppelungsstudien. *Agri Hortique Genetica*, **20**:23–62.
Laughnan, J. R. 1948. The action of allelic forms of the gene A in maize. I. Studies of variability, dosage and dominance relations. The divergent character of the series. *Genetics*, **33**:488–517.
———. 1952. The action of allelic forms of the gene A in maize. IV. On the compound nature of A^b and the occurrence and action of its A^d derivatives. *Genetics*, **37**:375–395.
Lea, D. E. 1955. *Actions of Radiations on Living Cells*. 2nd ed., Cambridge.
Lerner, I. M. 1954. *Genetic Homeostasis*. London.
———. 1958. *The Genetic Basis of Selection*. New York and London.
Levine, R. P. 1952. Adaptive responses of some third chromosome types of *Drosophila pseudoobscura*. *Evolution*, **6**:216–233.
———. 1955. Chromosome structure and the mechanism of crossing over. *Proc. Nat. Acad. Sci.*, **41**:727–730.
Levitan, M. 1954a. Position effects in natural populations. *Amer. Nat.*, **88**:419–423.
———. 1954b. Additional evidence of position effects in natural populations. *Genetics*, **39**:979.
———. 1958. Non-random associations of inversions. *Cold Spring Harbor Symposia Quant. Biol.*, **23**:251–268.
Lewis, E. B. 1945. The relation of repeats to position effect in *Drosophila melanogaster*. *Genetics*, **30**:137–166.
———. 1950. The phenomenon of position effect. *Advances in Genetics*, **3**:73–115.
———. 1951. Pseudoallelism and gene evolution. *Cold Spring Harbor Symposia Quant. Biol.*, **16**:159–174.
———. 1952. The pseudoallelism of white and apricot in *Drosophila melanogaster*. *Proc. Nat. Acad. Sci.*, **38**:953–961.

Lewis, H. 1954. Quantitative variation in wild genotypes of Clarkia. *Internat. Union Biol. Sci., B,* **15**:114–122.

———. 1962. Catastrophic selection as a factor in speciation. *Evolution,* **16**: 257–271.

Lewis, H. and P. H. Raven. 1958. Rapid evolution in Clarkia. *Evolution,* **12**:319–336.

Lewis, H. and M. R. Roberts. 1956. The origin of *Clarkia lingulata. Evolution,* **10**:126–138.

Lima-de-Faria, A. 1952. Chromomere analysis of the chromosome complement of rye. *Chromosoma,* **5**:1–68.

MacKey, J. 1954. Neutron and X-ray experiments in wheat and a revision of the speltoid problem. *Hereditas,* **40**:65–180.

Makino, S. 1951. *An Atlas of the Chromosome Numbers in Animals.* Ames, Iowa.

Mather, K. 1943. Polygenic inheritance and natural selection. *Biol. Rev.,* **18**: 32–64.

———. 1944. The genetical activity of heterochromatin. *Proc. Royal Soc., B,* **132**:308–332.

———. 1949. *Biometrical Genetics. The Study of Continuous Variation.* New York.

———. 1950. The genetical architecture of heterostyly in *Primula sinensis. Evolution,* **4**:340–352.

———. 1953. Genetical control of stability in development. *Heredity,* **7**:297–336.

———. 1955. Response to selection. *Cold Spring Harbor Symposia Quant. Biol.,* **20**:158–165.

Mather, K. and B. J. Harrison. 1949. The manifold effect of selection. *Heredity,* **3**:1–52, 131–162.

Mayr, E. 1954. Change of genetic environment and evolution. In, *Evolution as a Process,* ed. J. Huxley. London.

———. 1963. *Animal Species and Evolution.* Cambridge, Mass.

Mazia, D. 1954. The particulate organization of the chromosome. *Proc. Nat. Acad. Sci.,* **40**:521–527.

McClintock, B. 1953. Induction of instability at selected loci in maize. *Genetics,* **38**:579–599.

Mendel, G. 1866. Versuche über Pflanzenhybriden. *Verhandl. Naturforsch. Verein. Brünn,* **4**. (Translated and reprinted in various recent texts, i.e., in Sinnott, Dunn, and Dobzhansky, 1958.)

Mertens, T. R., A. B. Burdick, and F. R. Gomes. 1956. Phenotypic stability in rate of maturation of heterozygotes for induced chlorophyll mutations in tomato. *Genetics,* **41**:791–803.

Michaelis, P. 1929. Über den Einfluss von Kern und Plasma auf die Vererbung. *Biol. Zentralblatt,* **49**:302–316.

———. 1951. Plasmavererbung und Heterosis. *Zeitschr. Pflanzenzüchtung,* **30**: 250–275.

———. 1953. Der Nachweis einer Plasmavererbung beim Weidenröschen. *Die Umschau,* **9**.

———. 1954. Cytoplasmic inheritance in Epilobium and its theoretical significance. *Advances in Genetics.* **6**:287–401.

222   *Bibliography*

Mirsky, A. E. 1953. The chemistry of heredity. *Scientific American*, February 1953.

Mooring, J. 1958. A cytogenetic study of *Clarkia unguiculata*. I. Translocations. *Amer. Jour. Bot.*, **45**:233–242.

Moos, J. R. 1955. Comparative physiology of some chromosomal types in *Drosophila pseudoobscura*. *Evolution*, **9**:141–151.

Mukai, T. and A. B. Burdick. 1959. Single gene heterosis associated with a second chromosome recessive lethal in *Drosophila melanogaster*. *Genetics*, **44**:211–232.

Muller, H. J. 1935. On the dimensions of chromosomes and genes in Dipteran salivary glands. *Amer. Nat.*, **69**:405–411.

———. 1947. The Gene. *Proc. Royal Soc. London, B*, **134**:1–37.

———. 1959. The mutation theory re-examined. *Proc. 10th Internat. Genetics Congr.* (*Montreal*), **1**:306–317.

Muller, H. J. and A. A. Prokofyeva. 1935. The individual gene in relation to the chromomere and chromosome. *Proc. Nat. Acad. Sci.*, **21**:16–26.

Neel, J. V. 1949. The inheritance of sickle cell anemia. *Science*, **110**:64–66.

Novitski, E. and G. Braver. 1954. An analysis of crossing over within a heterozygous inversion in *Drosophila melanogaster*. *Genetics*, **39**:197–209.

Oehlkers, F. and C. Harte. 1943. Über die Aufhebung des Gonen- und Zygotenausfalls bei Oenothera. *Flora*, **37**:106–124.

Patterson, J. T. and W. S. Stone. 1952. *Evolution in the Genus Drosophila*. New York.

Patterson, J. T., W. Stone, S. Bedichek, and M. Suche. 1934. The production of translocations in Drosophila. *Amer. Nat.*, **68**:359–369.

Pfeiffer, J. 1948. Enzymes. *Scientific American*, December 1948.

Pontecorvo, G. 1953. The genetics of *Aspergillus nidulans*. *Advances in Genetics*, **5**:141–238.

———. 1958. *Trends in Genetic Analysis*. New York.

Preer, J. R. 1950. Microscopically visible bodies in the cytoplasm of the "killer" strains of *Paramecium aurelia*. *Genetics*, **35**:344–362.

Raffel, D. and H. J. Muller. 1940. Position effect and gene divisibility considered in connection with three strikingly similar scute mutations. *Genetics*, **25**:541–583.

Rees, H. and J. B. Thompson. 1955. Localisation of chromosome breakage at meiosis. *Heredity*, **9**:399–407.

———. 1956. Genotypic control of chromosome behavior in rye. III. Chiasma frequency in homozygotes and heterozygotes. *Heredity*, **10**:409–424.

Renner, O. 1928. Über Koppelungswechsel bei Oenothera. *Zeitschr. Abstammungs- u. Vererbungslehre*, suppl. 1928, **2**:1216–1220.

———. 1941. Über die Entstehung homozygotischer Formen aus komplexheterozygotischen Oenotheren. *Flora*, **35**:201–238.

Rhoades, M. M. and E. Dempsey. 1953. Cytogenetic studies of deficient-duplicate chromosomes derived from inversion heterozygotes in maize. *Amer. Jour. Bot.*, **40**:405–424.

Richardson, M. M. 1936. Structural hybridity in *Lilium martagon album* × *L. hansonii*. *Jour. Genetics*, **32**:411–450.

Rick, C. M. 1959. Non-random gene distribution among tomato chromosomes. *Proc. Nat. Acad. Sci.*, **45**:1515–1519.

Ris, H. 1957. Chromosome structure. *The Chemical Basis of Heredity,* ed. Wm. D. McElroy and B. Glass. Baltimore.

Russell, W. A. and C. R. Burnham. 1950. Cytogenetic studies of an inversion in maize. *Scientific Agriculture,* 30:93–111.

Sager, R. 1955. Non-Mendelian inheritance in Chlamydomonas. *Genetics,* 40:594.

Sager, R. and F. J. Ryan. 1961. *Cell Heredity.* New York.

Schnick, S. M., T. Mukai, and A. B. Burdick. 1960. Heterozygote viability of a second chromosome recessive lethal in *Drosophila melanogaster. Genetics,* 45:315–329.

Schuler, J. F. 1954. Natural mutations in inbred lines of maize and their heterotic effect. I. Comparison of parent, mutant and their F_1 hybrid in a highly inbred background. *Genetics,* 39:908–922.

Schultz, J. 1929. The minute reaction in the development of *Drosophila melanogaster. Genetics,* 14:366–419.

Sears, E. R. 1944. Cytogenetic studies with polyploid species of wheat. II. Additional chromosomal aberrations in *Triticum vulgare. Genetics,* 29:232–246.

———. 1959. The systematics, cytology and genetics of wheat. *Handbuch der Pflanzenzüchtung,* 2:164–187.

Sinnott, E. W., L. C. Dunn, and Th. Dobzhansky. 1958. *Principles of Genetics.* 5th ed., New York.

Sirks, M. J. 1956. *General Genetics.* 5th ed., transl., The Hague.

Snow, R. 1960. Chromosomal differentiation in *Clarkia dudleyana. Amer. Jour. Bot.,* 47:302–309.

Snow, R. and M. P. Dunford. 1961. A study of interchange heterozygosity in a population of *Datura meteloides. Genetics,* 46:1097–1110.

Sonneborn, T. M. 1950a. The cytoplasm in heredity. *Heredity,* 4:11–36.

———. 1950b. Partner of the genes. *Scientific American,* November 1950.

Spencer, H. 1884. *First Principles.* 5th ed., London.

Srb, A. M. and N. H. Horowitz. 1944. The ornithine cycle in Neurospora and its genetic control. *Jour. Biol. Chem.,* 154:129–139.

Srb, A. M. and R. D. Owen. 1952. *General Genetics.* San Francisco.

Stadler, L. J. and F. M. Uber. 1942. Genetic effects of ultraviolet radiation in maize. IV. Comparisons of monochromatic radiations. *Genetics,* 27:84–118.

Stebbins, G. L. 1938. Cytological characteristics associated with the different growth habits in the dicotyledons. *Amer. Jour. Bot.,* 25:189–198.

———. 1950. *Variation and Evolution in Plants.* New York.

———. 1958a. The inviability, weakness, and sterility of interspecific hybrids. *Advances in Genetics,* 9:147–215.

———. 1958b. Longevity, habitat, and release of genetic variability in the higher plants. *Cold Spring Harbor Symposia Quant. Biol.,* 23:365–378.

———. 1959. Genes, chromosomes, and evolution. In, *Vistas in Botany,* ed. W. Turrill, London.

Stebbins, G. L. and S. Ellerton. 1939. Structural hybridity in *Paeonia californica* and *P. brownii. Jour. Genetics,* 38:1–36.

Stebbins, G. L., J. A. Jenkins, and M. S. Walters. 1953. Chromosomes and phylogeny in the Compositae, tribe Cichorieae. *Univ. Calif. Publ. Bot.,* 26:401–429.

Steffensen, D. 1953. Induction of chromosome breakage at meiosis by a magnesium deficiency in Tradescantia. *Proc. Nat. Acad. Sci.,* 39:613–620.

———. 1959. A comparative view of the chromosome. *Brookhaven Symposia in Biology,* 12:103–124.

Stein, W. H. and S. Moore. 1961. The structure of proteins. *Scientific American,* February 1961.

Stephens, S. G. 1948. A biochemical basis for the pseudo-allelic anthocyanin series in Gossypium. *Genetics,* 33:191–214.

———. 1949. The cytogenetics of speciation in Gossypium. I. Selective elimination of the donor parent genotype in interspecific backcrosses. *Genetics,* 34:627–637.

———. 1950. The internal mechanism of speciation in Gossypium. *Bot. Rev.,* 16:115–149.

———. 1951*a.* Possible significance of duplication in evolution. *Advances in Genetics,* 4:247–265.

———. 1951*b.* "Homologous" genetic loci in Gossypium. *Cold Spring Harbor Symposia Quant. Biol.,* 16:131–141.

Stern, C. 1943. Genic action as studied by means of the effects of different doses and combinations of alleles. *Genetics,* 28:441–475.

———. 1949*a,* 1960. *Principles of Human Genetics.* 1st and 2nd ed., San Francisco.

———. 1949*b.* Gene and character. In, *Genetics, Paleontology, and Evolution,* ed. G. Jepsen et al. Princeton.

———. 1960. (See under 1949*a.*)

Stern, C., G. Carson, M. Kinst, E. Novitski, and D. Uphoff. 1952. The viability of heterozygotes for lethals. *Genetics,* 37:413–449.

Stubbe, H. 1953. Über mono- und di-gen bedingte Heterosis bei *Antirrhinum majus* L. *Zeitschr. Abstammungs- u. Vererbungslehre,* 85:450–478.

Sturtevant, A. H. 1921. A case of rearrangement of genes in Drosophila. *Proc. Nat. Acad. Sci.,* 7:235–237.

Sturtevant, A. H. and G. W. Beadle. 1936. The relations of inversions in the X chromosomes of *Drosophila melanogaster* to crossing over and disjunction. *Genetics,* 21:554–604.

———. 1939. *An Introduction to Genetics.* Philadelphia and London.

Sturtevant, A. H. and E. Novitski. 1941. The homologies of the chromosome elements in the genus Drosophila. *Genetics,* 26:517–541.

Swanson, C. P. 1957. *Cytology and Cytogenetics.* Englewood Cliffs, New Jersey.

Symposium. 1955. Pseudoallelism and the theory of the gene. *Amer. Nat.,* 89:65–122. (Papers by M. Green, E. B. Lewis, C. Stormont, and S. G. Stephens.)

Thoday, J. M. 1958. Natural selection and biological progress. In, *A Century of Darwin,* ed. S. A. Barnett. London.

Timoféeff-Ressovsky, N. W. 1934. Über den Einfluss des genotypischen Milieus und der Aussenbedingungen auf die Realisation des Genotyps. *Nachr. Ges. Wissensch. Göttingen, N.F.,* 1:53–106.

Tischler, G. 1951–1953. Allgemeine Pflanzenkaryologie. Handbuch der Pflanzenanatomie, vols. 2 and 3. Berlin.

Togby, H. A. 1943. A cytological study of *Crepis fuliginosa, C. neglecta,* and their F_1 hybrid, and its bearing on the mechanism of phylogenetic reduction in chromosome number. *Jour. Genetics*, **45**:67–111.

Waddington, C. H. 1962. New Patterns in Genetics and Development. New York.

Wagner, R. P. and H. K. Mitchell. 1955. Genetics and Metabolism. New York.

Wallace, B. 1959. Influence of genetic systems on geographical distribution. *Cold Spring Harbor Symposia Quant. Biol.*, **24**:193–204.

Wallace, B. and Th. Dobzhansky. 1959. *Radiation, Genes, and Man*. New York.

Walters, J. L. 1942. Distribution of structural hybrids in *Paeonia californica*. *Amer. Jour. Bot.*, **29**:270–275.

———. 1952. Heteromorphic chromosome pairs in *Paeonia californica*. *Amer. Jour. Bot.*, **39**:145–151.

Watson, J. D. and F. H. C. Crick. 1953. Molecular structure of nucleic acids. *Nature*, **171**:737–738.

Weismann, A. 1892. *The Germ-plasm. A Theory of Heredity*. Transl., New York.

Whaley, W. G. 1952. Physiology of gene action in hybrids. In, *Heterosis*, ed. J. W. Gowen. Ames, Iowa.

White, M. J. D. 1954. An extreme form of chiasma localization in a species of Bryodema (Orthoptera, Acrididae). *Evolution*, **8**:350–358.

———. 1959. Speciation in animals. *Australian Jour. Science*, **22**:32–39.

Wigan, L. G. 1949. The distribution of polygenic activity on the X chromosome of *Drosophila melanogaster*. *Heredity*, **3**:53–66.

Wilson, E. B. 1896. *The Cell in Development and Inheritance*. 1st ed., New York.

Winge, Ø. 1955. On interallelic crossing over. *Heredity*, **9**:373–384.

Wright, S. 1949. Adaptation and selection. In, *Genetics, Paleontology and Evolution*, ed. G. Jepsen et al. Princeton.

———. 1959. Genetics, the gene, and the hierarchy of biological sciences. *Proc. 10th Internat. Congr. Genetics (Montreal)*, **1**:475–489.

Wright, S. and Th. Dobzhansky. 1946. Genetics of natural populations. XII. Experimental reproduction of some of the changes caused by natural selection in certain populations of *Drosophila pseudoobscura*. *Genetics*, **31**:125–156.

Yarnell, S. H. 1962. Cytogenetics of the vegetable crops. III. Legumes. (A) Garden peas, *Pisum sativum* L. *Bot. Rev.*, **28**:465–537.

Yoon, C. H. 1955. Homeostasis associated with heterozygosity in the genetics of time of vaginal opening in the house mouse. *Genetics*, **40**:297–309.

Name index

Subject index

Adaptive gene combinations, 169 ff.
Adenine, 28–29
Adjacent disjunction, 177
Alcaptonuria, 40
Alleles, defined, 2
  interaction between, 53 ff.
Alternate disjunction, 177, 180–181,
  187–188
Amino acids, 22–23, 37
Anemia, 46–47
Anemone, 121
Anisomeric genes, 79, 84–85, 132
Antirrhinum majus, 59
Aquilegia, 203, 207, 212
Atropine, enzymatic breakdown in rab-
  bits, 40
Avena, *see* Oats

Bacteria, *see* Escherichia coli; Pneumo-
  coccus; Salmonella typhimurium
Bacteriophage, *see* Virus
Balanced lethals, 187–188
Balanced polygenic systems, 165 ff.
Barley, 59
Blood types, 55, 58; *see also* Hemo-
  globin
Brassica, 203
Breakage, of chromosomes, 10–12, 114,
  120 ff.
Bryodema, 121

Capsella bursa-pastoris, 75, 88–89
Ceanothus, 203
Centric fusion, 201
Chiasmata, localized, 121, 128
Chickens, 61
Chlamydomonas, 21, 122
Chromomere, 106–107
Chromosomal rearrangements, *types of*,
  114, 150 ff.
  and blocks of linked modifiers, 158 ff.
  position effect, 115, 119, 153 ff., 206–
  207
  in relation to linkage in homozygotes,
  150 ff.
  role in speciation, 205 ff.
  between species, 194 ff.
  see also Deficiencies; Duplications;
  Inversions; Translocations; Transposition
Chromosome, breakage, 10–12, 114,
  120 ff.
  in heredity, 7 ff.
  heterochromatin, 103–104
  organization of a segment, 105 ff.
  strands of DNA in, 30
  see also Preferential pairing; Salivary
  gland chromosomes
Chromosome maps, 13–14
Chromosome number, 135, 145, 198 ff.,
  204 ff.
Chromosome theory of heredity, 7 ff.

231